NUCLEAR WAR

www.penguin.co.uk

ANNIE JACOBSEN

NUCLEAR WAR

A SCENARIO

torva

TRANSWORLD PUBLISHERS
Penguin Random House, One Embassy Gardens,
8 Viaduct Gardens, London SW11 7BW
www.penguin.co.uk

Transworld is part of the Penguin Random House group of companies
whose addresses can be found at global.penguinrandomhouse.com

First published in Great Britain in 2024 by Torva
an imprint of Transworld Publishers
This edition published by arrangement with Dutton, an imprint of
Penguin Publishing Group, division of Penguin Random House LLC.

A CIP catalogue record for this book
is available from the British Library.

ISBNs
9781911709596 hb
9781911709602 tpb

Book Design by Aubrey Khan, Neuwirth & Associates, Inc.

Printed and bound in Great Britain by Clays Ltd, Elcograf S.p.A.

The authorized representative in the EEA is Penguin Random House Ireland,
Morrison Chambers, 32 Nassau Street, Dublin D02 YH68.

Penguin Random House is committed to a sustainable future
for our business, our readers and our planet. This book is made
from Forest Stewardship Council® certified paper.

For Kevin

"The Story of the human race is War.
Except for brief and precarious interludes,
there has never been peace in the world;
and before history began, murderous strife
was universal and unending."

—Winston Churchill

CONTENTS

x **Contents**

AUTHOR'S NOTE

S ince the early 1950s, the United States government has spent trillions of dollars preparing to fight a nuclear war, while also refining protocols meant to keep the U.S. government functioning after hundreds of millions of Americans become casualties of an apocalyptic-scale nuclear holocaust.

This scenario—of what the moments after an inbound nuclear missile launch could look like—is based on facts sourced from exclusive interviews with presidential advisors, cabinet members, nuclear weapons engineers, scientists, soldiers, airmen, special operators, Secret Service, emergency management experts, intelligence analysts, civil servants, and others who have worked on these macabre scenarios over decades. Because the plans for General Nuclear War are among the most classified secrets held by the U.S. government, this book, and the scenario it postulates, takes the reader up to the razor's edge of what can legally be known. Declassified documents—obfuscated for decades—fill in the details with terrifying clarity.

Because the Pentagon is a top target for a strike by America's nuclear-armed enemies, in the scenario that follows, Washington, D.C., gets hit first—with a 1-megaton thermonuclear bomb. "A Bolt out of the Blue attack against D.C. is what everyone in D.C. fears most," says former assistant secretary of defense for nuclear, chemical, and biological defense programs Andrew Weber. "Bolt out of the Blue" is how U.S. Nuclear Command and Control refers to an "unwarned large [nuclear] attack."

This strike on D.C. initiates the beginning of an Armageddon-like General Nuclear War that will almost certainly follow. "There is no such thing as a small nuclear war" is an oft repeated phrase in Washington.

A nuclear strike on the Pentagon is just the beginning of a scenario the finality of which will be the end of civilization as we know it. This is the reality of the world in which we all live. The nuclear war scenario proposed in this book could happen tomorrow. Or later today.

"The world could end in the next couple of hours," warns General Robert Kehler, the former commander of the United States Strategic Command.

INTERVIEWS

(U.S. Nuclear Command and Control positions are formerly held)

Dr. Richard L. Garwin: nuclear weapons designer, Ivy Mike thermonuclear bomb

Dr. William J. Perry: United States secretary of defense

Leon E. Panetta: United States secretary of defense, director of the Central Intelligence Agency, White House chief of staff

General C. Robert Kehler: commander, United States Strategic Command

Vice Admiral Michael J. Connor: commander, United States [nuclear] submarine forces

Brigadier General Gregory J. Touhill: first U.S. federal chief information security officer (CISO); director, Command, Control, Communications, and Cyber (C4) Systems, U.S. Transportation Command

William Craig Fugate: administrator, Federal Emergency Management Agency (FEMA)

Honorable Andrew C. Weber: assistant secretary of defense for nuclear, chemical, and biological defense programs

Jon B. Wolfsthal: special assistant to the president for national security affairs, National Security Council

Dr. Peter Vincent Pry: CIA intelligence officer, weapons of mass destruction, Russia; executive director, Electromagnetic Pulse Task Force of National and Homeland Security

Judge Robert C. Bonner: commissioner, Customs and Border Protection, Department of Homeland Security

Lewis C. Merletti: director, United States Secret Service

Colonel Julian Chesnutt, PhD: Defense Clandestine Service, Defense Intelligence Agency; U.S. defense attaché; U.S. air attaché; F-16 squadron commander

Dr. Charles F. McMillan: director, Los Alamos National Laboratory

Dr. Glen McDuff: nuclear weapons engineer, Los Alamos National Laboratory; laboratory historian

Dr. Theodore Postol: assistant to chief of naval operations; professor emeritus, MIT

Dr. J. Douglas Beason: chief scientist, United States Air Force Space Command

Dr. Frank N. von Hippel: physicist and professor emeritus, Princeton University (co-founder, Program on Science and Global Security)

Dr. Brian Toon: professor; nuclear winter theory (co-author with Carl Sagan)

Dr. Alan Robock: distinguished professor, climatologist, nuclear winter

Hans M. Kristensen: director, Nuclear Information Project, Federation of American Scientists

Michael Madden: director, North Korea Leadership Watch, Stimson Center

Don D. Mann: team manager, SEAL Team Six, Nuclear, Biological, and Chemical Program

Jeffrey R. Yago: engineer; advisor to Electromagnetic Pulse Task Force of National and Homeland Security

H. I. Sutton: analyst and writer, U.S. Naval Institute

Reid Kirby: military historian of chemical, biological, radiological, and nuclear defense

David Cenciotti: aviation journalist; 2nd Lt. (ret.), Aeronautica Militare (Italian Air Force, ITAF)

Michael Morsch: Neolithic archeologist, University of Heidelberg; co-locator Göbekli Tepe

Dr. Albert D. Wheelon: CIA director, Directorate of Science and Technology

Dr. Charles H. Townes: inventor of the laser; Nobel Prize in Physics, 1964

Dr. Marvin L. Goldberger: former Manhattan Project physicist, founder and chairman of the Jason scientists, science advisor to President Johnson

Paul S. Kozemchak: special assistant to director, DARPA (and its longest-serving member)

Dr. Jay W. Forrester: computer pioneer, founder of system dynamics

General Paul F. Gorman: former commander in chief, U.S. Southern Command (U.S. SOUTHCOM); special assistant to the Joint Chiefs of Staff

Alfred O'Donnell: Manhattan Project member, EG&G nuclear weapons engineer, Atomic Energy Commission

Ralph James Freedman: EG&G nuclear weapons engineer, Atomic Energy Commission

Edward Lovick Jr.: physicist, former Lockheed Skunk Works stealth technologist

Dr. Walter Munk: oceanographer, former Jason scientist

Colonel Hervey S. Stockman: pilot, first man to fly over the Soviet Union in a U-2, atomic sampling pilot

Richard "Rip" Jacobs: engineer, VO-67 Navy squadron, in Vietnam

Dr. Pavel Podvig: research fellow, United Nations Institute for Disarmament Research; research fellow, Moscow Institute of Physics and Technology

Dr. Lynn Eden: research scholar emeritus, Stanford University, U.S. foreign and military policy, nuclear policy, mass fire

Dr. Thomas Withington: researcher, electronic warfare, radar, and military communications, Royal United Services Institute, England

Joseph S. Bermudez Jr.: analyst, North Korean defense and intelligence affairs and ballistic missile development, Center for Strategic and International Studies

Interviews

Dr. Patrick Biltgen: aerospace engineer, former BAE Systems Intelligence Integration Directorate

Dr. Alex Wellerstein: professor, author, historian of science and nuclear technology

Fred Kaplan: journalist, author, nuclear weapons historian

Hell on Earth

**Washington, D.C.,
Possibly Sometime in the Near Future**

A 1-megaton thermonuclear weapon detonation begins with a flash of light and heat so tremendous it is impossible for the human mind to comprehend. One hundred and eighty million degrees Fahrenheit is four or five times hotter than the temperature that occurs at the center of the Earth's sun.

In the first fraction of a millisecond after this thermonuclear bomb strikes the Pentagon outside Washington, D.C., there is light. Soft X-ray light with a very short wavelength. The light superheats the surrounding air to millions of degrees, creating a massive fireball that expands at millions of miles per hour. Within a few seconds, this fireball increases to a diameter of a little more than a mile (5,700 feet across), its light and heat so intense that concrete surfaces explode, metal objects melt or evaporate, stone shatters, humans instantaneously convert into combusting carbon.

The five-story, five-sided structure of the Pentagon and everything inside its 6.5 million square feet of office space explodes into superheated dust from the initial flash of light and heat, all the walls shattering with the near-simultaneous arrival of the shock wave, all 27,000 employees perishing instantly.

Not a single thing in the fireball remains.

Nothing.

Ground zero is zeroed.

Traveling at the speed of light, the radiating heat from the fireball ignites everything flammable within its line of sight several miles out in every direction. Curtains, paper, books, wood fences, people's clothing, dry leaves explode into flames and become kindling for a great firestorm that begins to consume a 100-or-more-square-mile area that, prior to this flash of light, was the beating heart of American governance and home to some 6 million people.

Several hundred feet northwest of the Pentagon, all 639 acres of Arlington National Cemetery—including the 400,000 sets of bones and gravestones honoring the war dead, the 3,800 African American freedpeople buried in section 27, the living visitors paying respects on this early spring afternoon, the groundskeepers mowing the lawns, the arborists tending to the trees, the tour guides touring, the white-gloved members of the Old Guard keeping watch over the Tomb of the Unknowns—are instantly transformed into combusting and charred human figurines. Into black organic-matter powder that is soot. Those incinerated are spared the unprecedented horror that begins to be inflicted on the 1 to 2 million more gravely injured people not yet dead in this first Bolt out of the Blue nuclear strike.

Across the Potomac River one mile to the northeast, the marble walls and columns of the Lincoln and Jefferson memorials superheat, split, burst apart, and disintegrate. The steel and stone bridges and highways connecting these historic monuments to the surrounding environs heave and collapse. To the south, across Interstate 395, the bright and spacious glass-walled Fashion Centre at Pentagon City, with its abundance of stores filled with high-end clothing brands and household goods, and the surrounding restaurants and offices, along with the adjacent Ritz-Carlton, Pentagon

City hotel—they are all obliterated. Ceiling joists, two-by-fours, escalators, chandeliers, rugs, furniture, mannequins, dogs, squirrels, people burst into flames and burn. It is the end of March, 3:36 p.m. local time.

It has been three seconds since the initial blast. There is a baseball game going on two and a half miles due east at Nationals Park. The clothes on a majority of the 35,000 people watching the game catch on fire. Those who don't quickly burn to death suffer intense third-degree burns. Their bodies get stripped of the outer layer of skin, exposing bloody dermis underneath.

Third-degree burns require immediate specialized care and often limb amputation to prevent death. Here inside Nationals Park there might be a few thousand people who somehow survive initially. They were inside buying food, or using the bathrooms indoors—people who now desperately need a bed at a burn treatment center. But there are only ten specialized burn beds in the entire Washington metropolitan area, at the MedStar Washington Hospital's Burn Center in central D.C. And because this facility is about five miles northeast of the Pentagon, it no longer functions, if it even exists. At the Johns Hopkins Burn Center, forty-five miles northeast, in Baltimore, there are less than twenty specialized burn beds, but they all are about to become filled. In total there are only around 2,000 specialized burn unit beds in all fifty states at any given time.

Within seconds, thermal radiation from this 1-megaton nuclear bomb attack on the Pentagon has deeply burned the skin on roughly 1 million more people, 90 percent of whom will die. Defense scientists and academics alike have spent decades doing this math. Most won't make it more than a few steps from where they happen to be standing when the bomb detonates. They become what civil defense experts referred to in the 1950s, when these gruesome calculations first came to be, as "Dead When Found."

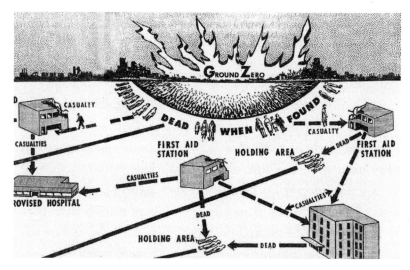

"Dead When Found." (U.S. Federal Civil Defense Administration)

At the Joint Base Anacostia-Bolling, a 1,000-acre military facility across the Potomac to the southeast, there are another 17,000 victims, including almost everyone working at the Defense Intelligence Agency headquarters, the White House Communications Agency headquarters, the U.S. Coast Guard Station Washington, the Marine One helicopter hangar, and scores of other heavily guarded federal facilities that cater to the nation's security. At the National Defense University, a majority of the 4,000 students attending are dead or dying. With no shortness of tragic irony, this university (funded by the Pentagon and founded on America's two-hundredth birthday) is where military officers go to learn how to use U.S. military tactics to achieve U.S. national security dominance around the world. This university is not the only military-themed higher-learning institution obliterated in the nuclear first strike. The Eisenhower School for National Security and Resource Strategy, the National War College, the Inter-American Defense College, the Africa Center for Strategic Studies, they all immediately cease to exist. This entire waterfront area, from Buzzard

Point Park to St. Augustine's Episcopal Church, from the Navy Yard to the Frederick Douglass Memorial Bridge, is totally destroyed.

Humans created the nuclear weapon in the twentieth century to save the world from evil, and now, in the twenty-first century, the nuclear weapon is about to destroy the world. To burn it all down.

The science behind the bomb is profound. Embedded in the thermonuclear flash of light are two pulses of thermal radiation. The first pulse lasts a fraction of a second, after which comes the second pulse, which lasts several seconds and causes human skin to ignite and burn. The light pulses are silent; light has no sound. What follows is a thunderous roar that is blast. The intense heat generated by this nuclear explosion creates a high-pressure wave that moves out from its center point like a tsunami, a giant wall of highly compressed air traveling faster than the speed of sound. It mows people down, hurls others into the air, bursts lungs and eardrums, sucks bodies up and spits them out. "In general, large buildings are destroyed by the change in air pressure, while people and objects such as trees and utility poles are destroyed by the wind," notes an archivist who compiles these appalling statistics for the Atomic Archive.

As the nuclear fireball grows, this shock front delivers catastrophic destruction, pushing out like a bulldozer and moving three miles farther ahead. The air behind the blast wave accelerates, creating several-hundred-mile-per-hour winds, extraordinary speeds that are difficult to fathom. In 2012, Hurricane Sandy, which did $70 billion in damage and killed some 147 people, had maximum sustained winds of roughly 80 miles per hour. The highest wind speed ever recorded on Earth was 253 miles per hour, at a remote weather station in Australia. This nuclear blast wave in Washington, D.C., destroys all structures in its immediate path, instantly changing the physical shapes of engineered structures including office buildings, apartment complexes, monuments, museums, parking structures—they disintegrate and become dust. That which is not crushed by blast is torn apart by whipping wind. Buildings collapse, bridges fall, cranes topple over. Objects as small as computers and cement blocks, and as large as 18-wheeler trucks and double-decker tour buses, become airborne like tennis balls.

The nuclear fireball that has been consuming everything in the initial 1.1-mile radius now rises up like a hot-air balloon. Up from the earth it floats, at a rate of 250 to 350 feet per second. Thirty-five seconds pass. The formation of the iconic mushroom cloud begins, its massive cap and stem, made up of incinerated people and civilization's debris, transmutes from a red, to a brown, to an orange hue. Next comes the deadly reverse suction effect, with objects— cars, people, light poles, street signs, parking meters, steel carrier beams—getting sucked back into the center of the burning inferno and consumed by flame.

Sixty seconds pass.

The mushroom cap and stem, now grayish white, rises up five then ten miles from ground zero. The cap grows too, stretching out ten, twenty, thirty miles across, billowing and blowing farther out. Eventually it reaches beyond the troposphere, higher than commercial flights go, and the region where most of the Earth's weather phenomena occurs. Radioactive particles spew across everything below as fallout raining back down on the Earth and its people. A nuclear bomb produces "a witch's brew of radioactive products which are also entrained in the cloud," the astrophysicist Carl Sagan warned decades ago.

More than a million people are dead or dying and less than two minutes have passed since detonation. Now the inferno begins. This is different from the initial fireball; it is a mega-fire beyond measure. Gas lines explode one after the next, acting like giant blowtorches or flamethrowers, spewing steady streams of fire. Tanks containing flammable materials burst open. Chemical factories explode. Pilot lights on water heaters and furnaces act like torch lighters, setting anything not already burning alight. Collapsed buildings become like giant ovens. People, everywhere, burn alive.

Open gaps in floors and roofs behave like chimneys. Carbon dioxide from the firestorms sinks down and settles into the metro's subway tunnels, asphyxiating riders in their seats. People seeking shelter in basements and other spaces belowground vomit, convulse, become comatose, and die. Anyone aboveground who was looking directly at the blast—in some cases as far as thirteen miles away—has been blinded.

Seven and a half miles out from ground zero, in a 15-mile diameter ring around the Pentagon (the 5 psi zone), cars and buses crash into one another. Asphalt streets turn to liquid from the intense heat, trapping survivors as if caught in molten lava or quicksand. Hurricane-force winds fuel hundreds of fires into thousands of fires, into millions of them. Ten miles out, hot burning ash and flaming wind-borne debris ignite new fires, and one after another they continue to conflate. All of Washington, D.C., becomes one complex firestorm. A mega-inferno. Soon to become a mesocyclone of fire. Eight, maybe nine minutes pass.

Ten and twelve miles out from ground zero (in the 1 psi zone), survivors shuffle in shock like the almost dead. Unsure of what just happened, desperate to escape. Tens of thousands of people here have ruptured lungs. Crows, sparrows, and pigeons flying overhead catch on fire and drop from the sky as if it is raining birds. There is no electricity. No phone service. No 911.

The localized electromagnetic pulse of the bomb obliterates all radio, internet, and TV. Cars with electric ignition systems in a

several-mile ring outside the blast zone cannot restart. Water stations can't pump water. Saturated with lethal levels of radiation,
the entire area is a no-go zone for first responders. Not for days will
the rare survivors realize help was never on the way.

Those who somehow manage to escape death by the initial
blast, shock wave, and firestorm suddenly realize an insidious truth
about nuclear war. That they are entirely on their own. Former
FEMA director Craig Fugate tells us their only hope for survival
is to figure out how to "self-survive." That here begins a "fight for
food, water, Pedialyte . . ."

How, and why, do U.S. defense scientists know such hideous
things, and with exacting precision? How does the U.S. government know so many nuclear effects–related facts, while the general
public remains blind? The answer is as grotesque as the questions
themselves because, for all these years, since the end of World War
II, the U.S. government has been preparing for, and rehearsing
plans for, a General Nuclear War. A nuclear World War III that is
guaranteed to leave, at minimum, 2 billion dead.

To know this answer more specifically, we go back in time, more
than sixty years. To December 1960. To U.S. Strategic Air
Command, and a secret meeting that took place there.

Part I

THE BUILDUP
(OR, HOW WE GOT HERE)

SAC headquarters, underground command post. The "big board."
View in early 1957. (U.S. Air Force Historical Research Agency)

CHAPTER ONE

The Top Secret Plan for General Nuclear War

December 1960, Strategic Air Command Headquarters, Offutt Air Force Base, Nebraska

O ne day not so long ago, a group of American military officials got together to share a secret plan that would result in the death of 600 million people, one-fifth of the world's then population of 3 billion people. Those in attendance that day included:

U.S. Secretary of Defense Thomas S. Gates Jr.
U.S. Deputy Secretary of Defense James H. Douglas Jr.
U.S. Deputy Director of Defense Research and Engineering John H. Rubel
The Joint Chiefs of Staff
Commander of U.S. Strategic Air Command General Thomas S. Power
Army Chief General George H. Decker
Navy Chief Admiral Arleigh A. Burke
Air Force Commander General Thomas D. White
Marine Corps Commandant General David M. Shoup
A multitude of additional top-ranking U.S. military officials

The room was located underground. Walls more than 150 feet long, several stories tall, with an overhead glass-enclosed balcony on the second floor. There were banks of desks, telephones, and maps. Panels of maps. A whole wall of maps. Strategic Air Command headquarters in Omaha, Nebraska, was where generals and admirals would run nuclear war when it happened. True then, true now in 2024—with the underground command center updated for twenty-first-century nuclear war.

Everything you are about to learn of this meeting comes from a firsthand witness—someone who was actually in the room that day—a business executive turned defense official named John H. Rubel. In 2008, in his late eighties, a few years before he died, Rubel revealed this information in a short memoir. As Rubel prepared for his own death, he summoned the courage to express a long-repressed truth. That he felt remorse for having participated in such a "heart of darkness" plan. For saying nothing for so many decades after the fact. What he was part of, Rubel wrote, was a plan for "mass extermination." His words.

Inside the large underground bunker in Nebraska that day, Rubel was seated alongside his fellow nuclear war planners in neat rows of folding chairs, the old-fashioned kind with wooden slats. The four-star generals sat in the front row, the one-star generals in the back. Rubel, U.S. deputy director of Defense Research and Engineering at the time, sat in the second row.

On a signal from Strategic Air Command commander General Thomas S. Power, a briefer stepped forward onstage. Then an aide appeared carrying an easel, and a second aide carrying a pointing stick. The first man was there to flip charts, the second to point things out. General Power (his actual name) explained to his audience that what was being witnessed was how a full-scale nuclear attack against the Soviet Union would go down. Two airmen walked forward and stood one at each end of the 150-foot-long wall of maps, each man carrying a tall stepladder. The map showed the Soviet Union and China (then called the Sino-Soviet bloc) and the surrounding countries.

Rubel recalled, "Each man climbed his tall ladder at the same brisk rate, reaching the top at the same instant as his counterpart. Each man reached up toward a red ribbon which, we now noticed, encircled a large roll of clear plastic. With a single motion, each untied the bowknot securing the ribbon at his end of the roll, whereupon the plastic sheet unrolled with a *whoosh!*, flapped a bit and then dangled limply in front of the map." The map showed hundreds of small black marks, "most of them over Moscow," each one representing a nuclear explosion.

The first of General Power's briefers began to describe the U.S. nuclear attack plan against the Soviet Union. The first wave of attacks would come from U.S. fighter jets that would take off from aircraft carriers stationed near Okinawa, Japan. "Wave after wave" of attacks would ensue. Successive bombing runs by Boeing B-52 long-range strategic bombers, each carrying in its bomb bay multiple thermonuclear weapons—each capable of thousands of times the destruction of the atomic bombs dropped on Hiroshima and Nagasaki, Japan. Each time the briefer described a new wave of attacks, Rubel wrote, the two men on their stepladders "would untie another pair of red ribbons, a plastic roll would come whooshing down and Moscow would be even further obliterated beneath the little marks on those layers of plastic sheets."

What shocked Rubel most, he wrote, was that with regards to Moscow alone, "the plan called for a total of forty megatons— *megatons*—on Moscow, about four thousand times more than the bomb over Hiroshima and perhaps twenty to thirty times more than all the non-nuclear bombs dropped by the Allies in both theaters during more than four years of World War II."

And yet, all during this meeting in 1960, Rubel sat in his chair and said nothing.

Not one thing. Not for forty-eight years. But the admission is remarkable—the first known instance where an attendee of this meeting dared reveal such personal details about what went on. Details that convey the simple truth to anyone outside that room: that this plan for nuclear war was genocide.

The airmen descended the ladders, folded them up, tucked them under their arms, and stepped out of view.

Four thousand times more explosive power than the bomb dropped on Hiroshima.

What does this even mean—and is it something one's brain can fully comprehend?

More immediately, can anyone stop the plan for mass extermination before it happens?

CHAPTER TWO

The Girl in the Rubble

August 6, 1945, Hiroshima, Japan

The atomic bomb that was dropped on Hiroshima in August 1945 killed more than 80,000 people in a single strike. The total numbers are debated still. In the days and weeks after the bombing, no accurate counting of the victims could be performed. The mass destruction of Hiroshima's government facilities, its hospitals, police, and fire departments created a state of total chaos and confusion in the immediate aftermath.

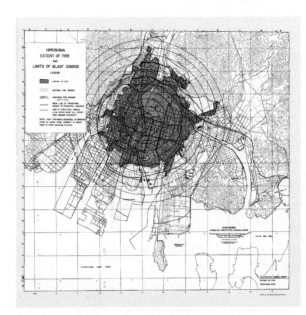

U.S. Strategic Bombing Survey map of Hiroshima's fire and blast damage. (U.S. National Archives)

Thirteen-year-old Setsuko Thurlow was 1.1 miles from ground zero when this atomic weapon, code-named Little Boy, detonated over Hiroshima at an altitude of 1,900 feet—an airburst, as it's known. This was the first nuclear weapon used in battle. Its burst height was based on a figure that had been precisely calculated by the American defense scientist John von Neumann, whose assigned task was to figure out a way to kill the most people possible on the ground below with this single atomic bomb. Exploding a nuclear bomb directly on the ground "wastes" a lot of energy, displacing massive volumes of earth, as military planners had figured out and agreed. Setsuko Thurlow was knocked unconscious by this blast.

When she first regained consciousness, Setsuko could not see or move. "Then I started hearing whispering voices of the girls around me," she recalled years later, and that she could hear them saying, "God, help me, mother help me. I'm here."

Sheltered by a collapsed building, Setsuko had somewhat miraculously survived the initial blast that comes with the detonation of an atomic bomb. Everything was very dark around her, she remembered. Her first sensation was that she had turned into smoke. After some time—seconds, or maybe minutes—it registered in her brain that the voice of a man was instructing her to do something.

"Don't give up," the man said. "I'm trying to free you."

This man, a stranger, was shaking Setsuko's left shoulder and pushing her from behind. "Get out . . . crawl as quickly as possible," she thought to herself.

At the time of the atomic bombing of Hiroshima, Setsuko Thurlow was an eighth-grade student attending a school for girls. She was one of more than thirty teenage girls who had been recruited and trained to do top secret recording work at the Japanese army headquarters in Hiroshima, which is where she was when the bomb went off.

"Can you imagine," Setsuko later reflected, "a 13-year-old girl doing such important work? That shows how desperate Japan was."

In these early moments after the atomic bomb exploded, Setsuko realized this man was trying to free her from the rubble and it was important she take action or she would likely die. She pushed and pushed. Began kicking. Somehow, she managed to crawl out of the rubble and through a doorway. "By the time I came out of the building, it was on fire," she remembered. "That meant about 30 other girls who were with me in that same place were burning to death."

The atomic bomb had been dropped out of a U.S. Army Air Forces airplane, which at the time was the only way to deliver such a bomb to its target. The weapon was ten feet long and weighed 9,700 pounds, about as much as a medium-sized elephant. A second plane flew directly behind the bomber plane, this one carrying three Los Alamos physicists, along with scores of scientific instruments with which to collect data.

The bomb's actual yield (the force required to produce an equivalent explosion) was for years debated among defense scientists and military officials. Finally, in 1985, the U.S. government settled on that number as being equivalent to 15 kilotons of TNT. A Strategic Bombing Survey conducted after the war estimated that 2,100 tons of conventional bombs would have had to have been dropped on Hiroshima all at once to achieve a similar effect.

Setsuko Thurlow made it outside. It was early in the morning, but it looked like night. The air was thick with dark smoke. Setsuko saw a black object shuffling toward her, followed by other black objects that, at first, she mistook for ghosts.

"Parts of the bodies were missing," she realized. "The skin and flesh were hanging from the bones. Some were carrying their own eyeballs."

Down the road a ways, Dr. Michihiko Hachiya, director of the Hiroshima Communications Hospital, had been lying on his living room floor, recovering from a night shift at work, when a strong flash of light—one that indicated the atomic bomb had detonated—startled him. Then came a second flash of light. He was knocked out, or was he? Through swirling dust Dr. Hachiya began to discern what was going on. Parts of his body, his thighs and his neck, were mangled and bleeding. He was naked. His clothes had been blown off. "Embedded in my neck was a sizable fragment of glass which I matter-of-factly dislodged," Dr. Hachiya later recalled, and that he wondered, "Where was my wife?" He looked at his own body again. "Blood began to spurt. Had my carotid artery been cut? Would I bleed to death?"

After some time, Dr. Hachiya found his wife, Yaeko-san. Their small house was collapsing around the two of them and they raced outside, "running, stumbling, falling," he remembered. "Getting to my feet I discovered that I had tripped over a man's head."

Setsuko Thurlow's survivor experience, and Dr. Hachiya's survivor experience, and countless others like theirs were for decades suppressed by the U.S. Army and its occupation forces in Japan. The effects that atomic weapons used in combat had on people and buildings were kept classified and proprietary because U.S. defense officials wanted that information for themselves. For another nuclear war. The Pentagon wanted to make sure it knew more about nuclear blast effects than any future enemy could possibly know.

In flashes of energy and light, two atomic bombs—one dropped on Hiroshima on August 6, 1945, and a second dropped on Nagasaki three days later—ended a world war in which 50 to 75 million people already had died. Now, starting in 1945, a small group of nuclear scientists and defense officials in the U.S.

began making new and bigger plans, to use scores of atomic weapons in the next world war. A war that could be expected to kill, at minimum, 600 million people, one-fifth of the entire world's population.

Which brings us back to the men seated in the underground bunker, in December 1960, listening to plans for General Nuclear War.

CHAPTER THREE

The Buildup

1945–1990:
Los Alamos, Lawrence Livermore,
and Sandia National Laboratories

The plan for nuclear war being secretly shown at Strategic Air Command headquarters in 1960 had been a year or so in the making. It was ordered for the U.S. president by the secretary of defense. Fifteen years had passed since the two atomic weapons were dropped on Japan, each one killing tens of thousands of people in an instant with tens of thousands more people burning to death in the ensuing firestorms.

Back in August 1945, the U.S. had a third bomb ready to be shipped out, with enough nuclear material in its arsenal to produce a fourth bomb by the end of the month, which was the plan of action had Japan not surrendered. "The original atomic bombs were like school science projects," says Dr. Glen McDuff, a long-serving Los Alamos nuclear weapons engineer and the former historian-curator of the laboratory's classified museum. "Nineteen out of every twenty pieces of scientific equipment they had," explains McDuff, "they designed and built themselves with only about eighty common vacuum tubes."

With the world war finally over, the fate of the Los Alamos

nuclear laboratory was anyone's guess. "After the war, with just one atomic bomb in the stockpile, the Los Alamos lab and town infrastructure crumbled," reflects McDuff. "It was a daily struggle just to keep the lights on. Half the Los Alamos staff left. Things looked bleak. Until, that is, the navy got involved."

The U.S. Navy was by far the most powerful maritime fighting force in the world and it was deeply worried about its looming obsolescence in this new age of atomic warfare. So it planned a live-action series of three atomic bomb tests—for all to see.

Atomic test Baker burst through the lagoon surface, lofting 2 million cubic yards of radioactive seawater and sediment into the air in 1946. (U.S. Library of Congress)

Operation Crossroads was a grand, celebratory affair. A massive, public-relations-based military test designed to demonstrate how eighty-eight naval vessels could survive—even thrive—in a future nuclear battle fought at sea. More than 42,000 people gathered at Bikini Atoll in the Marshall Islands. World leaders, journalists, dignitaries, heads of state—they traveled to this far corner of the Pacific to witness the live-fire atomic explosions. This was America's first use of an atomic weapon since the war. A demonstration of what lay ahead.

"For a crumbling Los Alamos in 1946," says McDuff, "the navy was their savior."

Operation Crossroads injected the atomic bomb program with new life. By mid-1946, the American nuclear stockpile grew to nine atomic bombs. After the test, the Joint Chiefs of Staff requested an evaluation of the "atomic bomb as a military weapon" to determine its next move. The report—classified until 1975—set the burgeoning military-industrial complex alight. The details were alarming.

Atomic bombs were "a threat to mankind and to civilization," warned the group of admirals, generals, and scientists who authored the report, "weapons of mass destruction" able to "depopulate vast areas of the Earth's surface." But they could also be very useful, the group told the Joint Chiefs of Staff. "If used in numbers," they wrote, "atomic bombs not only can nullify any nation's military effort, but can demolish its social and economic structures and prevent their reestablishment for long periods of time."

The board's recommendation was to stockpile more bombs.

Russia would soon have its own atomic arsenal, the report made clear, and that made America vulnerable to a surprise attack—later to be known as a Bolt out of the Blue attack. "With the advent of the atomic bomb," the board warned, "surprise has achieved supreme value so that an aggressor, striking suddenly and unexpectedly with a number of atomic bombs [could] insure the ultimate defeat of an initially stronger adversary"—meaning the United States.

What America had created presaged its own potential demise.

"The United States has no alternative but to continue the manufacture and stockpiling of weapons," the Joint Chiefs were advised. They took notice, and approved.

By 1947, the U.S. stockpile rose to 13 atomic bombs.

By 1948, there were 50.

By 1949, 170.

From declassified records, we now know that military planners agreed among themselves that 200 nuclear bombs provided enough firepower to destroy the entire Soviet empire. But come summer that same year, the U.S. monopoly on nuclear weapons came to its inevitable end. On August 29, 1949, the Russians exploded their first atomic bomb, an almost exact copy of the one the U.S. had dropped on Nagasaki four years earlier. The bomb's blueprints had been stolen from the Los Alamos laboratory by a German-born, British-educated, communist spy. A Manhattan Project scientist named Klaus Fuchs.

The race to build even more atomic bombs now accelerated dramatically. By 1950, the U.S. added 129 atomic weapons to its stockpile, bringing the total from 170 to 299. At the time, the Soviet Union had five.

The following year, in 1951, the number climbed again—this time to an astonishing 438 atomic weapons in the U.S. arsenal. More than twice the number the Joint Chiefs of Staff had been told could "depopulate vast areas of the Earth's surface leaving only vestigial remnants of man's material works."

The next year, there was a near-doubling of the near-doubling yet again.

By 1952, there were 841 atomic weapons in the U.S. stockpile. *Eight hundred and forty-one.*

With the U.S. monopoly on nuclear weapons now over, the race for nuclear supremacy had taken on a new urgency. Halfway across the world, the Soviets began building atomic weapons at a frenzied pace.

In just three years, the USSR grew its arsenal from one bomb to fifty.

But the atomic bomb—its extraordinary power, its mass-killing capacity—would soon pale in comparison to what was coming next. American and Russian weapons designers each had radical new plans on their individual drawing boards. What followed was the invention of "the most destructive, inhumane, and indiscriminate weapon ever created," in the words of a group of Nobel laureates. A climate-altering, famine-causing, civilization-ending, genome-changing, newer, bigger, even more monstrous nuclear weapon—one that the scientists involved called "the Super."

Indeed, "the Super . . . works better in large sizes than in small sizes," its designer, Richard Garwin, tells us. Confirming for readers of this book that "[yes] I am the architect of the Super . . . of this first thermonuclear bomb." Edward Teller conceived it, Richard Garwin drew it—at a time when no one else knew how.

The year 1952 saw the invention of the thermonuclear bomb, also called the hydrogen bomb. A two-stage mega-weapon: a nuclear bomb within a nuclear bomb. A thermonuclear weapon uses an atomic bomb inside itself as its triggering mechanism. As an internal, explosive fuse. The Super's monstrous, explosive power comes as the result of an uncontrolled, self-sustaining chain reaction in which hydrogen isotopes fuse under extremely high temperatures in a process called nuclear fusion.

An atomic bomb will kill tens of thousands of people, as did the ones dropped on Hiroshima and Nagasaki. A thermonuclear bomb, if detonated on a city like New York or Seoul, will kill millions of people in a superheated flash.

The prototype weapon Richard Garwin designed in 1952 had an explosive power of 10.4 megatons. The near equivalent of 1,000 Hiroshima bombs exploding all at once. It was an atrocious weapon. Garwin's own mentor, the Manhattan Project's Enrico Fermi, experienced a crisis of conscience at the very thought of such a horrifying weapon being built. Fermi and colleague I. I. Rabi temporarily broke ranks with their weapons-building colleagues and wrote to President Truman, declaring the Super to be "an evil thing."

Their words, in writing: "The fact that no limits exist to the destructiveness of this weapon makes its very existence and the knowledge of its construction a danger to humanity as a whole. It is necessarily an evil thing considered in any light."

But the president ignored the plea to stop building the Super, and Richard Garwin was given the go-ahead to draw the plans. "If the hydrogen bomb was inherently evil, it's still evil," Garwin says.

The Super was built. Its code name was Mike. The series was Ivy. "So it was the Ivy Mike test."

On November 1, 1952, it was test-fired on Elugelab island in the Marshall Islands. The Ivy Mike prototype bomb weighed around 80 tons (160,000 pounds), an instrument of destruction itself so physically enormous it had to be constructed inside a corrugated-aluminum building eighty-eight feet long and forty-six feet wide.

Ivy Mike exploded with unprecedented yield. The bomb crater left behind was described in a classified report as being "large enough to hold 14 buildings the size of the Pentagon." And while there is much to say about the inhumanely destructive power of thermonuclear weapons in general, two aircraft photographs—before and after shots of the Ivy Mike bomb test—tell the story.

In the top image on the following page, Elugelab island appears as it had since its geological origin.

In the bottom image, the entire island is gone. In its place is a crater two miles in diameter and 180 feet deep. Scorching the earth with mass extermination weapons had just been one-upped

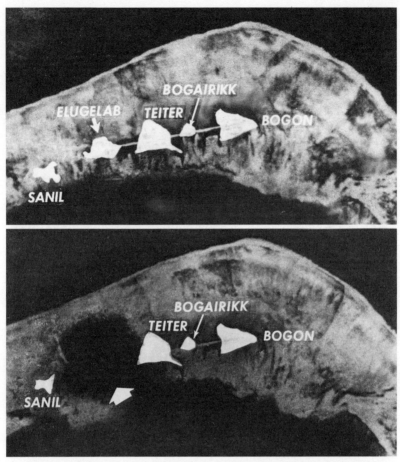

Elugelab island before and after the Ivy Mike thermonuclear bomb test in 1952.
(U.S. National Archives)

by an order of magnitude. The invention of the Super brought with it the existence of a weapon that can vanish land.

What happened after U.S. war planners saw what 10.4 megatons could instantly destroy simply boggles the mind. What came next was a mad, mad rush to stockpile thermonuclear weapons, first by the hundreds and then by the thousands.

In 1952 there were 841 nuclear bombs. The next year there were 1,169.

"The process became industrialized," Los Alamos historian Glen McDuff explains. "These were not science projects anymore."

By 1954, there were 1,703 nuclear weapons in the stockpile. The U.S. military-industrial complex was now churning out (on average) 1.5 nuclear weapons per day.

1955: 2,422. Almost two bombs per day, and with ten new systems introduced including three new styles of thermonuclear bombs.

1956: 3,692 bombs. The numbers continued to escalate to the point of dizziness. With production levels soaring, these mass-destruction weapons were now coming off literal assembly lines at an average pace of 3.5 nuclear bombs *per day.*

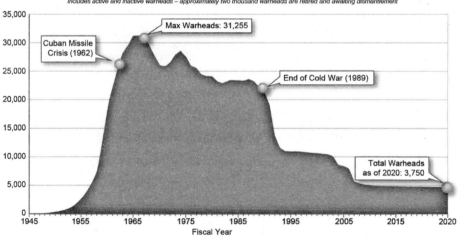

The frenzied buildup of the classified nuclear stockpile.
(U.S. Department of Defense; U.S. Department of Energy)

By 1957, there were 5,543 bombs in the U.S. stockpile. That is, 1,851 new nuclear weapons in a single year. More than five per day. And the numbers kept growing.

1958: 7,345.

And growing.

1959: 12,298.

By 1960, when the U.S. war planners met in the underground bunker in Nebraska, the U.S. stockpile contained 18,638 nuclear bombs.

By 1967, it reached an all-time high of 31,255 nuclear bombs.

Thirty-one thousand, two hundred and fifty-five nuclear bombs.

Why stockpile 1,000 or 18,000 or 31,255 nuclear bombs when a single one of them the size of Ivy Mike, dropped on New York City or Moscow, could leave some 10 million people dead? Why continue to mass-produce thousands of these weapons when the use of a single thermonuclear bomb will almost certainly ignite a wider, unstoppable, civilization-ending nuclear war?

A new term was afoot. A figure of speech known as "deterrence." To keep something from happening. But what does that even mean?

Deterrence

There are rules of nuclear war that guide U.S. nuclear policy. Concepts created by war planners starting in the 1950s to allegedly keep nuclear war from happening, while at the same time allowing war planners to figure out how to fight and win a nuclear war when it comes. Rule No. 1 is deterrence, sold to the public as the idea that maintaining a massive nuclear stockpile is imperative for the purpose of discouraging nuclear attack.

Deterrence guides nuclear policy. It works like this: Each nuclear-armed nation builds an arsenal of nuclear weapons that it keeps pointed at its nuclear-armed enemy, ready to launch in a few minutes' time. Each nuclear-armed nation vows never to use nuclear weapons unless they are forced to use them. Some people see deterrence as a peaceful savior. Others see it as doublespeak, asking, How could having nuclear weapons keep people safe from having a nuclear war?

For decades, deterrence has allowed the Defense Department to build tens of thousands of nuclear weapons, their delivery systems, and a complex system of counter-weapons to defend against nuclear attack. Trillions of dollars have been spent on nuclear weapons. There is no way to know the total for sure because the true numbers are classified. Rule No. 1 alleges to be simple: deterrence keeps the world safe from ever having a nuclear war. But what happens if deterrence fails?

CHAPTER FOUR

The SIOP

The Single Integrated Operational
Plan for General Nuclear War

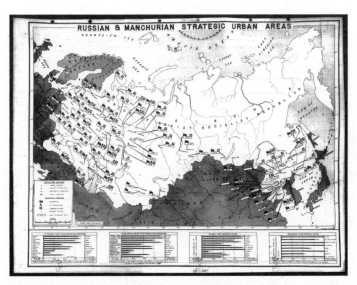

Less than two weeks after WWII ended, the U.S. military requested 466 nuclear bombs for the stockpile, the first known, systematic estimate of nuclear bombs it thought necessary to destroy Soviet and Manchurian targets. (U.S. National Archives)

As the U.S. nuclear stockpile was multiplying out of control, so were each of the individual U.S. military forces' plans for nuclear war. As crazy as this now seems, before December 1960, each U.S. Army, Navy, and Air Force chief had control over his own stockpile of nuclear weapons, their delivery systems, and target lists. In an attempt to rein in the potential for mayhem from these multiple, competing plans for nuclear war, the secretary of defense ordered all of them to be integrated into one single plan, which is how the Single Integrated Operational Plan—the SIOP—got its name.

In 1960, Strategic Air Command (later called U.S. Strategic Command) had 280,000 employees. To work on this new plan, 1,300 of them were corralled into a Joint Strategic Target Planning Staff. Men and women whose sole job was to integrate all the individual target packages into a single target deck. This amalgamated plan is what John Rubel and his colleagues learned about that December day in the bunker beneath Offutt Air Force Base. The secret plan that, if activated, would result in the deaths of at least 600 million people on the other side of the world.

This plan for General Nuclear War showed how the entire U.S. military force would be launched at Moscow in a preemptive first strike. How defense scientists had carefully calculated that 275 million people would be killed in the first hour, and that at least 325 million more people would die from radioactive fallout over the next six or so months. Roughly half of these deaths would be in the Soviet Union's neighboring countries—countries not at war with America, but who would be caught in the crosswinds. This included as many as 300 million Chinese.

In 1960, the world's population was 3 billion. What this meant was that the Pentagon had paid 1,300 people to compile a war plan that would kill one-fifth of the people on Earth in a preemptive nuclear first strike. It's important to note that this number did not account for the 100 million or so Americans who would almost certainly be killed by a Russian equal-measure counterattack. Nor did it account for another 100 million or so people in North and South America who would die from radioactive fallout over approximately the next six months. Or the untold numbers of people who would starve to death from the climate effects of a world set on fire.

After the briefing was concluded, a second classified plan of attack was demonstrated, one that Rubel described in his 2008 memoir as being an "attack on China given by a different speaker." It too involved similar theatrics with ladders and pointers and plastic sheets. "Eventually [this speaker] arrived at a chart showing deaths from fallout alone."

The briefer pointed to a graph. "It showed that deaths from fallout as time passed [would be] . . . 300 million, half the population of China," Rubel wrote.

After some time, the meeting was adjourned.

The following morning John Rubel participated in yet another meeting, smaller this time. It included himself, the secretary of defense, each of the Joint Chiefs of Staff, the secretaries of the army, navy, and air force, and the commandant of the marines. Rubel recalled that the chairman of the Joint Chiefs, Lyman Lemnitzer, "told everyone they had done a very fine job, a very difficult job, and that they should be commended for their work." Rubel recalled the army chief, George Decker, expressing similar congratulatory remarks. And he remembered how the chief naval officer, Arleigh Burke, "took his customary pipe out of his jaw and repeated the same message—hard job, well done, should be commended." That the last man to speak, General Thomas White of the air force, "ground out a comparable stream of the platitudes favored that morning in his gravelly voice always filled with a certain air of authority."

No one spoke up to object to the indiscriminate killing of 600 million people in a U.S. government–led, preemptive, first-strike nuclear attack, Rubel wrote. Not any of the Joint Chiefs. Not the secretary of defense. Not John Rubel. Then, finally, one man did. General David M. Shoup, the commandant of the U.S. Marine

Corps, a marine awarded the Medal of Honor for his actions in
World War II.

"Shoup was a short man with rimless glasses who could have
passed for a schoolteacher from a rural mid-American community," recalled Rubel. He remembered how Shoup spoke in a calm,
level voice when he offered a sole opposing view on the plan for
nuclear war. That Shoup said: "All I can say is, any plan that mur-
ders three hundred million Chinese when it might not even be their
war is not a good plan. That is not the American way." The room
fell silent, Rubel wrote. "Nobody moved a muscle."

Nobody seconded Shoup's dissent.

No one else said anything.

According to Rubel, everyone just looked the other way.

It was decades later that Rubel confessed that this U.S. plan for
nuclear war he participated in reminded him of the Nazis' plans
for genocide. In his memoir, he referred to a time in an earlier
world war when a group of Third Reich officials met at a lakeside
villa in a German town called Wannsee. It was there, over the
course of a ninety-minute meeting, that this group of allegedly
rational men decided among themselves how to move forward with
the genocide in a war they were presently winning—World War
II—so as to ensure total victory for themselves. Millions of people
needed to die, these Reich officials agreed.

Millions of them.

Finally, when John Rubel was in his late eighties, he articu-
lated key similarities he perceived between the meeting in Wannsee
and the meeting beneath the Offutt air base in Nebraska. "I
thought of the Wannsee Conference in January 1942," Rubel
wrote, "when an assemblage of German bureaucrats swiftly agreed
on a program to exterminate every last Jew they could find anywhere in Europe, using methods of mass extermination more tech-
nologically efficient than the vans filled with exhaust gases, the

mass shootings, or incineration in barns and synagogues used until then." Nearing the end of his life, Rubel decided to tell the world what he could not back in 1960. "I felt as if I were witnessing a comparable descent into the deep heart of darkness, a twilight underworld governed by disciplined, meticulous and energetically mindless groupthink aimed at wiping out half the people living on nearly one third of the earth's surface."

The Final Solution called for the extermination of all of Europe's millions of Jews and millions more people the Nazis considered subhuman. The plan for General Nuclear War that John Rubel and his colleagues signed off on—the Single Integrated Operational Plan—called for the mass extermination of some 600 million Russians, Chinese, Poles, Czechs, Austrians, Yugoslavians, Hungarians, Romanians, Albanians, Bulgarians, Latvians, Estonians, Lithuanians, Finns, Swedes, Indians, Afghans, Japanese, and others that U.S. defense scientists calculated would be caught in the crosswinds.

The Final Solution was enacted. The SIOP never has been—not so far. But a similar, still-classified plan exists today. Over the years, its name has changed. What began as the Single Integrated Operational Plan is now the Operational Plan, or OPLAN. For the Nuclear Information Project, in consort with the Federation of American Scientists, project director Hans Kristensen and senior researcher Matt Korda have identified the current Operational Plan as OPLAN 8010-12. And that it consists of " 'a family of plans' directed against four identified adversaries: Russia, China, North Korea, and Iran."

The number of nuclear weapons in the U.S. stockpile today is smaller than it was in 1960, but there still are 1,770 deployed nuclear weapons, a majority of which are on ready-for-launch status, with thousands more held in reserve, for a total inventory of more than 5,000 warheads. Russia has 1,674 deployed nuclear weapons, a majority of which are on ready-for-launch status, with thousands more in reserve, for a total inventory that is roughly the same size as the U.S.'s.

It is precisely the effects of this kind of mass extermination plan that *Nuclear War: A Scenario* is based upon.

"A nuclear war cannot be won and must never be fought," President Ronald Reagan and Soviet General Secretary Mikhail Gorbachev cautioned the world in a joint statement in 1985. Decades later, in 2022, President Joe Biden warned Americans that "the prospect of [nuclear] Armageddon" is at a terrifying new high.

So here we are now. Teetering at the edge—perhaps even closer than ever before.

BE PREPARED FOR A
NUCLEAR EXPLOSION

Nuclear explosions can cause significant damage and casualties from blast, heat, and radiation but you can keep your family safe by knowing what to do and being prepared if it occurs.

FEMA P-2149/March 2018

A nuclear weapon is a device that uses a nuclear reaction to create an explosion.

Nuclear devices range from a small portable device carried by an individual to a weapon carried by a missile.

A nuclear explosion may occur with a few minutes warning or without warning.

Bright FLASH can cause temporary blindness for less than a minute.	**BLAST WAVE** can cause death, injury, and damage to structures several miles out from the blast.	**RADIATION** can damage cells of the body. Large exposures can cause radiation sickness.	**FIRE AND HEAT** can cause death, burn injuries, and damage to structures several miles out.	**ELECTROMAGNETIC PULSE (EMP)** can damage electronics several miles out from the detonation and cause temporary disruptions further out.	**FALLOUT** is radioactive, visible dirt and debris raining down that can cause sickness to those who are outside.

Fallout is most dangerous in the first few hours after the detonation when it is giving off the highest levels of radiation. It takes time for fallout to arrive back to ground level, often more than 15 minutes for areas outside of the immediate blast damage zones. This is enough time for you to be able to prevent significant radiation exposure by following these simple steps:

GET INSIDE

STAY INSIDE

STAY TUNED

 Get inside the nearest building to avoid radiation. Brick or concrete are best.

 Stay inside for 24 hours unless local authorities provide other instructions.

Tune into any media available for official information such as when it is safe to exit and where you should go.

 Remove contaminated clothing and wipe off or wash unprotected skin if you were outside after the fallout arrived.

 Family should stay where they are inside. Reunite later to avoid exposure to dangerous radiation.

 Battery operated and hand crank radios will function after a nuclear detonation.

 Go to the basement or middle of the building. Stay away from the outer walls and roof.

Keep your pets inside.

 Cell phone, text messaging, television, and internet services may be disrupted or unavailable.

"Be Prepared for a Nuclear Explosion."
(U.S. Federal Emergency Management Agency)

Part II

THE FIRST 24 MINUTES

FOUR-TENTHS OF A SECOND
AFTER LAUNCH
Pyongsong, North Korea

Nuclear war begins with a blip on a radar screen.

It is 4:03 a.m. in North Korea, darkness before dawn. In a seemingly barren field twenty miles outside the capital, Pyongyang, a massive cloud of fire erupts just feet off the ground. Hot rocket exhaust spews from the tail end of North Korea's powerful intercontinental ballistic missile, an ICBM, as it launches off a 22-wheeled vehicle parked here in the dirt. The Hwasong-17, which analysts call "the Monster," begins ascent.

SBIRS satellite. (U.S. Department of Defense, Lockheed Martin)

Hovering 22,300 miles above planet Earth, as if floating in space, a car-sized sensor from the U.S. Defense Department's SBIRS ("*sibbers*") satellite system spots the fire from the missile's hot rocket exhaust through the cloud cover. This happens within a few tenths of a second after ignition.

SBIRS is a group of satellites in the U.S. Space-Based Infrared System of satellites, and because of how it moves, it seems to linger here in space—roughly one-tenth of the way to the moon. By circling the world at precisely the same speed as the Earth turns, a satellite in geosynchronous orbit behaves as if suspended.

SBIRS alarms: **BALLISTIC MISSILE LAUNCH, ALERT!**

1 TO 3 SECONDS AFTER LAUNCH
Aerospace Data Facility—Colorado

Buckley Space Force Base radomes. (U.S. Space Force, Tech. Sgt. JT Armstrong)

Raw data from space streams down into the Aerospace Data Facility, a National Reconnaissance Office (NRO) mission ground station at Buckley Space Force Base in Aurora, Colorado. The existence of this installation, as well as its sister ground stations at Fort Belvoir in Virginia and at White Sands in New Mexico, was classified until 2008. NRO's intelligence findings are among the most jealously guarded in the United States national security apparatus. Its motto is *Supra et Ultra*—Above and Beyond.

Everything in this facility is classified.

Every bit of data handled in this office is safeguarded by a labyrinth of highly classified protocols, many of them encrypted. Information here is often flagged "ECI," for Exceptionally Controlled Information.

NRO's officers are highly trained; there is no room for mistakes. Aerospace Data Facilities are responsible for command and control of Defense Department reconnaissance satellites. They analyze, report, and disseminate information about incoming nuclear threats.

Alarms wail.

BALLISTIC MISSILE LAUNCH, ALERT! has everyone's attention.

Co-located in this facility are hundreds of National Security Agency personnel, who begin sending encrypted emergency messages to three nuclear command centers located inside three separate command bunkers, each one fortified underground in three different places:

- The Missile Warning Center, Cheyenne Mountain Complex, Colorado
- The National Military Command Center, Pentagon, Washington, D.C.
- The Global Operations Center, Offutt Air Force Base, Nebraska

The NRO mission ground station here in Colorado is the nation's primary domestic downlink facility for all U.S. military satellites. "There are others," says former chief scientist Doug Beason of the U.S. Air Force Space Command. This includes an organization known as DEFSMAC (*"def-smack"*), the Defense Special Missile and Aeronautics Center, a classified facility located inside NSA headquarters at Fort George G. Meade in Maryland. Everything that will happen in a nuclear war when it comes hinges upon what analysts at these ground stations interpret as happening in the moment.

In this scenario, that means now.

4 SECONDS
Space

The SBIRS geo-sync satellite over North Korea is roughly the size of a metro bus with two twenty-foot-long solar wings extended wide on either side. SBIRS sensors have independent tasking capabilities, meaning they are able to scan wide swaths of territory and simultaneously fixate on a particular area of concern. Sensors so powerful they can see a single lighted match from 200 miles away.

The Space-Based Infrared System is America's twenty-first-century version of Paul Revere. But it's not the British who are coming, not on foot or on horseback. It is a nuclear-armed, intercontinental ballistic missile. The all-powerful, unstoppable, civilization-threatening ICBM.

Sensors aboard the U.S. satellite systems over North Korea perform their onboard signal processing, streaming colossal loads of early-warning sensor data down to planet Earth.

To think: the world's first satellite was launched by the Russians in 1957, a beach ball–sized spaceship called Sputnik, with radio antennas and silver-zinc batteries. Now, decades later, there are more than 9,000 high-powered, microprocessor-capable satellites circling the Earth, connecting people through telecommunication, aiding with navigation, forecasting the weather, entertaining with TV.

SBIRS does none of this; it keeps guard. Vigilantly waiting and watching, twenty-four hours a day, seven days a week, 365 days a year, for that initial, explosive spark of a nuclear threat.

A spark indicating an action that cannot be undone.

5 SECONDS
Aerospace Data Facility—Colorado

Inside the Aerospace Data Facility in Colorado, some of the fastest computer systems in the world sort raw SBIRS sensor data at a meteoric pace. They are busy measuring the dimensions of the launching ICBM's fiery plume. The hot rocket exhaust on a short-range ballistic missile differs dramatically in plume brightness and size from that on the intercontinental ballistic missile—each being precisely measurable from space.

Ballistic missile launches are not uncommon. They are also increasing at unprecedented speeds. In 2021, the U.S. Space Force tracked 1,968 missile launches around the globe, a number that "increased more than over three and a half times in 2022," says Space Systems Command's Colonel Brian Denaro. As of September 2023, Russia continues to notify the U.S. of its ballistic missile test launches.

No one wants to start a nuclear war by accident.

As a general rule, missile tests as significant as an ICBM launch are announced, usually to neighbors—through diplomatic channels, back channels, some other kind of channel, but almost always through a channel.

The exception is North Korea.

Between January 2022 and May 2023, North Korea test-launched more than 100 missiles, including nuclear-capable weapons that can hit the continental United States.

None of them were announced.

"They want to maintain the element of surprise," intelligence analyst Joseph Bermudez Jr. tells us. "To reinforce propaganda that they're a mighty and powerful nation."

Which is why Defense Department satellites remain "parked"

over North Korea. To examine ICBM exhaust, starting in the first fraction of a second after launch.

In Colorado, plume measurements confirm what analysts are seeing: an ICBM launch out of North Korea with a trajectory that is alarming. The missile is not heading into space, as it would be for a satellite launch, or toward the Sea of Japan, a commonplace trajectory in a demonstration-of-power test.

All critical components of America's colossal early-warning system are now correlating the missile's trajectory and integrating data streams. Working to characterize more precisely the exact nature of this event.

Is it a provocative test or a nuclear attack? A hack or a hoax?

At once, a vast worldwide network of U.S. intelligence, surveillance, and reconnaissance assets begins churning out every manner of intelligence information in the arsenal. SIGINT (signals intelligence), IMINT (image intelligence), TECHINT (technical intelligence), GEOINT (geospatial intelligence), MASINT (measurement and signature intelligence), CYBINT (cyber intelligence), COMINT (communications intelligence), HUMINT (human intelligence), and OSINT (open source intelligence)—all of it surging into the system in order to create an accurate picture of this detected event.

Every fraction of a second matters. Every byte of information counts.

6 SECONDS
National Military Command Center, Pentagon

The Pentagon. (U.S. Air Force, Staff Sgt. Brittany A. Chase)

The National Military Command Center beneath the Pentagon serves as the primary command and control facility in a nuclear war.

It may—or may not—also be the target.

In this scenario, it is 3:03 p.m. local time in Washington, D.C., March 30, early spring. It has been six seconds since the ICBM's launch. Computer algorithms in the National Military Command Center have already begun predicting the missile's intercontinental trajectory, based on available data, but a localized target area cannot yet be accurately discerned.

Is the missile headed for America? To Hawaii?

Or is the target the continental United States?

On any given day, at any given hour, there are hundreds of people working in this heavily fortified nuclear bunker beneath the

Pentagon. Each of them performing duties related to three primary missions assigned to the National Military Command Center
in its quest to ensure U.S. national security:

- The monitoring of military activity and events around
  the world
- The watching of the world for nuclear weapons activity
- The ability to respond to specific crises, as necessary—
  including the execution of the OPLAN (formerly the SIOP)

Now, mere seconds after the confirmation of an ICBM launch
out of North Korea, all eyes remain focused on a theater-size electronic screen mounted on the command center's wall. On a dot
moving ominously across the screen: an avatar for a nuclear-armed
Hwasong-17 ballistic missile.

As J-3 Operations Directorate officers pour into the National
Military Command Center, the J-2 deputy director of intelligence
works to get a North Korean official on the line. Among the Joint
Staff officers in the room delivering commands are:

- The J-32 deputy director for intelligence, surveillance and
  reconnaissance (ISR) operations (two-star general/flag
  officer)
- The J-36 deputy director for nuclear and homeland
  defense operations (one-star general/flag officer)
- The J-39 deputy director for global operations (one-star
  general/flag officer)

Not since 9/11 has everyone and their staff been in such an acute
state of heightened alert.

"It's hard to capture and explain the fog and friction of war,"
Colonel John Brunderman says of his experiences in the bunker

beneath the Pentagon on 9/11. A command post that "functions as the top of the pyramid for all U.S. command posts around the world." A classified facility that ensures "connectivity for the Single Integrated Operational Plan execution, worldwide situation monitoring, and crisis management." And yet, in the fog of war, uncertainty remains. "When you're looking for things that are abnormal," Colonel Brunderman warns, "a lot of things appear abnormal."

15 SECONDS
Buckley Space Force Base, Colorado

Buckley Space Force Base. (U.S. Space Force)

In Colorado, combat pilots run toward fighter jets waiting on the tarmac, ready to take to the air. Fifteen seconds have passed since launch and the ICBM has traveled far enough now that satellite sensors can determine its trajectory more precisely.

The outlook is catastrophic.

A worst-case scenario beyond comprehension.

The Hwasong-17 is traveling toward the continental United States.

Buckley Space Force Base is home to Space Delta 4, the missile-warning unit that operates defense satellites in space as well as ground-based early-warning radars around the world.

Space Delta 4 is in charge of reporting strategic warning information, via encrypted communications links, to three commands:

- NORAD—North American Aerospace Defense Command
- NORTHCOM—U.S. Northern Command
- STRATCOM—U.S. Strategic Command

Each of these three commands has an early-warning center located eighty miles down the road from the space force base, inside the Cheyenne Mountain Complex—America's legendary nuclear bunker, built inside a granite mountain during the Cold War.

Everyone with Space Delta 4 is hyper-focused on what appears to be an attacking intercontinental ballistic missile en route to the United States of America. The dreaded ICBM is unstoppable and nuclear capable.

Once launched, an ICBM cannot be recalled.

Across NORAD, NORTHCOM, and STRATCOM, everyone waits for an over-the-horizon ground radar system to confirm that a nuclear-armed missile is indeed attacking the United States.

This secondary corroboration is imperative.

Given the missile's trajectory, the first radar station to see the attacking missile as it comes over the horizon will be Clear Space Force Station in Alaska. Their state-of-the-art machine eyes remain focused on incoming threats from the Pacific.

It will take another eight minutes or so for the radars in Alaska to see the incoming missile. To analysts here, this will feel like an excruciating amount of time as the clock ticks on an incoming nuclear missile threat.

20 SECONDS

Clear Space Force Station, Alaska

Clear Space Force Station, Alaska, Long Range Discrimination Radar.
(U.S. Missile Defense Agency)

Clear Space Force Station in Alaska is a remote military installation strategically positioned on the outskirts of Fairbanks. In
late March the average temperature hovers in the teens. Most of
the snow has melted by now.

At the center of the base stands a five-story-tall search, track,
and discrimination radar called the Long Range Discrimination
Radar. This massive terrestrial sentinel is the newest component
in a decades-old early-warning radar system. Its job is to watch for
missiles attacking the U.S. from the Pacific theater, and to relay
warnings to NORAD, NORTHCOM, and STRATCOM.

From inside the structure, two massive, sixty-foot-diameter antennae scan the skies 24/7/365, in search of any indication of a missile attack. The radar system provides "an extra set of keen eyes that will paint the picture of any threat coming our way," NORAD's Lieutenant General A. C. Roper explains.

At twenty seconds after launch, the Arctic Airmen and Guardians assigned to the Space Warning Squadrons here outside Fairbanks have received word from Space Delta 4 of an attacking ICBM. But they see nothing. Not yet. Even the advanced, over-the-horizon radar systems can only see so far.

So the humans manning the systems must wait.

The massive radar system will remain blind to an attacking ICBM until that missile is in its Midcourse Phase—when the nuclear payload in its nose cone will be perilously closer to striking the United States.

Streams of data from ground radars feed to the command posts located thousands of miles across the North American continent. Into the classified underground Missile Warning Center inside Cheyenne Mountain, Colorado.

For now, the Long Range Discrimination Radar remains deceptively calm.

30 SECONDS
Cheyenne Mountain Complex, Colorado

Here in central Colorado, 2,000 feet below a triple-peaked mountain of igneous rock, alarms screech, lights flash, every computer generating a classified message to indicate the dreaded NUCLEAR LAUNCH ALERT.

Thirty seconds have passed since launch.

The Joint Operation Center in the Cheyenne Mountain Complex in 2023.
(North American Aerospace Defense Command, Thomas Paul)

The SBIRS satellites now have enough track data on the ICBM to determine it is heading toward a target somewhere on the East Coast of the United States.

Everyone in the Cheyenne Mountain Complex is alerted to the threat. Everyone is stunned by what is going on.

Sensor data from space and ground radar stations around the world inundate Missile Warning Center personnel, propelling them to task. Everyone is working to characterize the incoming threat. Everyone is seeing the same thing.

One, single, incoming ICBM.

Everyone is thinking the same thing.

One nuclear missile doesn't make any sense.

If North Korea really is attacking the U.S. with an ICBM, it will be considered a preemptive, nuclear first strike. If ordered by the president, the response from the U.S. military will be the overwhelming and unconditional use of nuclear force.

North Korea will be destroyed.

"This kind of Bolt out of the Blue attack is [characterized] as a surprise attack, a sneak attack," former secretary of defense

William Perry tells us. A military tactic as old as warfare itself. But in this age of nuclear weapons, it is national suicide for any country to be as foolhardy as to preemptively strike the United States. All deterrence is predicated on the idea that a Bolt out of the Blue attack against a nuclear-armed superpower all but ensures the attacking nation's total and complete destruction.

Surprise attacks change history.

But a surprise attack is designed to decapitate. To cut off the head of the snake. For that, you send the mother lode of weapons; you do not send one, single ICBM. Not against a country like the United States that has 1,770 nuclear weapons deployed, a majority of which are at the ready to launch.

"One, single, attacking missile would not make sense," former SecDef Perry adds. And that this kind of oddity "would require additional information [before] the president would be told."

With lights in the Cheyenne Mountain Complex flashing red, with warning sirens screeching alarm, every person in this complex acts as trained. Feet, fingers, eyeballs, intuition—all human faculties moving in ballet-like consort with their machine partners, sorting sensor data into actionable intelligence. The Missile Warning Center here in Cheyenne Mountain is a collection point for missile launch data worldwide. The people here decide whether or not to categorize the information coming in as a risk to North America, and to the United States.

"We are the brain stem that is pulling it all together," says Cheyenne Mountain's deputy director Steven Rose, "correlating it, making sense of it, and passing it up to the brain—whether it's [to] the commander at NORAD, NORTHCOM, or STRATCOM." The Cheyenne Mountain Complex is the brain stem that interprets data for the commanding generals and admirals to decide when, and if, to get the president on the line. The act of preparing a nuclear attack assessment for the commander in chief makes the Cheyenne Mountain Complex "the most critical part of the nervous system, and the most vulnerable," Rose warns.

Physically, the facility can withstand direct impact from a 1-megaton thermonuclear bomb. But the vulnerability here is a theoretical one. Here, now, there is no room for error in judgment.

No room for error of any kind.

The fate of the country, and the planet, and its people, is on the line.

60 SECONDS

U.S. Strategic Command (STRATCOM)
Headquarters, Nebraska

Sixty seconds have passed. Beneath Offutt Air Force Base in Nebraska lies U.S. Strategic Command Headquarters— STRATCOM, as it is known— a 916,000-square-foot complex of bunkers, command centers, medical facilities, dining halls, sleep centers, power stations, tunnels, and more.

This $1.3 billion nuclear command center, buried several stories underground, has also been designed to withstand a direct hit from a 1-megaton thermonuclear bomb. Of the more than 3,500 people who work here, all of them are now focused on the incoming nuclear threat.

Eeeeeeettt! Eeeeeeettt! Eeeeeeettt!

All classified alert systems sound.

"There's about ten different ways to make sure that the commander knows that it's time to move," says former STRATCOM commander General John E. Hyten.

BALLISTIC MISSILE LAUNCH, ALERT!

Electronic alert systems sound, screech, wail, blink, and vibrate all at once. It is impossible to work at STRATCOM headquarters and not know an attacking ICBM is now presumed to be on its way to the United States.

The person who matters most in this moment is the commander of U.S. Strategic Command—the STRATCOM commander, as he or she is known—the nation's most senior military commander responsible for nuclear operations. More than 150,000 soldiers, sailors, airmen, marines, guardians, and civilians follow the STRATCOM commander's orders. In the Nuclear Command and Control System, the STRATCOM commander advises the president, and then follows his direct orders.

There is no human being in between these two individuals. Not the secretary of defense, not the chairman of the Joint Chiefs of Staff, not the vice president.

The duty of the STRATCOM commander comes with a responsibility unlike any other in the world.

Retired general George Lee Butler, who commanded U.S. nuclear forces from 1991 to 1994, summed up his responsibility like this: "Should our warning systems detect an attack on the United States . . . my role was to advise the president that we were under attack; to characterize it in terms of the type and number of weapons and their targets; to advise him of his options as portrayed in the nuclear war plan; to elicit an execution order; and promptly transmit it to the operational forces to ensure their timely launch, survival and delivery of their weapons."

Sixty seconds into this unfolding nuclear crisis, the STRATCOM commander in this scenario exits his office and hurries into a private elevator that is his alone. The ride down into the command center's nuclear bunker, called the Global Operations Center, takes just seconds.

"Our strategic forces are always ready to respond and everybody should know that," STRATCOM commander General Hyten told CNN in 2018. "They are ready this minute—under the ground, under the sea, in the air—we are ready to respond to any threat, and the adversaries of the world, including Kim Jong Un, have to know that."

The elevator doors open.

"If somebody launches a nuclear weapon against us, we launch one back," says General Hyten. "They launch another, we launch another. They launch two, we launch two."

It's an "escalation ladder," Hyten says.

The STRATCOM commander in this scenario hustles into the underground Battle Deck, a 1,000-square-foot, concrete-walled room.

His eyes focus on a massive electronic screen that covers almost the entire wall. A display screen the size of a movie theater screen.

Three electronic clocks display three different time sequences, being tracked in seconds, as the attacking nuclear missile hurtles toward the United States. These time sequences are referred to as:

- RED IMPACT: time remaining until an incoming enemy missile arrives on target
- BLUE IMPACT: time remaining until the U.S. nuclear counterattack strikes the enemy
- SAFE ESCAPE: time remaining for the commander to exit the bunker and escape

Here inside the bunker, the Battle Deck staff briefs the commander in a well-rehearsed order that wastes no time. With the Red Impact and Safe Escape clocks counting down, getting the Blue Impact clock running is the top priority: counterattack.

At the back of the room, a soundproof divider comes down from the ceiling.

It locks into place.

The men and women in the Battle Deck maintain some of the highest security clearances in the U.S. Nuclear Command and Control System. They rehearse launch protocols day in and day out. But the information about to be discussed is far too sensitive for anyone but a small group of STRATCOM officers to hear.

The core group assembled now begins discussing launch plans.

1 MINUTE, 30 SECONDS
NORAD Headquarters, Peterson Space Force Base, Colorado

A little more than nine miles northeast of Cheyenne Mountain (as the crow flies), at NORAD headquarters in Colorado, deputies, officers, and military aides run down the corridors of Peterson Space Force Base and into the NORAD-NORTHCOM command center. The Peterson command center looks similar to the one inside Cheyenne Mountain, only it's bigger. Designed to accommodate an ever-growing staff assigned to handle new threats.

This is a central collection and coordination facility for early-warning sensor data currently being received from, and disseminated to, mission partners in the U.S. and around the world. Nuclear Command and Control is predicated on the concept of redundancy, with multiple organizations performing similar tasks in the event one component fails.

From inside this classified facility in the shadow of the Colorado Rockies, the NORAD commander prepares to convey his nuclear attack assessment to the secretary of defense and the chairman of the Joint Chiefs of Staff, co-located inside the Pentagon in Washington, D.C.

Using an encrypted, EMP-resistant, jam-resistant satellite communications system known as the Advanced Extremely High

Frequency System, the NORAD command center connects to its partner facility.

But the SecDef and the chairman are not quite inside the bunker beneath the Pentagon. Not yet.

2 MINUTES
National Military Command Center, Pentagon

Pentagon employees note how its center looks like a bull's-eye.
(Library of Congress, Theodor Horydczak)

Two minutes have passed. Two men move briskly through the Pentagon, running, not jogging, across the E-ring's high-shined, linoleum-tiled floors. One, the secretary of defense, wears a business suit, white shirt, and tie. The other, the chairman of the Joint Chiefs of Staff, is in military dress, resplendent with stars and bars and ribbons.

Each man moves quickly down multiple sets of stairs, through fire doors, down more stairs, through more doors, and into a high-security tunnel that leads into the National Military Command Center. Here, the nation's STRATCOM and NORAD commanders wait on satellite comms and video screens for the president's two most senior advisors. If STRATCOM and NORAD are the brain and the brain stem of nuclear war, the National Military Command Center beneath the Pentagon is the beating heart of nuclear World War III.

Originally called the War Room, this command post was first conceived for the Pentagon, in 1948, as a place to run the next world war. It has been in use—24/7/365—every day of every year, ever since.

Two minutes have now passed since detected launch. The SecDef and the chairman arrive just seconds apart. Via secure satellite video comms from Colorado, the NORAD commander speaks.

His assessment is brief and to the point.

Tracking data has confirmed a worse worst-case scenario.

An attacking intercontinental ballistic missile is on its way to the East Coast of the United States.

The ICBM

26 minutes, 40 seconds to Armageddon

Ballistic missile trajectory in three phases of flight:
Boost, Midcourse, and Terminal. (U.S. Missile Defense Agency)

An intercontinental ballistic missile is a long-range missile that delivers nuclear weapons to targets across continents. ICBMs exist to kill millions of people on another side of the world. Back in 1960, when the ICBM had just been invented, the Pentagon's chief scientist, a man named Herb York, wanted to know precisely how many minutes it would take for one of these mass-extermination rockets to get from a launchpad in Soviet Russia to a city in the United States. York hired a group of defense scientists, called the Jason scientists, to whittle that number down to its most accurate form.

The result, Herb York learned, was 26 minutes and 40 seconds from launch to annihilation.

Just 1,600 seconds. That is it.

A copy of this secret assessment lies hidden among Herb York's personal papers at the Geisel Library in San Diego. Perhaps York left it there out of carelessness, or maybe he wanted the world to know for certain what war planners and weapons builders have known for decades, but have never revealed in such cold, hard terms. That there is no way to win a nuclear war.

It simply happens too fast.

The speed at which nuclear war will unfold, and then escalate, all but guarantees that it will end in nuclear holocaust.

"The nuclear armed ICBM threatens us with annihilation," York wrote. "The outlook is admittedly bleak."

The Jason scientists calculated that an ICBM's 26 minutes and 40 seconds of travel time occurs in three phases of flight:

- Boost Phase, which lasts 5 minutes
- Midcourse Phase, which lasts 20 minutes
- Terminal Phase, which lasts 1.6 minutes (100 seconds)

The five-minute-long Boost Phase includes the time it takes for the missile to ignite its rocket motors on the launchpad, head into space, and finish powered flight. After powered flight, the warhead is released, typically at an altitude of between 500 and 700 miles.

The Midcourse Phase lasts twenty minutes and includes the time it takes for the released warhead to coast through space in an arc-like trajectory around the Earth.

The Terminal Phase, or final stage, is incredibly short. Just 1.6 minutes. One hundred seconds. The Terminal Phase begins when the warhead reenters Earth's atmosphere and ends when the nuclear weapon detonates on its target.

The attacking Hwasong-17 in this scenario is a two-stage, liquid-fueled, road-mobile intercontinental ballistic missile. As of 2024, not a lot has been verified about its warhead capabilities, if it carries one or more nuclear warheads, if its payload is thermonuclear, and of what yield. What is known is that it can strike any target in the continental United States.

The Jason scientists' 26 minutes and 40 seconds launch-to-target calculation for Herb York was done in 1960, when the Soviet Union was the only other nuclear superpower in the world.

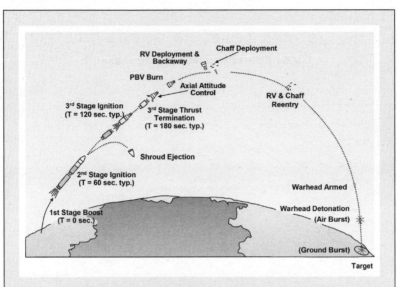

ICBM launch-to-target flight sequence. (U.S. Air Force)

Today, nine countries possess nuclear weapons: the United States, Russia, France, China, the United Kingdom, Pakistan, India, Israel, and North Korea. Given North Korea's geographical location, the launch-to-target time frame from the Korean peninsula to the East Coast of the United States is slightly longer. MIT professor emeritus Theodore "Ted" Postol has done the math for us.

It is 33 minutes.

The clock is ticking.

In this scenario, 2 minutes have passed.

Once launched, an ICBM cannot be recalled.

The classified papers stashed away in Herb York's dusty archives forewarned the world of Armageddon, and here we are now.

The ICBM threatens us with annihilation, York wrote.

True in 1960, true today.

2 MINUTES, 30 SECONDS

U.S. Strategic Command, Nebraska

Flooded tarmac, STRATCOM headquarters, Offutt Air Force Base,
Nebraska, in 2019. (U.S. Strategic Command)

U.S. Strategic Command headquarters in Nebraska sits less than ten miles south of Omaha, two miles west of the Missouri River. Its original name was Fort Crook. Ruinous regional weather includes tornadoes, cyclones, and floods. Deadly tornado funnels menace America's most important strategic nuclear headquarters with increasing regularity. In 2017, ten aircraft were damaged when a tornado hit Offutt Air Force Base.

The floods here are catastrophic. During the 2019 season, 700 Offutt airmen filled 235,000 sandbags in what was described by the *Air Force Times* as "a valiant, but ultimately unsuccessful, effort to hold the waters back." Some 720 million gallons of sewage-infested waters flooded the base, ruining 137 buildings and destroying 1 million square feet of workspace, including 118,000 square feet of Sensitive Compartmented Information Facility space (also known as SCIF space) for handling classified material. Half a mile of runway was submerged.

The runway at Offutt Air Force Base is a critical piece of nuclear counterattack infrastructure, never more so than now in this scenario, with a nuclear-armed ICBM headed to the U.S. The runway here services the mini-fleet of America's airborne nuclear command posts, known ominously as its Doomsday Planes. These retrofitted Boeing aircraft are always at the ready, always prepared to command a nuclear war from the air.

"Our military is very powerful, very lethal," says Captain Ryan La Rance, an officer who manages the airmen on a Doomsday Plane, "but it doesn't happen without communication."

Inside the Doomsday Plane is where the STRATCOM commander can receive launch orders during a nuclear crisis, then execute those orders, even after America's Nuclear Command and Control facilities on the ground have been destroyed.

Which is why the STRATCOM commander is now hyperfocused on getting the Blue Impact, or Counterattack, clock running. Then on getting himself out of STRATCOM's underground bunker and into a Doomsday Plane that idles here on the tarmac—engines spinning, awaiting his arrival for takeoff.

STRATCOM's Global Operations Center at Offutt Air Force Base is considered to be a top ten nuclear target on every enemy's target list. But its commander won't leave the bunker until he speaks with the president first.

Track data on the incoming ICBM has determined the missile's end point to be somewhere on the East Coast, presumably either New York City or Washington, D.C.

But it will be another two to three minutes before the designated target becomes more precisely defined.

2 MINUTES, 45 SECONDS
National Military Command Center, Pentagon

Inside the nuclear command bunker beneath the Pentagon, the secretary of defense and the chairman of the Joint Chiefs of Staff discuss rapidly what the NORAD commander has just told them, over video comms. An attacking ICBM appears headed for the East Coast of the United States.

The secretary of defense takes charge. Along with the chiefs of the other command facilities, he formulates what he might say to the president when asked. The individuals on this video call are men and women whose professional lives are dedicated to Nuclear Command and Control. Who live and breathe hypothetical nuclear war.

Once ground radar confirms that an attacking ICBM is on its way to the East Coast, an impossibly dangerous, next-step feature of U.S. nuclear warfighting strategy comes to the fore.

This feature centers around a decades-old policy called Launch on Warning.

"Once we are warned of a nuclear attack, we prepare to launch," former secretary of defense William Perry tells us. "This is policy. We do not wait."

Launch on Warning policy is why—and how—America keeps a majority of its deployed nuclear arsenal on ready-for-launch status, also known as Hair-Trigger Alert.

HISTORY LESSON NO. 3

Launch on Warning

Launch on Warning policy means America will launch its nuclear weapons once its early-warning electronic sensor systems *warn* of an impending nuclear attack. Said differently, if notified of an impending attack, America will *not wait* and physically absorb a nuclear blow before launching its own nuclear weapons back at whoever was irrational enough to attack the United States.

Launch on Warning "is a key aspect of nuclear war planning the public rarely hears about," says William Burr, a senior analyst at the National Security Archive at George Washington University in Washington, D.C.

Launch on Warning—in place as policy since the height of the Cold War—is also incredibly high-risk.

"Inexcusably dangerous," presidential advisor Paul Nitze warned us decades ago. Launch on Warning during a "time of intense crisis" is a recipe for catastrophe, Nitze said.

During the presidential campaign of George W. Bush in 2000, the future president vowed to address this perilous policy if elected. "Keeping so many weapons on high alert may create unacceptable risks of accidental or unauthorized launch," Bush said. "High-alert, high-trigger status [is] another unnecessary vestige of Cold War confrontation."

No change was made.

Barack Obama echoed the same fundamental concern during his campaign.

"[K]eeping nuclear weapons ready to launch on a moment's notice is a dangerous relic of the Cold War," Obama declared. "Such policies increase the risk of catastrophic accidents or miscalculation."

Like his predecessor, President Obama made no change.

When President Biden took office, physicist Frank von Hippel urged him to eliminate the perilous policy. "President Biden . . . should end the launch-on-warning option and the danger it entails of an unintended nuclear Armageddon," von Hippel wrote in the *Bulletin of the Atomic Scientists*.

But like his predecessors, President Biden has made no change.

And so, decades later, we're still here. With Launch on Warning in effect.

3 MINUTES
National Military Command Center, Pentagon

Inside the bunker beneath the Pentagon, the secretary of defense and the chairman of the Joint Chiefs of Staff consult with the vice-chairman of the Joint Chiefs, a woman in this scenario who (like General Ellen Pawlikowski) previously commanded the NRO Space Command in Colorado, as well as the Space and Missile Systems Center in California.

Her experience makes her uniquely qualified to assess what is going on in this moment, just three minutes after launch of an ICBM from a field north of Pyongyang.

The vice-chairman of the Joint Chiefs has studied enough track data on launched North Korean ICBMs—set to fly on preset trajectories so as to land in open water—to recognize for herself that what she is looking at is not one of these preset trajectories.

This missile's trajectory has it headed for the United States.

Brilliant, fierce, and not known to mince words, the vice-chairman points to the small black ICBM avatar moving ominously across the screen.

She inhales, exhales.

Addresses the secretary of defense directly.

You should get the president on comms, the vice-chairman says.

3 MINUTES, 15 SECONDS
The White House, Washington, D.C.

It's 3:06 p.m. EST in this scenario and the president is in the White House dining room, reading his midday briefing

The White House. (Photograph by Jett Jacobsen)

documents, drinking coffee, and eating an afternoon snack. He will not finish what he is doing.

The national security advisor rushes into the room, phone in hand. He informs the president that the secretary of defense is calling from the National Military Command Center beneath the Pentagon—2.1 miles away.

The president puts the phone to his ear.

The secretary of defense tells the president: *North Korea has launched an attacking missile at the U.S.*

It is a statement that at first seems implausible.

The secretary of defense tells the president: *NORAD and STRATCOM commanders have validated the assessment. We are awaiting secondary confirmation from ground radar in Alaska.*

The president turns to the national security advisor. He asks if this is some kind of a test.

National security advisor: *This is not a test.*

3 MINUTES, 30 SECONDS
National Military Command Center, Pentagon

B eneath the Pentagon, the secretary of defense watches the missile's trajectory as it moves across the massive screen in front

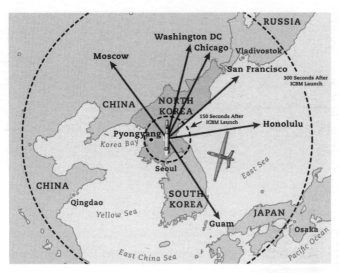

Drone engagement range against a Hwasong ICBM in Boost Phase, as devised by
Richard Garwin and Theodore Postol. (Image redrawn by Michael Rohani)

of him. Just three minutes and thirty seconds have passed (210
seconds), which means the ICBM missile is still in Boost Phase.
The missile's avatar will soon cross North Korea's northern border
into Chinese airspace.

The job of the secretary of defense is to ensure civilian command of the military, a position that is second only to the president,
who serves as the commander in chief. The secretary of defense
and president are the only two civilian positions within the military
chain of command.

Standing beside the secretary of defense is the chairman of the
Joint Chiefs of Staff, the nation's highest-ranking and most senior
military officer. The chairman's job is to advise the president, the
secretary of defense, the National Security Council members, and
others on military matters. The vice-chairman is second to him.

While the chairman of the Joint Chiefs outranks all other officers in the military, he or she does not—and cannot—command
the military. The job is to advise the president and the secretary of

defense. To help them decide what is best to do. What actions are the right next actions to take, including in a nuclear war.

Everyone here in the underground National Military Command Center is intensely focused on the task at hand. Everyone is also in a state of shock; everyone trained to act like they are not.

A nuclear crisis is not a worst-case scenario, it is *the* worst-case scenario.

The so-called unthinkable, and yet, most definitely, not unrehearsed.

The ramifications regarding what is about to happen are almost impossible to comprehend. Nuclear war is unprecedented. Over decades, there have been several significant false alarms. In this scenario, what is happening is real.

The president now faces an inexorably small decision-making window of time. What must happen next has been rehearsed by everyone presently in attendance on satellite comms, "except, most likely, the president himself," former secretary of defense Perry tells us. The president in this scenario, like almost all U.S. presidents since John F. Kennedy, is entirely underinformed about how to wage nuclear war when it happens.

The president has no idea that as soon as he has been briefed on what is happening, he will have just six minutes to deliberate and decide which nuclear weapons to launch in response.

Six minutes.

How is that even possible? Six minutes is roughly the amount of time it takes to brew a ten-cup pot of coffee. As former president Ronald Reagan lamented in his memoirs, "Six minutes to decide how to respond to a blip on a radar scope and decide whether to release Armageddon! How could anyone apply reason at a time like that?"

Nuclear war, we are about to learn, robs man of reason.

4 MINUTES
The White House, Washington, D.C.

The president is on his feet in the White House dining room, his cloth napkin on the floor. There are roughly 8 billion people on the planet. In the coming six minutes, the president will be asked to make a decision that can kill tens of millions of human beings on the other side of the world—just minutes (not hours) after his authorization.

With Launch on Warning policy in effect, and nuclear war on the horizon, so much hangs in the balance.

"Civilization as we know it is about to end," former secretary of defense Perry tells us of such a moment as this. "This is not an exaggeration," he says.

Here in the White House, the national security advisor stands a few feet from the president. He is trying to get a North Korean official on the phone, when he is knocked into by the special agent in charge of the presidential protective detail. Of all the people in the room prepared for crisis response, the Secret Service agents on the president's detail are among the best rehearsed.

Day in and day out, the U.S. Secret Service trains for this.

Into the emergency bunker now, the special agent in charge shouts at the president. Members of the detail hover close by, the agents all speaking into their ear and hand comms in sync.

There is a flurry of activity. Two Secret Service agents grab the president by his armpits, his hand still clutching his cell phone. The generals and admirals who are watching all this on satellite comms sit or stand in their respective bunkers while waiting on the president's every word.

The emergency plans book, the national security advisor says.

Keep him with the satchel, says the special agent in charge. *We're taking him to the Sit Room.*

The president does not fully comprehend all that is going on. How fast a nuclear counterattack must unfold. This hasn't fully landed with him yet.

"No one—not even the president—has complete knowledge of what is going on in a crisis zone or in a conflict," let alone in a nuclear war, says Jon Wolfsthal, a former national security advisor to President Obama.

"Many presidents come to the office uninformed about their role in a nuclear war," former secretary of defense Perry explains. "Some seem not to want to know."

Once, at a press conference in 1982, President Reagan went so far as to incorrectly tell the public that "submarine ballistic missiles are recallable."

After the Berlin Wall came down, and the Soviet Union was dissolved, William Perry found in his experience as secretary of defense that "many people clung to the idea that nuclear war was no longer a threat." When in fact, he now says, "nothing could be farther from the truth."

In a nuclear war, confusion over protocol and speed of action will have unintended consequences beyond anyone's grasp. It will send the United States of America into the heart of darkness that defense official John Rubel warned about in 1960.

Into what he called "a twilight underworld governed by disciplined, meticulous and energetically mindless groupthink aimed at wiping out half the people living on nearly one third of the earth's surface."

HISTORY LESSON NO. 4

ICBM Launch Systems

*Since the launch of this ballistic missile in 2012, North Korea's ICBMs
have gotten increasingly more powerful, and more menacing.
(The Pentagon Channel via Korean Central News Agency)*

The Hwasong-17 missile on its way to Washington, D.C., in this
scenario was road-mobile, meaning it got carried to its launch
site by a 22-wheeled vehicle called a transporter erector launcher.
The missile itself stands eighty-five feet tall. In its nose cone it carries a warhead bus that may or may not include dummy (or fake)
warheads designed to confuse America's missile defense systems
that are about to try to shoot it down.

In 2021, defense analysts predicted 50 percent of North Korea's
ICBMs would succeed in hitting their targets inside the U.S. In
2022, Japan's defense minister publicly confirmed the Hwasong-17

can travel 9,320 miles, far enough to reach the continental United States.

The Hwasong-17 ICBM is too heavy to drive around the countryside along North Korea's cheaply paved roads and so it gets driven on dirt roads, along sturdy ground, no recent rain or snow. The U.S. does not have road-mobile missile launchers. All 400 of its ICBM missiles are housed in underground silos across America. Most U.S. citizens do not accept as reasonable a road-mobile missile loaded with nuclear warheads being driven through their town or city, past their homes, or near where their children go to school.

Road-mobile rocket launchpads (invented by Nazi rocket scientists circa 1944) give North Korea a strategic advantage. Whereas the precise location of all 400 of the ICBM silos in America is available on the internet (and on maps before that), North Korea's road-mobile ICBMs are continually on the move—so the Defense Department cannot easily target them for destruction before or during nuclear war.

At Buckley Space Force Base in Colorado, analysts with NRO's Aerospace Data Facility examine satellite imagery from the minutes and hours before the missile launched off the truck bed parked in the dirt field. They confirm its identity as a Hwasong-17. Looking back at NRO's satellite images from earlier in time, analysts can see it was being transported along a dirt road to its launch location twenty miles north of Pyongyang.

While very little is known about the Hwasong-17's warhead capabilities, quite a lot is known about its rocket motor, the RD-250, including that it is Russian made. In November 2017, North Korea first flew an ICBM powered by this motor, which led four missile experts—American scientist Richard Garwin and MIT professor emeritus Ted Postol, along with German rocket engineers Markus Schiller and Robert Schmucker—to sound an alarm.

"The Russian engine was probably stolen from a storage unit after the Soviet Union collapsed," Postol tells us, "later sold to North Korea."

Theft of nuclear weapons and their delivery systems is often how nations accelerate their fledgling nuclear programs. Property theft saves a nation not just time but treasure—by avoiding complex research and development programs. Back in the 1940s, after Klaus Fuchs stole blueprints for the atomic bomb dropped on Nagasaki, he gave them to his handler in Moscow. From that moment, it was only a matter of time before Stalin had his own atomic bomb. Until the Hwasong-17's Russian RD-250 rocket engine was put into play, says Postol, North Korea couldn't get a missile anywhere near the East Coast of the United States. This likely theft by North Korea "fast-tracked in just four months a technical devel- opment" that would have taken the Hermit Kingdom decades to accomplish, he says.

Ted Postol and Richard Garwin warned colleagues about North Korea's capability in a 2017 paper. Postol is an expert on missile technology, a former advisor to the chief of naval operations, and professor emeritus at MIT. Richard Garwin, having drawn the plans for the world's first thermonuclear bomb, knows as much (or more) about nuclear weapons as anyone else alive. Garwin has been at the fore of nuclear weapons development and national security ever since. He worked on developing the world's first spy satellites and is considered one of the ten founders of the National Reconnaissance Office.

In their 2017 paper, Garwin and Postol argue that because of North Korea's particular geographical location, traditional missile defense against their ICBM is near to impossible. There are blind spots around the North Pole, they write in their paper—and propose that the best way to defend against the Hwasong-17 is to fly armed MQ-9 Reaper drones (the big-wing variant built during the War on Terror) over the Sea of Japan, close to North Korea's coast, twenty-four hours a day, seven days a week, 365 days a year. "Ready to take out an attacking missile 240 to 290 seconds into flight," Postol clarifies.

This time frame is imperative because just a few seconds later, the ICBM will complete powered flight and go dark.

Meaning it can no longer be seen and tracked by early-warning space satellites.

"Satellites can only see hot rocket exhaust," says Postol. "They cannot see the rocket after the rocket motor stops."

This is a dark black hole in national defense against ICBMs, Postol and Garwin warn.

4 MINUTES, 30 SECONDS
STRATCOM Headquarters, Nebraska

Everyone at STRATCOM has eyes on tracking screens. Four minutes and thirty seconds have passed since the launch of the Hwasong-17.

The ICBM is now in its last few seconds of Boost Phase. Once the missile enters Midcourse Phase it becomes almost impossible to stop. Now is the last opportunity to shoot down the attacking ICBM, but this cannot happen because the U.S. Defense Department has no system in place.

"We told all kinds of people in D.C. about this and all of them disregarded the idea," Postol tells us.

"We proposed a joint initiative with Russia," Garwin reveals. "They also have an interest in keeping North Korea from launching a nuclear weapon. Just as we do." But Postol's and Garwin's suggestions fell on deaf ears. There are no Reaper drones presently patrolling over the Sea of Japan, to try to shoot down this attacking ICBM.

275 seconds pass. 285 . . . 295 . . .

The rocket motor burns out.

Boost Phase ends.

The Hwasong-17 releases its warhead, which continues ascent.

Midcourse Phase begins.

The multibillion-dollar SBIRS constellation of early-warning satellites can no longer see what remains of the North Korean ICBM. It can no longer see the nuclear warhead en route to the United States. The warhead has gone ballistic and is now all but invisible to the satellite's sensors, coasting as it is on a high-speed trajectory to an apogee, or high point, somewhere over planet Earth.

5 MINUTES

U.S. Missile Defense Agency Headquarters,
Fort Belvoir, Virginia

Missile Defense Agency headquarters, Fort Belvoir, Virginia. (U.S. Army)

Twelve miles south of the Pentagon, at Fort Belvoir in Virginia, personnel at the Missile Defense Agency's headquarters command center are freaking out. There is a myth among Americans that the U.S. can easily shoot down an incoming, attacking ICBM. Presidents, congresspeople, defense officials, and countless others in the military-industrial complex have all said as much. This is simply not true.

The U.S. Missile Defense Agency is the organization responsible for shooting down incoming missiles in mid-flight. Its flagship system, the Ground-Based Midcourse Defense system, was built in the wake of North Korea's accelerated ICBM program that began in the early 2000s.

The U.S. system centers around forty-four interceptor missiles, each one fifty-four feet tall and designed to hit a fast-flying nuclear warhead with a 140-pound projectile called an exoatmospheric kill vehicle. The incoming North Korean warhead will be traveling at speeds of around 14,000 miles per hour, while the interceptor's kill vehicle will be traveling at speeds of around 20,000 miles per hour, making this action, if successful, "akin to shooting a bullet with a bullet," according to the Missile Defense Agency's spokesperson.

From 2010 to 2013, not a single one of the early interceptor tests was successful.

Not one.

The following year, the U.S. Government Accountability Office reported the system was not really operational because "its development was flawed." That each interceptor missile was only "capable of intercepting a simple threat in a limited way." After five years, and many billions of U.S. tax dollars spent, nine out of twenty hit-to-kill U.S. interceptor tests failed, which means there is only an approximate 55 percent chance that a Hwasong-17 will be shot down before it reaches its target.

At any given time, these forty-four interceptor kill vehicles are on alert, siloed at two separate locations in the continental United States. Forty of these missiles are located in Alaska, at Fort Greely, and four are located in California, at Vandenberg Space Force Base near Santa Barbara.

Forty-four missiles total.

That is it.

The intercept sequence is a ten-step process, three of which, in this scenario, have already happened by now:

1. The enemy has launched an attacking missile.
2. Space-based infrared satellites have detected the launch.
3. Ground-based early-warning radars have tracked the attacking missile through Boost Phase until Midcourse Phase begins.

The attacking North Korean missile now releases its warhead and decoys so as to confuse the sensor system on the exoatmospheric kill vehicle that is attempting to track (by sensors and an onboard computer) and intercept it. Distinguishing between a single warhead and other possible warheads and decoys in the warhead bus poses a new set of challenges for the U.S. Missile Defense Agency.

These are challenges that must be dealt with in seconds, not minutes. For this, attention moves out to sea, to the classified, $10 billion Sea-Based X-Band Radar station, known as the SBX.

6 MINUTES
North of Kure Atoll, North Pacific Ocean

Twenty miles north of the coral-ringed Kure Atoll, floating in the vast North Pacific Ocean more than 1,500 miles from Honolulu, the SBX radar station is a sight to behold. This one-of-a-kind, stadium-sized, seagoing, self-propelled radar station weighs 50,000 tons, requires 1.9 million gallons of gas to run, can

Sea-Based X-Band (SBX) Radar at sea. (U.S. Missile Defense Agency)

withstand thirty-foot-tall waves, is larger than a football field, rises twenty-six stories out of the ocean, requires eighty-six crew members to carry out its mission, and claims to be the most sophisticated phased-array, electro-mechanically steered X-band radar system in the world.

The original platform of the SBX was built by a Norwegian company that specializes in offshore vessels for oil drilling. It was purchased by the U.S. Defense Department and modified. Now it houses the world's most expensive missile defense radar, its bridge, workspaces, control rooms, living quarters, power-generating areas, and a helicopter pad.

The SBX was sold to Congress by leaders of the Missile Defense Agency as the most capable system of its kind, able to detect, track, and discriminate incoming missile threats. One catchy descriptor that SBX advocates use to explain how powerful the SBX is, is to say if placed in the Chesapeake Bay, its radars would be able to see a baseball-sized object in San Francisco from an observation post in Washington, D.C., some 2,900 miles away. This is true, sort of. The baseball needs to be hovering 870 miles above San Francisco in a direct line of sight with the radar in D.C. in order to be seen.

The goal of the SBX is to provide U.S. interceptor missiles with precise data about where an attacking nuclear warhead is in the atmosphere, in Midcourse Phase flight.

Inside a very small window of time, as in seconds.

Most Americans have never heard of the SBX and have no idea about its strengths, or its flaws. Mike Corbett, a retired air force colonel who oversaw the program for three years, had by 2017 already predicted it would fail. "You can spend an awful lot of money and end up with nothing," Corbett told the *Los Angeles Times* in 2015, "billions and billions [were spent] on these [SBX] programs that didn't lead anywhere."

Critics call the SBX radar system "the Pentagon's 10-billion-dollar radar gone bad."

By the time most people learn firsthand of the SBX's litany of flaws, it will be far too late.

7 MINUTES

U.S. Army Space and Missile Defense Command, Fort Greely, Alaska

To discern a nuclear warhead from a decoy is the job of the one-of-a-kind SBX radar system at sea. It is what taxpayers have paid billions of dollars to develop, and hundreds of millions more, annually, to maintain. (A recent Congressional Budget Office report indicates Pentagon missile defense costs from 2020 to 2029 could reach $176 billion.) In this critical moment, seven minutes after an attacking missile has been launched from Asia at the United States, U.S. national defense depends entirely on the exoatmospheric kill vehicle (inside the interceptor missile) communicating with the SBX radar system in order to determine what it must hit-to-kill.

Here in the Alaskan wilderness, 100 miles southeast of Fairbanks, a set of clamshell-shaped silo doors blast open. A 50,000-pound, 54-foot-tall interceptor missile fires up into the air from the U.S. Army Space and Missile Defense Command, Fort Greely, with an explosive howl.

In the history of warfare, the goal in battle is to meet attacking sword with defensive shield. The intention of the interceptor missile system is to shield the continental U.S. from a limited nuclear attack. "Limited" is the key word here because the total number of interceptor missiles is forty-four. As of early 2024, Russia has 1,674 deployed nuclear weapons, the majority of which are on ready-for-launch status. (China has a stockpile of more than 500; Pakistan and India each have around 165; North Korea has around 50.)

With forty-four missiles in its entire inventory, the U.S. interceptor program is mostly for show.

In press photographs released by the Missile Defense Agency, a rising interceptor missile in action is presented as glamorous-looking and powerful, with a plume of fire and smoke trailing out behind an ascending rocket body, on a backdrop of purple sky. In reality, it is far from salvational.

U.S. interceptor missile in Boost Phase.
(U.S. Missile Defense Agency)

As the interceptor rises into space, its onboard sensors communicate with radar systems on the ground and at sea in a process known as telemetry, the remote collection, measurement, and relay of data. When the interceptor missile completes its own Boost Phase, its exoatmospheric kill vehicle separates from its rocket body and continues on ascent.

This (allegedly) is the shield. This is what promises to keep an attacking missile from striking a target in the U.S.

There is no other shield. This is it.

"Hit-to-kill means it must collide with the warhead to destroy it in flight," Richard Garwin clarifies.

Missile expert Tom Karako anthropomorphizes the process, explaining that now is when "the kill vehicle [would] open its eyes, unbuckle its seatbelt, and get to work." But the real-world capabilities of a warhead on a Hwasong-17 suggest there could be up to five decoys contained in its warhead bus.

Will the interceptor succeed or fail?

9 MINUTES
Clear Space Force Station, Alaska

Roughly one hundred miles west of the interceptor missile fields at Fort Greely, the powerful Long Range Discrimination Radar at Clear Space Force Station gets its first sight of the attacking missile as it comes over the horizon. The Defense Department calls Alaska "the most strategic place in the world," when it comes to ballistic missile defense, and says that its long-range radar has the necessary "field of view" to detect incoming threats.

Nine minutes have passed.

Inside the classified Fire Direction Center, an airman seated at a desk picks up the red phone in front of her.

This is Clear, she says. *Site report is valid. Number of objects is one.*

The dreaded secondary confirmation of an attacking ICBM, headed to the East Coast of the United States, has just been made.

The facility here in Alaska is one of several early-warning ground radar facilities keeping watch for nuclear attack since the early days of the Cold War. Other facilities like it are located in:

- California, at Beale Air Force Base
- Massachusetts, at Cape Cod Space Force Station
- North Dakota, at Cavalier Space Force Station

- Greenland, at Pituffik Space Base (formerly Thule Air Base)
- United Kingdom, at Royal Air Force Fylingdales

For decades, these ground radar systems the size of small pyramids have been relied on to scan the skies for an incoming ballistic missile attack.

To err is human; but machines also make mistakes. These same systems have been responsible for several near-catastrophic false alarms. Once, in the 1950s, early-warning radars interpreted a flock of swans as a fleet of Russian MiG fighter jets en route to the U.S. by way of the North Pole. In October 1960, computers at the ground radar site in Thule, Greenland, misread the moon rising up over Norway as being the radar returns from 1,000 attacking ICBMs. In 1979, a simulation test tape mistakenly inserted into a NORAD computer deceived analysts into thinking the U.S. was under attack by Russian nuclear-armed ICBMs and nuclear ballistic submarines.

Former secretary of defense Perry tells us about the sheer madness involved when a person's brain tries to process the horrific supposition that America is actually under nuclear attack. The NORAD test tape debacle happened on Perry's watch (he was undersecretary of defense for research and engineering at the time), and for a few short minutes he prepared to notify then President Jimmy Carter that the dreaded time had come. That the president needed to launch a nuclear counterattack.

Instead, that early-warning notification turned out to be notification of a phantom attack.

"What came through on the computer was a simulation of an actual attack," Perry remembers. "It looked very, very real." So real that he actually believed it was real.

But back in 1979, instead of waking up President Carter in the middle of the night, as was Perry's job, the chief nuclear watch officer on duty at NORAD that night "dug into it [further] and concluded it was an error," Perry explains. For several terrifying minutes, William Perry believed nuclear war was about to begin. "I'll never forget that night," he tells us, now in his nineties, and that "right now, we are closer to having a nuclear war happen, even by accident, than we were during the Cold War." The scenario presented here is "not fearmongering," Perry confirms. That, rather, it should be understood "as entirely possible [of] happening."

In the twenty-first century, U.S. satellite systems have replaced ground systems as the initial bell ringer in a sneak nuclear attack. Ground radar stations around the world exist to provide secondary confirmation regarding what the Nuclear Command and Control System ostensibly already knows.

What the Fire Direction Center has just reported in this scenario is not a simulation tape, a flock of swans, or the rising moon.

It is real.

9 MINUTES, 10 SECONDS
U.S. Army Space and Missile Defense Command,
Fort Greely, Alaska

The U.S. Army Space and Missile Defense Command at Fort Greely and the Clear Space Force Station in Anderson sit roughly 100 miles apart from each other, as the crow flies. In this intense moment of missile defense, everyone at both bases is focused on precisely the same action: shooting down the attacking ICBM with an interceptor missile.

Hundreds of miles above, up in space, the interceptor completes powered flight.

Its boosters burn out and fall away.

The exoatmospheric kill vehicle in the nose cone is let loose and begins seeking the Hwasong-17's nuclear warhead by using sensors, an onboard computer, and a rocket motor designed to steer it to its target.

The final step in the interception process has begun.

The kill vehicle hurtles through space at a velocity of around 15,000 miles per hour. It opens its infrared "eyes" and tries to locate the target. Tries to find a signal from the warhead's warm surface on an otherwise dark background of space. Once the kill vehicle locates what it thinks is the warhead, attempting to destroy it is an even more radical challenge. To destroy the warhead as it hurtles through space, the kill vehicle must rely on its own propulsive energy and an extremely precise, physical collision. There are no explosives involved in this interception. This is where the "akin to shooting a bullet with a bullet" statement applies. There are significant problems. We know from the history of the interceptor program that its highly scripted tests have been riddled with failure. In missile defense terms, this means a disastrous success rate. In 2017, the tests plummeted to below a 40 percent success rate. Perhaps embarrassed by what it called "design flaws," the Missile Defense Agency announced it was giving the kill vehicle program a "strategic pause." That the agency would instead focus on a new system it calls "next generation." But as of 2024, all forty-four interceptors remain on ready-for-launch status, despite the unacceptable flaws.

The clock is ticking.

Interception by the exoatmospheric kill vehicle is attempted.

The system fails.

In immediate succession, a second kill vehicle from a second interceptor missile seeks the target and fails. Ground-based interceptors are not employed in what is known as a "shoot, look, shoot" type of profile; there isn't enough time.

The sequence is immediately followed by a third, then a fourth attempt.

All four interceptor missiles have failed to stop the attacking North Korean ICBM. In the words of one critic, former assistant secretary of defense and U.S. chief weapons evaluator Philip Coyle, "If you miss by an inch, you miss by a mile."

The die is cast.

The time has come. The president must act.

10 MINUTES
The White House, Washington, D.C.

The president was en route from a White House dining room to a command center beneath the West Wing, when he was redirected to the Presidential Emergency Operations Center, a more hardened facility under the East Wing. This bunker, known as the PEOC ("*pee-oc*"), was designed during World War II as a place to hide President Roosevelt should enemy forces penetrate U.S. air defense systems and bomb Washington, D.C., with attacking aircraft.

The PEOC is a location made famous in the weeks after 9/11 because it is where Secret Service agents took Vice President Dick Cheney in the heat of the moment after the national security apparatus realized America was under terrorist attack. It was from inside this fortified operations center that the vice president was able to override the official national command structure and assume control of U.S. military assets, including fighter jets.

Guiding American decisions about nuclear war are a series of procedures and protocols laid out in "highly, highly, highly" classified documents, former STRATCOM commander General

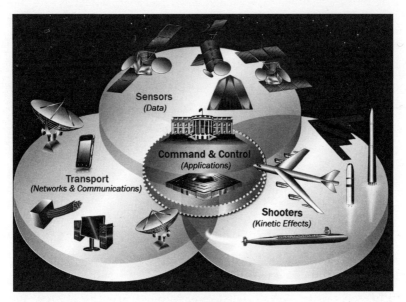

Military departments, nuclear force commanders, and the defense agencies provide the president with the means to authorize the use of nuclear weapons in a crisis. (U.S. Department of Defense)

Robert Kehler tells us. But America the democracy also releases information to the public—command structure and nuclear inventory included. From the unclassified "Nuclear Matters Handbook 2020," a Defense Department reference manual, much can be discerned.

A military command hierarchy follows strict rules. Each person carries out orders based on orders received from another person within the chain of command. Orders are delivered from the top down. Drawn as a diagram, the military chain of command resembles a pyramid of power. There are lots of people at the bottom. The president, as commander in chief, sits at the top.

The U.S. president—as odd as this may seem—has sole authority to launch America's nuclear weapons.

The president asks permission of no one.

Not the secretary of defense, not the chairman of the Joint Chiefs of Staff, not Congress. In 2021, the Congressional Research Service published a review to confirm that the decision to launch nuclear weapons is the president's and the president's alone. "The authority is inherent in his role as commander in chief," the research found. The president "does not need the concurrence of either his [or her] military advisors or the U.S. Congress to order the launch of nuclear weapons."

With the Red Impact clock counting down minutes and seconds until the incoming nuclear missile strikes its target inside the United States, the time has come for the president to launch a nuclear counterattack. This will get the Blue Impact, or Counterattack clock running.

On occasion, a debate arises as to whether America actually has a Launch on Warning policy. That the commander in chief really is expected to launch nuclear weapons while America is still under *threat* of nuclear attack, though not yet physically hit. Former secretary of defense Perry sets the record straight.

"We have a Launch on Warning policy," he says. Period, full stop.

In this scenario, the president's advisors rush to brief him on counterattack options.

To get the Blue Impact clock running.

With the briefing underway, the six-minute deadline for deliberation has begun. The president has just six minutes to deliberate, and make a decision regarding what nuclear weapons to use, and what enemy targets to instruct STRATCOM to strike. In the words of former launch control officer and nuclear weapons expert Dr. Bruce Blair, "A six-minute deadline for deliberation and decision is ridiculous." Meaning, nothing can prepare a man for this. It's too little time. And yet this is exactly where we are.

Standing beside the president in the PEOC is a military aide, known colloquially as the "mil aide," carrying the president's emergency satchel, a handheld aluminum and leather bag also known as the Football. This leather satchel is with the president at all times. Once, when President Clinton was visiting Syria, President Hafez al-Assad's handlers tried to prevent Clinton's mil aide from riding in an elevator with him. "We could not let that happen, and did not let that happen," former Secret Service director Lewis Merletti tells us. Merletti was the special agent in charge of President Clinton's detail at that time; he later became director of the U.S. Secret Service. "The Football must always be with the president," Merletti clarifies. "There are no exceptions."

Inside the Football are papers that are (arguably) the single-most highly classified set of documents in the United States government. Called Presidential Emergency Action Documents (PEADs), they are executive orders and messages that can be put into effect the moment an emergency scenario like a nuclear attack comes to pass. "They are designed 'to implement extraordinary presidential authority in response to extraordinary situations,'" reports the Brennan Center for Justice. "PEADs are classified 'secret,' and no PEAD has ever been declassified or leaked."

Where did this extraordinary presidential authority come from? The early history of the Football has long been shrouded in mystery. Los Alamos National Laboratory declassified its origin story for this book.

The President's Football

O ne day in December 1959, a small group of officials from the Joint Committee on Atomic Energy visited a NATO base in Europe to examine joint-custody nuclear bomb protocols. The NATO pilots there flew Republic F84F jets. Operation Reflex Action was in effect, meaning air crews were ready to strike predetermined targets in the Soviet Union in less than fifteen minutes from the call to nuclear war.

One of the men on the visit was Harold Agnew, a scientist with a unique history. Agnew was one of the three physicists assigned to fly on the Hiroshima bombing mission as a scientific observer. He carried a movie camera with him and took the only existing film footage of the atomic bombing of Hiroshima, as seen from the air. Now, in 1959, Agnew was at Los Alamos overseeing thermonuclear bomb tests; he later became the lab's director.

During the trip to the NATO base, Agnew noticed something that made him wary. "I observed four F84F aircraft . . . sitting on the end of a runway, each was carrying two MK 7 [nuclear] gravity bombs," he wrote in a document declassified in 2023. What this meant was that "custody of the MK 7s was under the watchful eye of one very young U.S. Army private armed with a M1 rifle with 8 rounds of ammunition." Agnew told his colleagues: "The only safeguard against unauthorized use of an atomic bomb was this single G.I. surrounded by a large number of foreign troops on foreign territory with thousands of Soviet troops just miles away."

Back in the United States, Agnew contacted a project engineer at Sandia Laboratories named Don Cotter and asked "if we could insert an electronic 'lock' in the [bomb's] firing circuit that could prevent just any passerby from arming the MK 7." Cotter got to work. He put together a demonstration of a device, a lock and coded switch, that functioned as follows: "[a] 3-digit code would be entered, a switch was thrown, the green light extinguished, and the red light illuminated indicating the arming circuit was live."

Agnew and Cotter went to Washington, D.C., to demonstrate this locking device—first to the Joint Committee on Atomic Energy, then to the president's top science advisor, and finally to the president himself. "We presented it to President Kennedy, who ordered it be done," Agnew recalled.

The military objected. The man in charge of nuclear weapons at the time, General Alfred D. Starbird, opposed the idea. Glen McDuff, who coauthored (with Agnew) the now declassified paper on the subject, summed up the general's documented concerns. "How is a pilot, U.S. or foreign, somewhere around the world, going to get a code from the President of the United States to arm a nuclear weapon before being overrun by a massively superior number of Soviet troops?" For the U.S. military, the locking device issue opened Pandora's box. "If gravity bombs were coded," McDuff explains, "why not all nuclear weapons including missile warheads, atomic demolition munitions, torpedoes, all of them." The president decided they needed to be.

The answer came in the creation of the Football, the president's emergency satchel. During Agnew and Cotter's meeting with President Kennedy, the original SIOP was in its final stages—the plan that gave the president, not the military, control of America's nuclear arsenal. This new device, called a Permissive Action Link, or PAL, would now be part of the new system of control. With the invention of the Football, the order to launch nuclear weapons—and the ability to physically arm them—would come from *only* the president. The commander in chief. "This is how the president got the Football," said Agnew.

10 MINUTES, 30 SECONDS
The White House, Washington, D.C.

The president stares at the Football. Inside this emergency satchel is a set of documents known as the Black Book, a list of nuclear strike options that a U.S. president must choose from—to commence nuclear war. From a declassified (but heavily redacted) document, "SIOP Briefing for [the] Nixon Administration," we know this set of documents has, for decades, been called the *Decisions Handbook*. Details of some of the other items contained in the Football have been leaked. These details include:

- What nuclear weapons to use
- What targets to hit
- Estimated casualties that will result

The nuclear weapons at the president's disposal in this scenario astound even him. Even more so is the truly perilous policy known as Hair-Trigger Alert.

Hair-Trigger Alert works in consort with Launch on Warning. So as to guarantee the annihilation of a devious enemy who defies deterrence and strikes another nuclear-armed nation in a decapitation event, U.S. nuclear forces maintain an arsenal of weapons on so-called Hair-Trigger Alert, also known as ready-for-launch status.

This means the president has the ability to order the launch of one, ten, one hundred, or all of America's nuclear weapons at his or her choosing, twenty-four hours a day, seven days a week, 365 days a year. All he has to do is follow the directions inside the Football.

Which brings us to the U.S. nuclear triad: the triptych of nuclear weapons the president has the authority to launch—by land, by air, and by sea. The U.S. nuclear triad includes:

- On land: 400 ICBMs, each carrying one warhead
- In the air: 66 nuclear-capable bombers (B-52 bombers and B-2 stealth bombers), each carrying multiple nuclear warheads
- At sea: 14 nuclear-armed submarines, each carrying multiple submarine-launched ballistic missiles (SLBMs) outfitted with multiple nuclear warheads
- (The 100 tactical nuclear bombs at NATO bases in Europe are not officially considered part of the triad.)

The time has come for the president to make a decision. In this scenario, nuclear weapons are about to be launched by the U.S. for the first time since World War II. The mil aide opens the Football in front of him. The president stares at the Black Book.

STRATCOM commander: *Sir.*

No one but the most senior-level officials in U.S. Nuclear Command and Control ever sees the contents of the Black Book. The number of people who have written about what they've seen is extremely limited: the targets involved, what kind of weapons would be used (kilotonnage versus megatonnage), the mass casualty numbers that will result. John Rubel is one of them, Daniel Ellsberg of the Pentagon Papers fame is another. Ted Postol and Jon Wolfsthal are among the individuals who have seen the contents of the Black Book, but have never shared what they learned. What is detailed in the Black Book is a secret most men take to their graves, perhaps for reasons like the ones Rubel shared with us before he died.

President Clinton's military aide, a colonel named Robert "Buzz" Patterson, once likened the Black Book to a "Denny's breakfast menu." He made the analogy that choosing retaliatory targets from a predetermined nuclear strike list was as simple as deciding on a combination of food items at a restaurant, "like picking one out of Column A and two out of Column B."

Los Alamos historian and nuclear weapons engineer Dr. Glen McDuff has never seen the Black Book himself, but knows many who have. "It's called the Black Book because it involves so much death," McDuff says.

A flurry of voices shout at the president. Everyone vying for his attention.

The president says aloud, to no one in particular:

Quiet.

11 MINUTES
National Military Command Center, Pentagon

Beneath the Pentagon, inside the National Military Command Center, the secretary of defense and the chairman of the Joint Chiefs of Staff face the president on satellite video comms. It is 3:14 p.m. Federal employees are still at work. This presents a for-better-or-for-worse situation for the secretary of defense and the chairman.

On the one hand, the president's two most important advisors in a nuclear crisis are immediately available to him for advice. On the other hand, these two individuals are standing under one of two likely targets. If they remain where they are, and the nuclear weapon strikes Washington, D.C., they will be killed.

The president focuses his attention on the chairman of the Joint Chiefs of Staff.

Tell me what to do.

It's a natural thing to say. No one but a madman would want to launch nuclear weapons of their own accord.

The chairman tells the president that he, as chairman, is part of the "chain of communication," not the "chain of command" for authorizing a nuclear launch. The chairman of the Joint Chiefs of Staff gives advice, not orders.

Advise me, the president commands. Seconds pass.

The chairman briefs the president on the situational awareness that's been developed. On counterstrike options. On what needs to happen next. "There is an actual script that the president will be walked through," former special assistant to the president Jon Wolfsthal tells us. "It is literally written down, and the lead officer from the National Military Command Center will walk him through it." There are just a few minutes remaining for him to order a counterstrike, the chairman says. But before the president can launch nuclear weapons, he must move the status of forces to Defense Readiness Condition 1: maximum readiness, immediate response, prepare for nuclear war. The military has never been raised to DEFCON 1, at least not as far as the public has been made aware. During the Cuban Missile Crisis, in 1962, U.S. forces were placed at DEFCON 2, meaning war involving nuclear weapons was presumed to be imminent.

Okay fine, move to DEFCON 1, says the president. Then, to the secretary of defense, wild-eyed, almost frantic now, he says out loud what he is thinking privately. What no one else dares to say: *Is this even real?*

Chairman: *Yes.*

President: *Good God.*

Secretary of defense, cautious: *We are waiting for more information to come in.*

What do we do? the president wonders.

And here is where advice and options can dangerously diverge.

Hold, the secretary of defense in this scenario says, and advises the president to consult with his counterparts in Russia and China first.

SecDef: *We must gather information, Mr. President.*

The gathering of information decreases the likelihood of making a catastrophic mistake.

The president's national security advisor remains preoccupied. Getting North Korea on the phone has failed. Now he is working to get Moscow on the line.

From satellite comms in the Nebraska bunker, the STRATCOM commander disagrees with the SecDef.

An enemy is attacking the homeland with a nuclear weapon, sir, he says. Emphasis on "nuclear."

The president requests information from the casualty officer.

We are looking at hundreds of thousands of casualties in D.C. alone, the casualty officer says.

The chairman corrects that number: *It will be upwards of 1 million, Mr. President. Sir.*

STRATCOM commander: *Launch on Warning allows us to change their decision calculus, sir.*

We retaliate to decapitate, says the chairman—acting now in a manner colloquially known as "jamming the president," whereby generals and admirals pressure the president to quickly launch nuclear weapons while the U.S. is still under suspicion of attack.

But the SecDef is adamant: *No. Mr. President. We must wait.*

Which is when the SecDef clarifies his comments with what everyone fears, but no one else dares to say.

SecDef: *To launch now all but guarantees a wider war.*

12 MINUTES
STRATCOM Headquarters, Nebraska

In the bunker beneath Offutt Air Force Base, the STRATCOM commander stands facing the president and his mil aide on video comms.

The time has come to discuss and finalize nuclear options.

As the president's mil aide was opening the Football in the bunker beneath the White House, a similar action was taking place here at STRATCOM, inside its bunker, the Battle Deck. A black safe in this nuclear operations center contains an identical copy of the president's nuclear *Decisions Handbook*, the Black Book.

"The [Black Book inside the] president's football and our black book are duplicates," former STRATCOM battle watch commander Colonel Carolyn Bird told CNN. And that the two books "contain the same information in the same way so that we are talking off the same documents when we are discussing nuclear options."

Nuclear options.

The time has come to act.

Standing beside the STRATCOM commander is the nuclear strike advisor, an individual whose job it is to study the contents of the Black Book "on a daily basis." Lieutenant Colonel Kristopher Geelan once served in this position. To explain the macabre complexity of his job, Geelan used language that only touches the surface.

"My responsibility as the STRATCOM nuclear strike advisor," Geelan told *60 Minutes*, "is to be the expert on the Nuclear Decisions Handbook and the alert status of all U.S. nuclear forces."

"All U.S. nuclear forces" refers to the triptych of sea-air-land nuclear weapons. The 400 ICBMs, the 66 nuclear-capable bombers, and the 14 nuclear-armed subs.

Standing beside the nuclear strike advisor in the STRATCOM bunker is the weather officer, whose job it is to brief the president on how many people will likely die from nuclear fallout after a U.S. counterstrike. It's a ghastly job. One that requires math and accounting skills to calculate and report accurate and thus astonishingly high-number death tolls. During the 1960 nuclear strike plan against Moscow, as relayed to us by John Rubel, the nuclear fallout numbers in China alone included "half the population of China." Today, that would mean more than 700 million Chinese citizens would be dead from radiation poisoning after a nuclear strike on Russia.

The STRATCOM commander briefs the president on his Launch on Warning options, presented in the Black Book as Alpha, Beta, and/or Charlie options. Choices based on STRATCOM's promise to "deliver a decisive response" if deterrence fails. According to missile launch officer Bruce Blair (who died in 2020), there are approximately eighty targets in North Korea, in categories that include its "nuclear-war sustaining industry" and its leadership.

The president stares at the Black Book.

The STRATCOM commander has eyes on the Red Impact clock, the nuclear fuse getting shorter by the second.

STRATCOM commander: *Mr. President, we are awaiting your orders.*

Chairman of the Joint Chiefs: *Advise strike option Charlie.*

National security advisor: *Why would anyone be so goddamn stupid as to start a nuclear war?*

The STRATCOM commander focuses on getting the Blue Impact clock ticking: *Emphasis on military targets, sir.*

The secretary of defense is desperately trying to get his counterpart in Moscow on his phone.

It is insanity for us to launch without informing Moscow, the SecDef warns.

STRATCOM commander: *Mr. President, sir!*

SecDef: *Don't do it, not yet.* Then: *Who's calling China?*

Chairman: *We are ready for your orders, sir.*

National security advisor: *North Korea has nuclear facilities in a ring around Pyongyang, where nearly 3 million civilians reside.*

Reading from the Black Book, the president considers his options. He focuses on option Charlie, as the chairman of the Joint Chiefs suggests.

The chairman clarifies numerous military targets in North Korea: in Pyongyang, Yongbyon, Yongjo-ri, Sangam-ni, Tongchang-ri, Sino-ri, Musudan-ri, Pyongsan, Sinpo, Pakchon, Sunchon, and Punggye-ri.

The national security advisor's deputy has China on the line.

North Korea's Tongchang-ri missile launch complex is less than forty miles from the border city of Dandong, population 2.2 million Chinese, someone says.

STRATCOM commander to the president: *Deploy six bombers over the peninsula. Move submarines into position around the globe.*

Nuclear weather officer to SecDef: *The fallout estimate on option Charlie is 400,000 to 4 million Chinese nationals.*

Secretary of defense: *Still no Moscow on the line.*

National security advisor: *Punggye-ri is roughly 200 miles from Vladivostok, Russia. Population 600,000.*

Vladivostok is home to the Russian Pacific Fleet, with dozens of surface warships stationed there.

The Red Impact clock indicates twenty-one minutes remain until a nuclear bomb destroys Washington, D.C.

We can't reach the Kremlin, says the SecDef—still on hold. Which is not implausible. In November 2022, after a Russian missile was incorrectly reported to have struck NATO territory in Poland, the chairman of the Joint Chiefs of Staff, General Mark Milley, was unable to reach his Russian counterpart for more than twenty-four hours. "My staff was unsuccessful in getting me linked up with General Gerasimov," Milley conceded during a press conference a day and a half after the incident.

Aides everywhere across the National Military Command Center floor are frantically dialing the U.S.-Russia deconfliction hotline, a communication link set up to avoid military misunderstanding between the two nuclear-armed superpowers.

National security advisor, phone in hand: *China says killing Chinese citizens with radiation poisoning is an act of war.*

Everyone on comms talking over one another.

Someone says: *Hushhhh.*

The commander of the U.S. Indo-Pacific Command speaks for the first time: *There are 28,500 U.S. troops in South Korea, sir.* U.S. servicemen and -women who are at risk, not only from lethal radiation from any U.S. nuclear counterattack on Pyongyang but also from a counter-counterattack by North Korea.

All eyes are on the president.

The STRATCOM commander awaits orders, with 150,000 individuals beneath him also waiting on the president's command. No one can, or will, take action until the president chooses a nuclear strike option from the Black Book.

We are waiting, sir, the STRATCOM commander repeats.

The president hesitates.

He flips a page in the Black Book, his eyes darting across numbers, letters, words. *Get the bombers up,* he says as he reads. U.S. nuclear-armed bombers are the only leg of the triad that can be recalled.

Chairman and SecDef simultaneously: *Send the bombers, now.* The scramble alert is sounded. But everyone is acutely aware of the timing involved. U.S. bombers are not deployed with their nuclear weapons on board. Loading them takes time.

President: *How can we be sure this is not some kind of electronic simulation?*

STRATCOM commander: *Multiple early-warning systems confirm launch.*

President: *A spoof designed to trick me into launching nuclear weapons in error.*

A twenty-first-century version of the VHS simulation tape William Perry saw in 1979.

Chairman: *We are certain this is very real, sir.*

STRATCOM commander: *We need to get the Blue Impact clock running.*

Chairman: *Now.*

Everyone is watching the avatar of an ICBM making its way over the North Pole.

And we know there's a nuclear warhead inside? the president asks.

A fair question. The answer from the SecDef: *We don't.*

President: *What?*

STRATCOM commander: *There is no way of certifying what's inside an ICBM warhead until after it explodes.*

President: *What if there is no nuclear warhead inside?*

Imagine starting a nuclear war by mistake.

Chairman: *You don't launch an ICBM at the United States unless you expect to be counterattacked.*

President: *But what if . . . ?*

STRATCOM commander: *The warhead could be a chemical or a biological weapon.*

President: *So, we don't know?*

SecDef: *We don't know.*

STRATCOM commander: *Sir, the gold codes.*

Chairman: *Sir. Now.*

The president reaches into his wallet for the laminated nuclear codes card he must carry with him at all times. The "Biscuit," in national security terms. Wallet in hand, he begins to pull out the card. As he does, the PEOC's vault doors fly open.

Ten men armed with SR-16 gas-operated, air-cooled carbines and AR-15 assault rifles burst into the room.

They rush the president and grab him by the armpits, his feet no longer touching the ground.

12 MINUTES, 30 SECONDS

Andersen Air Force Base, Guam

B-2 nuclear bomber. (U.S. Air Force, Master Sgt. Russ Scalf)

Eight thousand miles from Washington, D.C., at Andersen Air Force Base on the Micronesian island (and U.S. territory) of Guam, two B-2 stealth bombers prepare to roll out of a hangar and onto the runway. This is not a test flight.

The B-2 is a $2 billion, 172-foot-long flying wing that carries in its weapons bay up to sixteen nuclear bombs. Traveling at 628 miles per hour, a B-2 flies 6,000 miles without refueling. There are twenty in the fleet, based out of Whiteman Air Force Base in Missouri, with individual aircraft deploying to bases around the world, including ones in Iceland, the Azores, and in Diego Garcia. Flying out of Guam, it will take a B-2 bomber roughly three hours to get within striking distance of Pyongyang.

So much can happen in three hours of nuclear war.

The B-2 uses stealth technology to penetrate enemy air defenses without being seen by radar. It is the only long-range, nuclear-capable U.S. aircraft able to perform this feat. Each B-2 has a crew of two. A pilot in the left seat, a commander in the right. The B-2 carries the B61 Mod 12 thermonuclear gravity bomb, also known as a nuclear bunker buster because of its earth-penetrating component, which makes it more effective at destroying deeply buried targets.

Targets like the bunkers that North Korea's supreme leader is presently suspected to be hiding inside.

"The main advantage of the B61-12 is that it packs all the gravity bomb capabilities against all the targeting scenarios into one bomb," nuclear weapons expert Hans Kristensen tells us. "That spans from very low-yield tactical 'clean' use with low fallout, to more dirty attacks against underground targets."

The B-2 stealth bomber is the most expensive aircraft in history. And the most effective. But what the generals in the Pentagon know, and no one really wants to say, is that loading nuclear weapons onto the aircraft takes time. Coupled with the requisite flight time, by the time the B-2s get anywhere near Pyongyang in a scenario such as this, a General Nuclear War will be well underway.

Which also means that by the time the $2 billion stealth aircraft needs fuel, given where the B-2 bomber is going, there will be nowhere to refuel, and nowhere to land.

13 MINUTES
Mount Weather, Virginia

The administrator of the Federal Emergency Management Agency is being driven along Highway 267, toward Dulles airport to catch a flight, when his driver is notified by the Department

of Homeland Security to pull over and wait for a FEMA search
and rescue team. The team is just minutes away from the FEMA
chief's location and will pick him up along the side of the road.

The White House is invoking "the Program."

As chief of FEMA, he will be taken by helicopter to the Mount
Weather Emergency Operations Center, as is protocol. The highway pickup is but one element of nuclear crisis protocols that were
first put in place back in the early days of the Cold War. In the
1950s, President Eisenhower created the U.S. highway system with
this kind of dual-use in mind. He modeled America's original
"National System of Interstate and Defense Highways" after "the
superlative system of German autobahn," he wrote in his presidential memoirs. Not only could U.S. highways facilitate large-scale
evacuation of cities in a nuclear war, but the broad, flat interstate
lanes could be used as runways for takeoff and landings on bombing runs. For setting down a helicopter in the median strip, or
along the side of the road in the grass. This is how many of
America's mid-century transportation systems were designed.

FEMA is the government entity assigned to prepare for nuclear
war. Its special access programs are highly classified. They also
hide, or obscure, a misperception. The truth is, there is no federal
agency to help citizens survive a nuclear war per se. What FEMA
does is focus on how to save specific government officials in the
event of a nuclear attack. This is part of a classified FEMA program built upon classified information called the Continuity of
Operations Plan, or COOP.

"The Program" in government-speak.

This is not to be confused with the Continuity of Government
program, former FEMA director Craig Fugate clarifies. "There is
the Continuity of Government and then there is the Continuity of
Operations Plan," Fugate explains. "Continuity of Government is
the constitutional succession of the acting president and agency

heads. The Continuity of Operations program is the 'essential functions' list that agencies are required to identify, and to be able to reconstitute [or reconstruct] those 'essential functions,' on a very bad day." As for what constitutes a very bad day, Fugate says, "That's the euphemism for nuclear war."

The job of FEMA after the invocation of "the Program" boils down to a basic, terrifying concept.

"Can you keep enough of the government intact?" Fugate asks rhetorically. "The Continuity Program is built around low-probability, high-consequence events," he tells us. "And it's built around this concept of no matter how bad something is, [including] a full-blown nuclear exchange, can the government continue to function in a lawful manner? That's what we [at FEMA] are shooting for."

Separate from the Continuity Program is another program called Population Protection Planning. This involves FEMA organizing first responders to help U.S. citizens in the aftermath of an emergency crisis like a hurricane, a flood, or an earthquake. But a nuclear war is what FEMA calls a Bolt out of the Blue attack. "If it's a Bolt out of the Blue attack," says Fugate, "population protection planning is a different animal. With a Bolt out of the Blue attack, population protection planning won't happen because everyone will be dead."

In this scenario, the FEMA chief's driver pulls the vehicle over to the side of the road, as instructed.

The helicopter carrying the FEMA search and rescue team lands in the grass.

The FEMA chief boards the rotary-wing aircraft and takes off, the vehicle he was driven in idles by the side of the road. People stare briefly, accustomed as they are to government vehicles showing up in and around D.C. Some take photographs, post them on social media, get back to their own lives. After a little rubbernecking, traffic moves along again.

Flying now to Mount Weather, the FEMA chief joins the satellite comms. Extraordinary challenges lie ahead, he understands. In a nuclear attack, "from the time we get a detection of something [nuclear] happening," Fugate tells us, "everything becomes about counting down. Looking at the time frame . . . in a nuclear attack . . . I'm looking at fifteen minutes," Fugate says. So the question becomes "How fast can you move? How fast can you spin up? Because when things are moving so fast, miscalculations and mistakes take place."

In a scenario such as this, a well-informed FEMA chief like Fugate suspects that the world is about to end.

From this moment forward, the job of the FEMA chief is to stay focused on the Program. Everything else must be ignored. "You'd have to get over the fact that after a nuclear strike, you couldn't do anything for [most] people," Fugate warns. He says that if someone in his position were to focus on the reality of what is about to go down in a Bolt out of the Blue nuclear attack, "you'd be paralyzed," he opines. "It's almost like you'd have to disassociate yourself from the horrors. Our line of work is low-probability, high-consequence events. I mean, we plan for asteroids."

The FEMA chief knows to prepare for the worst. And short of an asteroid hitting planet Earth, there is nothing more catastrophic than a nuclear attack.

Fugate reasons, "After the attack, the first question you have to ask is, what's left and who's left?" Then you must focus on "how do you keep them alive?"

From there, it will get far, far worse. In the hours and days after a nuclear attack, "it really now becomes about the survival," Fugate predicts. "This isn't about getting back to normal. This isn't about traditional response. This is about: What can we [FEMA] do to keep the most of us that have survived the initial attack alive?" And the truth is, he says, "the best the federal government could do is to tell people . . . people who still have a radio . . . what they can do for *themselves* to self-survive."

Things like: "Stock water. Drink Pedialyte. Stay indoors. Don't forget your morals."

Self-survive.

14 MINUTES
The White House, Washington, D.C.

The heavily armed men who just entered the Presidential Emergency Operations Center are members of the Counter Assault Team, or CAT, the Secret Service's paramilitary unit. They've been called here by the special agent in charge of the president's detail, also known as the SAC ("*the sack*"), who also ordered the Element, a three-man, emergency CAT team. They're here to move the president to a secure location outside Washington, D.C.

The CAT Element took longer than usual to show up. This is because the special agent in charge instructed them to pass by the White House headquarters office, to get whatever parachutes were there, and to bring them to the PEOC. Nighthawk One, Secret Service code for Marine One, is not equipped with parachutes, and the SAC's job is to always be thinking ahead.

When the CAT Element arrives, the SAC is on his phone calling for a status update on KNEECAP, Secret Service code for a Doomsday Plane when carrying POTUS, which is the acronym for "president of the United States."

The Element rushes to the president. Dressed in black, wearing helmets and night vision goggles, ammoed up and with secure comms, the CAT operators grab the president by his arms and pull him to his feet. They are here to move POTUS, not to discuss or debate.

In nineteen minutes, a nuclear weapon will strike D.C. The president must board Marine One and evacuate the White House complex in four minutes or Nighthawk One risks being too close to ground zero when the bomb detonates. A host of deadly threats loom, including getting knocked out of the sky from the shock wave blast and the ensuing several-hundred-mile-per-hour winds. But most concerning to the SAC are the potentially catastrophic effects from nuclear EMP, or electromagnetic pulse, a fast three-phase burst of current that can destroy Marine One's electronic systems and cause the helicopter to crash.

The Counter Assault Team Element brought parachutes to tandem jump POTUS out of the aircraft if the pilot cannot get them out of the danger zone before the Red Clock zeros out.

SAC: *Out to the South Lawn. We are moving you now, sir!*

Over video comms, the STRATCOM commander challenges the move.

STRATCOM commander: *We need launch orders first, Mr. President.*

Chairman concurs: *I advise Charlie option, sir. STRATCOM requires gold codes.*

SAC: *We are moving POTUS now.*

STRATCOM commander: *We require launch orders from POTUS first.*

Chairman: *Orders for EAMs, sir.*

EAMs are Emergency Action Messages, coded nuclear launch orders that get transmitted to battlefield commanders around the world.

National security advisor: *The only way we don't start World War III is to wait and see if we physically get hit.*

Chairman disagrees: *You have a duty to launch on attack, sir.*

SecDef to SAC: *Get POTUS out. Take him to Site R.*

We are moving POTUS, says the special agent in charge.

The mil aide closes the Football. He locks the satchel and begins to move, always maintaining an arm's length from the president, as trained.

15 MINUTES
National Military Command Center, Pentagon

Inside the National Military Command Center beneath the Pentagon, the secretary of defense is hyper-focused on an issue secondary to launch, namely Continuity of Government. Holding one of only two civilian positions in the military chain of command as he does, the secretary of defense is seriously concerned about keeping the federal government functioning in the aftermath of a nuclear attack.

When a nuclear bomb hits Washington, D.C., chaos will grip the nation. Without a functioning government, there will be no rule of law. Democracy will be replaced by anarchy. Moral constructs will disappear. Murder, mayhem, and madness will prevail. In the words of Nikita Khrushchev, "The survivors will envy the dead."

Continuity of Government, if implemented correctly, allows the president and his advisors to direct the U.S. military to fight a full-scale nuclear war from inside a backup command post like the Pentagon's Alternate National Military Command Center outside D.C., colloquially known as the Raven Rock Mountain Complex, or Site R. This underground command center is located seventy miles northwest of the White House, near Blue Ridge Summit, Pennsylvania. It is considered to be the safest underground bunker in closest proximity to the White House.

Now, with just minutes remaining on the Safe Escape clock, the secretary of defense considers evacuating to Site R too.

He turns to his deputy chief of staff. *Is there an Osprey on the helipad?* he asks.

16 MINUTES
Battle Deck, STRATCOM Headquarters, Nebraska

The STRATCOM commander is furious. He stares into the White House Presidential Emergency Operations Center via satellite comms. He sees the advisors and the aides, the officers and the deputies. But not POTUS. How can the president of the United States not be available for the STRATCOM commander in this DEFCON 1 posture? How dare the Secret Service do what they've done.

I NEED POTUS! the STRATCOM commander shouts at the video screen.

Without launch codes from the president, the STRATCOM commander remains hamstrung. He waits.

And just when one thinks the unfolding situation could not get any worse, new data comes in from NRO's Aerospace Data Facility in Colorado.

SBIRS sensors have detected the hot rocket exhaust on a submarine-launched ballistic missile. This second attacking missile has breached the surface of the ocean, roughly 350 miles off the California coast. The only nuclear-capable missile that can get closer to its target, and therefore strike and hit a target—in this case inside the United States—faster than an ICBM launched from across the globe is a submarine-launched ballistic missile. The dreaded SLBM.

Oh. My. God, someone in the bunker says.

17 MINUTES
Beale Air Force Base, California

Seventeen minutes have passed since a nuclear-capable ICBM lifted up off a dirt field in Pyongsong, North Korea, headed for the East Coast of the United States. Now an early-warning satellite in high Earth orbit tracks this second ballistic missile as it moves through Boost Phase toward California.

There is little data to discern who owns this missile, or the submarine it was launched from—not now, not in real time. But everyone's best guess is North Korea. Satellites do not have eyes under the sea. Submarines hide under ocean cover, rise close to the surface, fire their missiles, and disappear.

Analysts at Beale Air Force Base, outside Yuba City, California, acquire, track, and confirm this second event as a ballistic missile moving at hypersonic speed.

Generals and admirals at underground control centers in Colorado, Nebraska, and Washington, D.C., no longer hold facial expressions at neutral. So many of them thinking, even saying out loud, similarly shocking truths.

One missile could be a misread. Two is not a mistake.

Deterrence has failed.

Nuclear war is happening. Now.

Most of them knowing, *This is the beginning of the end of the world.*

One incoming attacking missile could be a terrible accident. An anomalous event. But two attacking missiles, from two separate launch sites, rises to the threshold of a coordinated nuclear attack.

There can be only one response from the United States. A counterattack aimed at decapitating an enemy who just launched a preemptive nuclear strike. The time has come to turn North Korea into ancient Carthage. Into salted earth.

STRATCOM commander, again over comms: *Where is POTUS?!*

Chairman: *We need codes!*

But the president is still in the stairwell outside the PEOC, on the move.

High in space, the Advanced Extremely High Frequency satellite constellation is working as designed, but the president's Black

Book remains secured inside the Football, swinging from the mil aide's hand.

17 MINUTES, 30 SECONDS
The White House, Washington, D.C.

T he president runs up a set of stairs. Behind him, the vault doors to the Presidential Emergency Operations Center close and lock. Some of the president's advisors have stayed behind. They've read briefings about this kind of scenario and have made peace with what is happening. Like President Carter and President Reagan are said to have decided, they will go down with the ship.

The members of the CAT Element usher the president down another hallway and through two sets of blast doors.

Up another stairwell, then another after that.

Down a corridor. Through another set of doors.

They are outside the White House now. There is fresh air. Green buds on the Jackson Magnolia trees. The low hum of helicopter rotor blades. Marine One ready to take flight. The CAT operators jog with the president across the White House lawn. No green grass yet, just cold wet earth.

18 MINUTES
National Military Command Center, Pentagon

I nside the National Military Command Center beneath the Pentagon, the secretary of defense decides what he should do. An ICBM hurtling toward the United States is about to destroy everything in Washington, D.C.

A second ballistic missile en route to the West Coast will detonate somewhere in California or Nevada, in minutes. The SecDef knows if he stays where he is, he'll be killed. Even if the hardened walls and ceiling protect him from the initial blast, he will burn to death when the National Military Command Center beneath the Pentagon becomes like a furnace.

Former secretary of defense William Perry tells us what a secretary of defense might be considering in a moment such as this. When there is still time for a SecDef to try to save himself and get out.

"In this case, if it was a [nuclear] bomb in Washington, D.C., the cabinet would likely be decapitated and an emergency government [would have] to be brought into play," Perry says. "An immediate consequence of a nuclear strike [would be] that democracy would be completely gone and military rule would take place." Perry believes that if military rule is ever imposed on today's America, "it would be almost impossible to undo military rule" in the United States.

The cabinet is the president's principal advisory body. It includes the vice president and the heads of fifteen executive departments, as well as the White House chief of staff, the U.S. ambassador to the United Nations, the director of national intelligence, and a handful of other bureaucrats, just about every one of whom has an office in D.C. It is 3:21 p.m. Federal employees and staff are still hard at work, meaning in a matter of minutes, all of the president's principal advisors will likely be dead.

Seeing as many of the president's cabinet members are also named in the line of succession (how power gets passed if the president dies), the best move for the secretary of defense is to get out of the Pentagon immediately. According to William Perry, the move would be to get to Raven Rock—and fast.

"I'd have a discussion with the chairman of the Joint Chiefs," he says.

He'd say: *One of us needs to stay, one of us needs to go.*

"Objectively the wisest move would be for me to try and save myself," Perry explains, "because I might end up being the leader of the country." In the presidential line of succession, the secretary of defense is number six. The first twelve are:

1. vice president
2. speaker of the House
3. president pro tempore of the Senate
4. secretary of state
5. secretary of the treasury
6. secretary of defense
7. attorney general
8. secretary of the interior
9. secretary of agriculture
10. secretary of commerce
11. secretary of labor
12. secretary of health and human services

"The smart thing for me and the vice-chairman of the Joint Chiefs of Staff to do [would be] to get out," Perry clarifies. "To get on a helicopter. To get out of there."

If the bomb strikes D.C., the first five individuals in the presidential line of succession—all of whom are in D.C. in this scenario—will all, almost certainly, be killed. The chairman of the Joint Chiefs will almost certainly choose to remain at the Pentagon. "My position, as secretary of defense," Perry continues, "would be for me and the vice-chairman . . . to be in a secure command post," not inside the Pentagon.

Somewhere safe. Like Site R.

The SecDef's deputy chief of staff speaks on comms with the Pentagon Army Heliport, the pentagon-shaped helicopter pad on the northern side of the building. In order to get there, the SecDef must sprint like a teenager.

Meet us in the parking lot, the deputy chief of staff tells Army Heliport command, a move that will save the secretary of defense precious time.

Go, the chairman tells the SecDef. *You too,* he instructs the vice-chairman.

A nuclear decapitation strike against the Pentagon will upend the national command authority—that is, the way presidential authority is exercised and operational command and control is conducted. The chairman knows this, and he does a Dick Cheney. He overrides protocol and takes charge of strategic decisions until the Football is reopened and the president is back on comms.

The chairman of the Joint Chiefs tells the STRATCOM commander that the president will likely want to use submarine forces in a nuclear counterattack.

Submarines are the most survivable leg of the nuclear triad because when electronic communication systems soon fail, submariners will still be able to receive launch orders from STRATCOM using very low frequency/low frequency (VLF/LF) radio wave technology developed, rehearsed, and mastered during the Cold War. These subsurface radio systems behave differently from others working in the atmosphere, systems that can easily be destroyed by electromagnetic pulse. The second reason is because submarines cannot easily be located by an enemy force.

"It's easier to find a grapefruit-sized object in space than a submarine at sea," former vice admiral Michael J. Connor, commander of the United States (nuclear) submarine forces tells us. And that, conversely, "anything fixed is destroyable."

Launch on Warning policy dictates that now is the time to try to decapitate North Korean leadership before it can launch any more nuclear missiles at the United States. The U.S. submarine force is the fastest way to get missiles on these targets. In preparation for the president's presumed wishes, the USS *Nebraska*, an Ohio-class nuclear-armed, nuclear-powered submarine, moves into position out at sea. Far from America's shores, in the vast Pacific Ocean north of the island of Tinian. The SecDef and the vice-chairman race to leave the Pentagon.

Nuclear war is about to begin.

An Osprey leaves the Pentagon.
(U.S. Marine Corps, Lance Cpl. Brian R. Domzalski)

HISTORY LESSON NO. 6

Nuclear-Armed Submarines

A nuclear-armed, nuclear-powered submarine is a nightmare weapon system. An object as dangerous to human existence as an incoming asteroid. These submarines are called many things: boomers, vessels of death, nightmare machines, handmaidens of the apocalypse. They are unlocatable and armed to the teeth. Each of the fourteen Ohio-class submarines in the U.S. arsenal can empty itself of up to eighty nuclear warheads in a matter of minutes, and disappear.

Russia maintains a fleet of approximate parallel capability.

Fearsome and revered, they are masterpieces of engineering. Self-contained ecosystems that generate their own power, make their own oxygen and potable water, and can remain at sea, underwater, almost indefinitely, or until the crew runs out of food. Hidden from reconnaissance satellites, submarines move around the ocean with impunity. Because they have zero detectability, they're immune from first-strike attack, or almost any attack, until they're forced to surface upon return to port.

Stretching two football fields in length, each Ohio-class submarine is capable of launching twenty submarine-launched ballistic missiles—the dreaded SLBMs. Forty-four feet in length, eighty-three inches in diameter, and weighing 130,000 pounds at launch, each SLBM is armed with multiple nuclear warheads in its nose cone.

The firepower on one of these submarines can pretty much destroy a nation.

Nuclear submarine strike capabilities differ from those of land-based ICBMs in significant ways. Because they are undetectable under the sea, they can sneak up very close to a nation's coast and launch a first-strike attack, lowering launch-to-impact time from approximately thirty minutes to a fraction of that. Submarines launch nuclear missiles in unique ways. Long range across continents, and shorter range by using a depressed (lower) trajectory. For example, a Russian sub lurking off the U.S. West Coast can launch its missiles near simultaneously, at targets in all fifty states, all at once. This is because the multiple warheads in the nose cone of each missile can be deployed to individual targets hundreds of miles away. This is a primary driver of the Launch on Warning policy, and why the U.S. nuclear triad—like Russia's nuclear triad—remains on Hair-Trigger Alert.

And it is why the president has a six-minute window to deliberate and decide on a nuclear counterattack.

"If Washington was attacked by a Russian sub 1,000 kilometers [621 miles] from our coast, the time of flight would be less than seven minutes from launch to impact," warns Ted Postol. "The president would have no time to escape, and a 'designated successor' would then have to take nuclear command."

Back in 1982, in his capacity as advisor to the chief of U.S. naval operations, Postol was asked to give a classified briefing at the Pentagon on the power and speed of an attacking Russian submarine. His briefing slides were hand-drawn. "The early personal computers did not have any graphics capabilities," says Postol.

The normal method for briefing Pentagon officials back then was for a security-cleared expert to submit slides to the Office of the Draftsman (to formalize for presentation). Ted Postol was an exception to the rule. His opinions were highly regarded, and when they were needed, they were needed fast. Decades later, one of these formerly classified slides, captioned "Near Simultaneous Launch," seems oddly childlike, given the Armageddon-like consequences at hand.

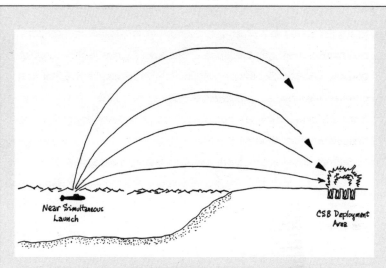

Theodore Postol's Pentagon briefing slide, from 1982.
(Courtesy of Theodore Postol)

But the decades-old slide is significant, Postol tells us, because "it pointed out that a Soviet submarine [can] launch all of its missiles at roughly five-second intervals, unloading all its missiles in about eighty seconds." And each missile has multiple warheads in its nose cone. "This fire-to-strike time is so short that if the United States had an attack submarine trailing the Soviet ballistic missile submarine, it could not fire a torpedo in time to sink the submarine before it was empty of missiles."

Then, as now, Postol's drawing underscores the reality that there is no defense against a nuclear-armed submarine. And yet back in 1982, this particular slide managed to stun the very individuals who were in charge of waging submarine warfare at the time. "This fact was shocking to the Chief of Naval Operations Jim Watkins," Postol recalls. "He had no idea this was possible." Even crazier, Postol notes, "because Watkins [himself] was a submariner, and had certainly been involved in operations where a submarine under his command was shadowing a Soviet ballistic missile submarine."

It's the speed with which submarines can launch nuclear weapons that makes them handmaidens of the apocalypse. In the words of defense analyst Sebastien Roblin, "ballistic-missile submarines promise the unstoppable hand of nuclear retribution—and should deter any sane adversary from attempting a first strike, or resorting to nuclear weapons at all."

But not all adversaries are sane, as history makes clear.

"There are those who are like Napoleon," thermonuclear weapons designer Richard Garwin warns. Leaders whose mindset echoes *"Après moi, le déluge."*

After me, the flood.

In discussing the rules of nuclear war, Garwin, like former secretary of defense Perry, acknowledges that all it takes is one nihilistic madman with a nuclear arsenal to start a nuclear war no one can win. A ruler like the one in this scenario, from North Korea, whose family has managed to rule the country for decades, imposing totalitarian-style martial law and monitoring citizens for the tiniest hint of dissent.

In North Korea, any infraction—speaking ill of the leader, leaving a speck of dust on his portrait, wearing skinny jeans—can result in arrest, torture, imprisonment, death. TVs and radios churn out state propaganda. Borders are closed. Ordinary people have little idea of what life outside the Hermit Kingdom is like. "I [had] never seen a map of the world," defector Yeonmi Park told Joe Rogan on his podcast. "As an Asian, I did not even know that I was Asian. The regime told me I was a Kim Il Sung race. [That] the calendar begins when Kim Il Sung was born."

Much of the country's landscape is rugged, mountainous terrain. Barely 17 percent of its land can support basic farming. Crops are said to be fertilized with human excrement. Malnutrition is commonplace.

Outside the capital, people forage for grasshoppers and other insects to eat. Livestock is considered property of the state. It is essentially illegal to own a cow. After an undernourished border guard's dramatic 2017 escape was caught on video, doctors found ten-inch parasitic worms in his intestines. It is as if North Korea's pauperized citizens are deprived of even the tiniest modicum of power, figuratively—and literally. When NASA released a satellite image of the Korean peninsula at night (taken by an Expedition 38 crew member on the International Space Station), bright city lights lit up the southern half of the peninsula but the northern half was dark. In a caption accompanying the image, NASA wrote, "North Korea is almost completely dark compared to neighboring South Korea and China. The darkened land appears as if it were a patch of water joining the Yellow Sea to the Sea of Japan." While the citizens of North Korea suffer and starve, a succession of its leaders have built for themselves a warren of underground command and control bunkers to keep themselves in power before, during, and after nuclear war. And to avoid decapitation from a strike by the United States.

Like other nations, North Korea pursued atomic fission during the Cold War. In the 1990s, it began developing nuclear weapons. By 1994, the CIA told President Clinton North Korea might have already produced one or two nuclear warheads. Clinton dispatched his Secretary of Defense William Perry to Pyongyang to try to convince Kim Jong Il to abandon the program in exchange for economic bene-fits. The result was nil. In 2002, North Korea admitted it had been developing nuclear weapons for years. By 2003, their first reactor was producing weapons-grade plutonium. In 2006, they tested a nuclear bomb. In 2009, they demonstrated a successful second test. By 2016, North Korea had thermonuclear weapons. By 2017, they had engineered an ICBM able to "reach anywhere in the world."

Augmenting its nuclear arsenal, North Korea maintains an unusual fleet of as many as eighty submarines. If accurate, this means it has one of the largest submarine forces in the world (the U.S. Navy reports having a total of seventy-one). These vessels in North Korea's fleet are old and clunky. "Not nuclear-powered, not even close," Postol says. But at least one of them likely can carry a submarine-launched ballistic missile. We know this because in October 2019, North Korea conducted a successful test launch from an underwater platform, simulating a submarine launch. And two years later, North Korea fired into the open waters off the coast of Japan what was likely an actual submarine-launched ballistic missile. "The world's most powerful weapon," the Korean Central News Agency (the state-run news agency of North Korea) declared.

And one submarine-launched ballistic missile is all a mad king requires.

While experts disagree on whether a North Korean submarine could realistically sneak up close to the U.S. and launch a missile (Garwin says unlikely), Ted Postol maintains it most certainly could. "It would be a tricky operation," he says, "but not impossible. I've done some analysis. I wouldn't rule it out."

Postol's calculations go like this.

North Korea's diesel submarine in this scenario is a modified 1950s-era attack submarine of the Romeo class. "These diesel-electric submarines are really hard to find in the ocean," he affirms, "except when they recharge their batteries. Then they're vulnerable." A diesel-electric submarine gets its power from a diesel motor, which drives electric generators and charges its batteries. "When the submarine wants to be covert," Postol notes, "the submarine operates only on batteries and it's under the surface, and it's an electric-powered system, so it's very quiet." Eventually, batteries run down and need to be recharged. For this, a diesel engine needs air. And to explain how this works, Postol puts himself in the shoes of a North Korean submariner.

"So, what I do is, I get up close to the surface and I extend up to the water surface a device that's called a snorkel. Basically, a pipe—typically with a hat on top of it to protect against waves. And at the same time, I keep it low to the water. You don't want the pipe up too high. Modern radar systems are pretty able to see things like a snorkel sticking above the water."

The submarine would have to travel very slowly. "Slowly, as in about five knots." This is because most battery power consumed by a diesel-electric submarine is for hotel load. "Meaning keeping people warm, fans blowing to keep the oxygen generating." Postol surmises that in a primitive submarine like this, one "that doesn't have the most advanced batteries, you could probably stay underwater for seventy-two to ninety-six hours, going at five knots, before you have to snorkel." And to give us a sense of how much power the vessel would consume if going fast: "If you're going at twenty-five knots, your power is gone in less than one hour, so you've got to be slow. But if you are a North Korean submariner, you're pretty tough," Postol imagines. He calculates. "So, say I can do a hundred hours at a time, at five knots without having to snorkel—to surface and recharge the batteries—that means I can cover about 500 nautical miles between snorkeling events, if I'm careful and quiet." Difficult but not impossible. "If I were a North Korean submariner, I'd snorkel for a couple of hours and try to make sure that nobody sees me, which is not hard to do because there's a lot of ocean out there. So let's say the transit is five or six thousand nautical miles. So, it's a couple of months. And you need a lot of food, you probably don't expect to make it home, but if you're North Korean that's part of the job."

Postol also worked out the route. "If you wanted to pose a threat to the United States, you would try to hug the southern coast of Alaska," he suggests, citing the underwater geography involved. "You want to stay on the continental shelf in shallow water, which is not so shallow that a submarine can't use it, because if you go into the deep water, there's a good chance we'll find you. Because the sound of the snorkeling submarine in deep water is potentially detectable at hundreds of miles."

The detectability of submarines is not simply how "noisy they are," Postol asserts. "It is what is going on in whatever kind of environment they are operating in"—a concept known as the echo effect, which Postol has spent hours not just thinking about but explaining to officials at the Pentagon. "When a submarine is in shallow water it is nearly impossible to hear it, even with a very advanced acoustic system." An advanced sonar system like SOSUS (Sound Surveillance System), developed by the U.S. Navy during the Cold War to track Soviet submarines and create its strategy for anti-submarine warfare. SOSUS has advanced over the years. It's how, in June 2023, the navy was able to hear an underwater implosion that was likely the *Titan* submersible. But SOSUS works in deep ocean waters, not shallow waters. And the reason it's nearly impossible to detect has to do with the complexity of the signals from reflections off the ocean's surface and bottom—the echo-chamber effect. "In shallow water," says Postol, "there are too many echoes. You can't hear or 'see' shit."

In this scenario, North Korea's diesel-electric Romeo-class submarine crosses the ocean, hugs the continental shelf along Alaska, then heads south. "And, suddenly, you find yourself off the coast of the United States and able to strike with a short-range ballistic missile."

That is the scenario we're looking at now. It is how the North Korean navy managed to get a ballistic-missile submarine within striking distance of the West Coast of the United States. And now, eighteen minutes after the Hwasong-17 ICBM first launched, a nuclear-capable, submarine-launched short-range ballistic missile has emerged from the ocean.

It ends powered flight and begins Midcourse Phase. Tracking data indicates it is headed toward the middle to bottom half of California, population 25 million souls.

19 MINUTES
Aerospace Data Facility—Colorado

At the Aerospace Data Facility in Colorado, analysts with NRO, NSA, and Space Force all see the data at the same time. They all understand that there is now a second ballistic missile attacking the United States. This one, flying at a speed of Mach 6, or 4,600 miles per hour, on a quasi-ballistic trajectory, appears to be headed for Southern California or maybe Nevada. It is less than 300 miles away from the shore.

The missile is the KN-23, a North Korean short-range ballistic missile similar to one that analysts watched successfully fire from a subsurface platform off the coast of Sinpo in October 2021. The intended purpose of the KN-23, analysts believed back then, was to deliver a nuclear weapon to a target in South Korea. Now one of them is flying toward Southern California, moving at a rate of six times the speed of sound.

The KN-23 is roughly twenty-five feet long and has fins. Its operational range is somewhere between 280 and 430 miles, depending on the payload. It can carry in its nose cone a 1,100-pound warhead. But the target that the KN-23 nuclear missile is headed for will be utterly catastrophic, no matter the yield. The target is protected by Article 15 of the Geneva Conventions, a set of treaties and protocols that form the core of international humanitarian law and regulate the conduct of armed conflict. But as the world is about to learn, there are no laws in nuclear war. The premise of deterrence is that nuclear war is never supposed to happen.

The Aerospace Data Facility alerts military commands in Nebraska, Colorado, and Washington, D.C. With all U.S. military forces at DEFCON 1, all personnel at all eleven combatant commands in the United States and around the world are already poised for imminent nuclear battle. Confirmation of this second attacking missile ratchets up the degree of force that will be used in the U.S. counterattack.

Because of the missile's low apogee (high point), its short flight time, and the maneuverability from its fins, the Defense Department faces an unmitigated nightmare. The KN-23 missile is capable of evading traditional U.S. missile defense. And a launch-to-target distance of less than 400 miles, traveling at a speed of Mach 6, means the missile will remain in the air for less than three minutes.

20 MINUTES
U.S. Strategic Command Headquarters, Nebraska

Duty officers at STRATCOM's Battle Deck in Nebraska receive sensor data from the Aerospace Data Facility in Colorado confirming launch and travel time. Based on plume measurements and missile trajectory, this second attacking ballistic missile is heading into Southern California or possibly lower Nevada. Likely targets include:

- China Lake, the Naval Air Weapons Station near Inyokern
- Fort Irwin, the army garrison in the Mojave Desert
- Naval Base Coronado, the Pacific Fleet's home port off San Diego
- Nellis Air Force Base, the air force installation in southern Nevada

On satellite comms, all commanders wait for the president's orders, as he is still in the process of being evacuated by CAT operators onto Marine One. As tracking data comes in, Nuclear Command and Control computing systems calculate and project the target more accurately. The missile now appears to be heading toward Vandenberg Space Force Base, roughly fifty miles northwest of Santa Barbara. Machine analysis is never perfect and the missile has fins that can change its trajectory at any time.

Seconds pass.

As it turns out, the algorithmic estimation is off by some thirty-five miles. The target is up the coast from Vandenberg Space Force Base. The target is a civilian facility, on an ocean bluff just north of Avila Beach, California.

The target is the Diablo Canyon Power Plant—a nuclear power plant with two, thousand-plus-megawatt pressurized water reactors.

Diablo Canyon Power Plant in central California.
(Courtesy of Pacific Gas and Electric Company)

21 MINUTES

Diablo Canyon Power Plant,
San Luis Obispo County, California

The incoming short-range ballistic missile races toward Diablo Canyon Power Plant, a 750-acre facility sitting eighty-five feet above the Pacific Ocean.

It is a warm day at the end of March, 12:24 p.m. local time, the hour that security guards at Diablo's southern-facing gate are generally known to eat lunch, often outside in the sun. There are seagulls resting along the tops of fence poles here. Pelicans are visible on the beach below, catching prey in their large throat pouches and swallowing fish whole. It is near to low tide. Seaweed covers the rocks. As of 2024, Diablo is the only nuclear power plant in California that remains active. The gate guard here, eating his lunch in the sun, is one of some 1,200 employees and 200 subcontractors who work on-site at Diablo. None of them has any idea that in just a few seconds they will all be cremated on the spot.

To defend against short-range ballistic missiles, the U.S. Navy has developed its Aegis program, an anti-ballistic missile system mounted on navy Aegis cruisers and destroyers at sea. Unlike the faulty interceptor program, Aegis missiles have a shoot-down record of 85 percent. But these battleships are out on patrol in the Atlantic and Pacific Oceans, and in the Persian Gulf—defending America's NATO and Indo-Pacific partners from attack. They are thousands of miles away from being anywhere near shooting range of America's West Coast.

The Pentagon also operates a land-based missile defense program called the Terminal High Altitude Area Defense, or THAAD, system—one that fires anti-ballistic missiles from launchers mounted on flatbed trucks. But as with the Aegis missile defense systems, all of America's THAAD systems are presently deployed overseas. Years back, after North Korea first successfully fired a KN-23 missile, Congress discussed setting up THAAD systems along America's West Coast, but as of 2024 has not done so yet.

In this moment, all of these missile defense systems are a moot point. The SBIRS space satellites spotted the hot rocket exhaust on this sub-launched missile just a fraction of a second after launch, but now roughly four minutes have passed. Boost Phase and Midcourse Phase have begun and ended. The warhead bearing down on the Diablo Canyon Power Plant now enters Terminal Phase.

In the laws of war, there exists a promise among nations never to attack a nuclear reactor. Expanding on the Geneva Conventions Protocol II, Article 15, the International Committee of the Red Cross calls this Rule 42.

Practice Relating to Rule 42.
Works and Installations Containing Dangerous Forces

Section A. Additional Protocol II

Article 15 of the 1977 Additional Protocol II provides:

Nuclear electrical generating stations shall not be made the object of attack, even where these objectives are military objectives.

But as history demonstrates, mad rulers disobey rules of war. In words often attributed to Adolf Hitler, "If you win, you need not have to explain."

Directly attacking a nuclear reactor with a nuclear-armed missile is a worst-case scenario beyond measure. In terms of outcome, there are few nuclear attack realities that can get any worse. Nuclear weapons exploded in the air, at sea, and on land create varying degrees of radiation and fallout based on yield (size of explosion) and weather (rain vs. wind). Radiation let loose in the atmosphere dissipates over time, rising into the troposphere and moving with the wind. But attacking a nuclear reactor with a nuclear missile all but guarantees a core reactor meltdown that in turn results in a thousands-of-years-long nuclear catastrophe.

What is about to happen in Southern California is known by energy officials as the Devil's Scenario, a phrase also used in secret discussions led by the Japan Atomic Energy Commission chairman, Dr. Shunsuke Kondo, and others, after the Fukushima Daiichi Nuclear Power Plant disaster of 2011. In that case, after the plant's six nuclear reactors were catastrophically impacted by a magnitude 9.0 earthquake and a forty-six-foot-tall tsunami wave, the plant suffered major damage and officials feared the worst. During a closed-door emergency meeting, Japan's cabinet members acknowledged that Fukushima Daiichi was on the brink of core reactor meltdown and hydrogen fire if they were unable to get its cooling system back online. Were this to happen, a blanket of dense radioactive smoke would spread out across eastern Japan, rendering a 150-mile stretch of land from Fukushima to Tokyo impassible to humans for an untold number of years.

"That was the Devil's Scenario that was on my mind," Japan's chief cabinet secretary, Yukio Edano, later explained. And that he feared "common sense dictated that, if that came to pass, then it was the end of Tokyo." As in the entire city.

But Japan was spared. Three of the six nuclear reactors at Fukushima Daiichi sustained severe core damage and released radioactive materials, but they did not melt down. The Devil's Scenario did not come to pass. "Japan dodged a bullet," wrote Declan Butler in *Nature* magazine. In its 2014 report called "Reflections on Fukushima," the U.S. Nuclear Regulatory Commission warned that what happened in Japan should serve the world as a "cautionary tale."

All nuclear power plants generate electric power using heat from enriched uranium. Every five years, each plant's spent nuclear fuel rods lose their full capacity and must be removed, stored, and kept cool; these rods remain highly radioactive for thousands of years. At Diablo Canyon, there are more than 2,500 spent fuel assemblies being continually cooled in on-site cooling pools, which use water from the Pacific Ocean. Were these pumps to fail, by accident or by attack, a catastrophic meltdown would occur.

Every three years, the U.S. Nuclear Regulatory Commission carries out force-on-force maneuvers where security guards practice how to counter a direct attack. Exercises include tabletop games, like chess, and mock drills that simulate combat against an adversary force like a terrorist organization. But there has never been such a thing as a rehearsal against an incoming nuclear missile. This is because no such defense exists. Rule 42, like the concept of deterrence, is psychological. A theoretical supposition predicated on supposed future behavior and follow-on consequences that promise to work—until it doesn't work.

Fifty-eight miles up, the nuclear warhead from the submarine-launched ballistic missile reenters the atmosphere, traveling now at a speed of more than 4,000 miles per hour.

Thirty seconds remain until the bomb's triggering system is set to explode.

A Nuclear Regulatory Commission report finds that a small-to-medium-sized fire at a facility like Diablo Canyon would displace 3 to 4 million people. "We'd [be] talking about trillion-dollar consequences," Frank von Hippel, professor emeritus at Princeton University and cofounder of its Program on Science and Global Security, said of such a catastrophe. But a nuclear strike against Diablo Canyon Power Plant will not produce a fire that is small or even medium-sized. It will be a radioactive inferno. The beginning of the apocalypse.

Twenty seconds remain.

A nuclear strike against a nuclear reactor guarantees a nuclear core collapse, also known as a nuclear core materials meltdown. In an article from the *New York Times*, published in 1971, former Manhattan Project physicist Ralph E. Lapp described what happens were a nuclear reactor to experience a core collapse. Citing facts from the Atomic Energy Commission's Ergen Report, Lapp detailed the horror: first an explosion, then fire, then the uncontrollable spewing out of radioactive debris. But what happens deep inside the reactor core is the real threat, Lapp explained. "This molten debris could accumulate at the bottom of the reactor vessel . . . [a] huge, molten, radioactive mass . . . would sink into the earth and continue to grow in size for about two years." A "high temperature mass," a liquified "hot sphere" of radioactive lava and smoldering fire "about a hundred feet in diameter might form and persist for a decade."

Four. Three. Two. One.

The KN-23's nuclear warhead detonates on its target.

The entire Diablo nuclear power plant is consumed in a flash of nuclear light. There is a massive fireball. A building-destroying blast. A nuclear mushroom cloud *and* a nuclear core meltdown.

The Devil's Scenario has come to pass.

22 MINUTES
Cavalier Space Force Station, North Dakota

The Cavalier Space Force Station in eastern North Dakota sits fifteen miles from the Canadian border. Here, inside an eight-story-tall concrete structure, a massive octagon-shaped radar system scans the sky. Given Cavalier's position on the globe, its radar sees the attacking warhead let loose by the Hwasong-17

ICBM as it comes over the horizon in Midcourse Phase, from the north. This occurs approximately twenty-two minutes after launch. The ground radar's observation will be the last over-the-horizon tracking data the Space Force records before the bomb detonates over D.C.

Ten or eleven minutes remain. There is now enough data to pinpoint the target within a half-mile distance. The target is either the Pentagon or the White House.

What is happening in this scenario is a decapitation event.

Radar building at Cavalier Space Force Station, North Dakota.
(U.S. Space Force)

23 MINUTES

The White House, Washington, D.C.

I n Washington, D.C., the president gets strapped into Marine One, its rotor blades spinning, ready for ascent. It has been several minutes since the president climbed inside and yet the helicopter still hasn't left. The special agent in charge of the president's detail is screaming at the president's national security advisor, who is yelling into his own cell phone while standing in the doorway of Marine One. The SAC is about to get physical. It's his duty to protect the president with his own life.

SAC: *Helicopter needs to leave now!*

The fierce argument between the two men has been over the available number of parachutes in Marine One. The controversy has wasted precious time. The three-man Counter Assault Team Element has chutes for themselves, for the president, for the special agent in charge, and for the mil aide; the sum total of parachutes in Marine One. There are fourteen people in Marine One, meaning the rest of the passengers will go down with the aircraft if it goes down.

The national security advisor gives up the fight. He decides to take his chances, gets into the helicopter, and straps in. Already inside are a few individuals from the executive office of the president—sometimes called the permanent government—including the national cyber director and the executive secretary of the National Space Council. The White House chief of staff, the assistant to the president for homeland security and counterterrorism, and half a dozen others are running toward a second marine helicopter ready to lift off from farther down the lawn.

The Marine One fleet is reinforced with ballistic armor, has anti-missile defense, and a missile-warning threat system. As the newly built Sikorsky VH-92A carrying the president and his advisors begins to rise, CAT operators up and down the White House lawn scan for threats.

But the threat is not coming from the ground.

The threat is approaching from above.

Only minutes remain until a nuclear bomb will strike Washington, D.C.

Inside Marine One, multiple people are shouting at the president over satellite video comms displayed in front of him. The president's family, his wife, and their children, are in upstate New York with his in-laws. The SecDef and the vice-chairman are on route to Site R. The vice president's whereabouts have yet to be confirmed. A system of antennas and satellite dishes contained in a communications bubble attached to the helicopter's tail boom has the president connected with STRATCOM. Nuclear Command, Control, and Communications, or NC3, is a complex system of systems that exist on the ground, in the air, and in space. Its components include receivers, terminals, and satellites to keep the Nuclear Triad under the president's control. The NC3 system inside Marine One is said to be hardened against the electromagnetic pulse that accompanies a nuclear flash. But no one has any idea if the system will endure or fall apart in a nuclear war. When analyzing its efficiency in 2021, the Government Accountability Office did not make public its recommendations and the Defense Department did not comment.

Seated next to the president, the mil aide opens the Football, inside of which is the Black Book. As the helicopter leaves the White House complex airspace, the chairman of the Joint Chiefs of Staff speaks first, over comms.

Chairman: *We've been hit with a nuclear bomb in California.*

Jesus Christ, didn't we have a few more minutes? the president asks.

National security advisor: *A second missile.* He stumbles. *A different one.*

Chairman: *In Southern California, at a nuclear power plant.*

STRATCOM commander: *We anticipate the Pentagon will be hit next, sir.*

The national security advisor points to a time clock on an electronic screen inside Marine One, counting down seconds.

Chairman: *Launch orders, sir!*

The president removes the laminated code card from his wallet. The Biscuit. With the gold codes.

Chairman: *Advising option Charlie from the Black Book, sir.*

Just minutes from now the chairman will be dead.

The president confirms option Charlie. A nuclear counterstrike designed as the Launch on Warning response to a North Korean nuclear strike against America. Eighty-two targets, or "aimpoints," that include North Korea's nuclear and WMD facilities, its leadership, and other war-sustaining facilities. This counterstrike launches fifty Minuteman III ICBMs and eight Trident SLBMs (each Trident carries four nuclear warheads in its nose cone), for a total of eighty-two nuclear warheads at eighty-two targets on the northern half of the Korean peninsula. This mother lode of force is but a fraction of what the original SIOP for nuclear war called for in its opening salvo against Moscow. Here, in this scenario, the eighty-two nuclear warheads about to be launched all but guarantee the deaths of millions of people, or maybe even tens of millions of people, on the Korean peninsula alone.

It is nearly noiseless inside Marine One.

Speaking in a normal tone, the president reads the nuclear launch codes out loud.

23 MINUTES, 30 SECONDS
National Military Command Center, Pentagon

Beneath the Pentagon, the deputy director of operations authenticates as fact that the man who just ordered a nuclear counterstrike against North Korea is the president of the United States. This is not done by state-of-the-art voiceprint biometrics, but rather the old-school way. By challenge-and-response code: two letters from the NATO phonetic alphabet spoken by a human voice.

Foxtrot, Tango, the deputy director of operations says in this scenario. These are the last two words he will ever say to the president.

From inside Marine One, the president reads his response.

Yankee, Zulu, he says.

As the helicopter leaves the White House complex airspace, the president stares out the window of Marine One, watching as the distance between himself and the city expands.

The end of the world has been set in motion by two code words spoken aloud.

24 MINUTES
Missile Alert Facility, Wyoming

One thousand, six hundred miles from Washington, D.C., in a field in Wyoming, a patch of hardpack snow shimmers in the afternoon sun. There is chain-link fence, motion-detection equipment, and a 110-ton concrete door lying flush with the earth. Facing the sky.

To passersby, this is cowboy country. Ranchers' land. To Strategic Command, it's ICBM silo country. Home to one-third of

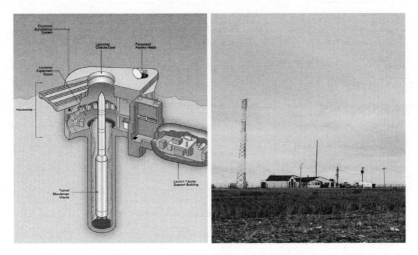

Minuteman III ICBM belowground (left) and
aboveground (right) launch facility. (U.S. Air Force)

the nation's 400 land-based nuclear missiles. To those not in the
know, the Echo-01 launch facility in this scenario is simply a non-
descript cluster of buildings: house, barn, electric tower, garage.
But beneath the blast doors, hidden in the field, sits an
eighty-foot-deep missile silo tunnel with concrete walls that are
four feet thick. An elevator shaft connects the launch crew to living
quarters, a power station, and an escape tunnel so the two-person
missile crew can get out after launch.

Most of the space down in the silo is consumed by a Minuteman
III missile—60 feet tall, 80,000 pounds, and with a 300-kiloton
thermonuclear weapon in its nose cone. A weapon that is now
being readied for launch.

The clock reads 1:27 p.m. local time when the clarion call
sounds. Combat missile crews and support personnel assigned to
the 90th Missile Wing leap from their seats in every outpost across
the state, each person moving at speeds only DEFCON 1 can
incentivize. America's 400 land-based ICBMs are generally
accepted as the leg of the U.S. nuclear triad most vulnerable to

attack because their locations are publicly known and don't change. This also makes them among the first weapons systems to be launched in a nuclear counterattack—a concept known to insiders as the "use them or lose them" strategy. Launch your ICBMs fast or expect them to be targeted and destroyed.

An ICBM can be launched—meaning the time it takes from the moment a launch order is received, to the weapon's physical launch—faster than any other weapon system in the arsenal, including those on submarines. "They weren't called Minutemen for nothing," wrote former ICBM launch officer Bruce Blair. "The process of arming and targeting and firing the missiles [happens] in a grand total of 60 seconds."

Each of the 400 ICBM silos like Echo-01 is strategically positioned across America (west of the Mississippi River)—in Montana, Wyoming, North Dakota, Nebraska, and Colorado. They've been built beneath private ranches, inside national forests, on Native American reservations and family farms. Some are outside small towns, others down the road from local mini-malls. A few facilities are so remotely located, it takes missile crews several hours to get there by vehicle, on good-weather days.

Missile Alert Facility Echo-01 sits inside a 9,600-square-mile parcel that makes up Wyoming's vast underground nuclear missile field. "If Wyoming were a nation," journalist Dan Whipple points out, F. E. Warren Air Force Base outside Cheyenne "would make it one of the world's major nuclear powers."

At Missile Alert Facility Echo-01, the two-man missile crew has been preparing every day for this day. During each morning's elevator ride down, the launch officers remove their air force patches from a Velcro strip and replace them with patches from Strategic Command. In the event of nuclear war, they report directly to the STRATCOM commander. For seven decades, this act has been preparatory. Today it is real.

Now that the president's launch order has been validated, the ICBM launch sequence begins. A Minuteman launch control center controls ten ICBMs. Across Wyoming, launch crews inside missile silos receive encrypted orders; each order is said to be 150 characters long.

Five launch control center crews, including those at Echo-01, open their locked safes bolted into the missile silos' concrete walls.

Each launch officer compares the recently updated Sealed Authenticator System codes with the codes they've just received from the Emergency Action Team at the National Military Command Center beneath the Pentagon.

Each officer retrieves a fire-control key—small, silver in color, made of metal, with a key ring and a descriptive tab.

Each launch crew enters a war plan code into a launch computer, retargeting each of the ICBMs from open ocean default presets (for safety) to a predetermined target in the option Charlie attack plan from the president's Black Book.

Fifty new target coordinates are typed in.

Launch keys turn.

Fifty Minuteman III missiles, each with a 300-kiloton nuclear warhead in its nose cone, are now armed.

Fifty ICBMs transporting a total of 15 megatons of explosive yield.

Across the state of Wyoming, fifty 110-ton concrete silo doors blow open wide.

Through clouds of smoke and fire, fifty nuclear-armed missiles begin to rise. It takes 3.4 seconds for a Minuteman missile to exit its missile silo and take flight.

After a minute, the first-stage booster of each 80,000-pound missile completes powered flight and drops free.

The second-stage rocket booster ignites, dropping parts of itself as the missile climbs.

After roughly twelve minutes, each missile will accelerate to extremely high velocities, before reaching an ultimate cruising height of 500 to 700 miles above the surface of the Earth.

But before any of these fifty ICBMs reach this final speed and height, a phone call gets made by an old man living down the road from one of these launch facilities here in Wyoming.

The old man is a Russian spy.

"There are spies everywhere, watching nuclear-launch facilities across the United States," the CIA's first science and technology director, Dr. Albert "Bud" Wheelon, told us before he died.

The old Russian spy picks up his phone and calls Moscow.

The ICBMs have launched, he says into the phone.

Part III

THE NEXT 24 MINUTES

24 MINUTES

Rancho San Miguelito, Point Buchon, California

Diablo Canyon, California. On detonation, a 300-kiloton nuclear bomb releases 300 trillion calories of energy within one-millionth of a second.
(Courtesy of Pacific Gas and Electric Company)

In central California on the coast, four miles northwest of the Diablo Canyon Power Plant, high on a hilltop near Point Buchon, a cattle rancher is tending to his animals when he is blown off his feet by the blast from a 300-kiloton nuclear bomb.

There was no sound at first, no warning.

Just a wall of dense air that hit him like a bulldozer, the wind ripping the clothes off his body. As fate and circumstance had it, the cattle rancher was facing away from the bomb when it exploded, sparing him blindness.

He is alive owing, in part, to geography. To the forms and features of the land surfaces around him. A series of low mountains and sloping cliff formations separate the rancher from ground zero, the point where the bomb detonated. The earth and stone buffered some of the bomb's deadly thermal radiation—light and heat that causes third-degree skin burns and sets combustible materials on fire—but not all. "Large, hilly land masses tend to increase air blast effects in some areas and to decrease them in others," U.S. army scientists learned from the Hiroshima and Nagasaki bombings. There are no buildings here on this sea-facing bluff, nothing to topple over and crush the rancher to death. No glass windows to shatter and impale him. The overpressure from the bomb tore off his clothes and threw him to the ground. He is old as dirt and tough as hell. He gets on his feet. Spins around.

He sees the mushroom cloud.

The rancher's great-grandfather purchased this land in the early 1900s, before the invention of Ford's automobile. Staring at the mushroom cloud rising over the land, he almost can't believe his eyes.

The rancher's cattle—their fur singed from thermal radiation—run for the hills. He stands alone. An old, naked man. He was born in July 1945, the same month and year that Manhattan Project scientists built and tested the first atomic bomb, code name Trinity, as in Father, Son, and Holy Ghost.

The old rancher looks around for his clothes. He sees his smartphone in the dirt, spared localized EMP effects owing to the surrounding terrain. He picks up the remarkable little machine and begins taking video with its camera system. The old rancher knows history. Knows the Trinity bomb was exploded in the Jornada del Muerto desert, which means the Journey of the Dead Man.

And now, here he stands in Diablo Canyon, in the Devil's Gorge, watching the mushroom cloud expand.

Everything associated with nuclear weapons is saturated in evil and in death, he has read in books. Always has been this way. He is old enough to remember when Mutual Assured Destruction was first sold to the public as a savior; when really the old rancher knows that MAD is madness. He remembers Bert the Turtle. Duck and cover drills. Project Sunshine, that Atomic Energy Commission program that collected bones of the dead and baby teeth of living children. To secretly test tissue in human body parts for levels of radiation exposure.

The rancher keeps filming.

He is aware of his own mortality. Of the lethal levels of radiation he is no doubt receiving right now. Of death by radiation poisoning, and how it is an abominable way to die. He uploads to Facebook more video. Images of this grayish-brown mushroom cloud rising over a nuclear power plant sitting nearly equidistant between San Francisco and Los Angeles. Between two of the most populous cities in America's most populous state.

This is the Devil's Scenario made real.

The bomb's localized electromagnetic pulse destroyed AC power systems up and down the coast, but the rancher's cell phone still has battery juice. It connects to the internet by way of a communications satellite passing overhead. The rancher's video posts to social media sites and begins making its way around the digital world. People in Paris and Peoria, in Karachi and Kuala Lumpur, are now seeing images of this mushroom cloud appearing across social media in near real time.

Reports begin to flood the internet.

#NuclearWar #Armageddon #EndOfTheWorld.

25 MINUTES
Data Center, Sacramento, California

Tens of millions of people across America hurry to their smartphones and log on to social media platforms. If the internet is the road, the app is the destination—and in this moment people flood Facebook, X, Instagram, whatever their trusted news app happens to be—everyone desperate to gather information about what is happening on California's coast, in real time.

To see is to believe.

People need to see the rancher's video with their own eyes.

X is the first to implode. At its data center in Sacramento, the power shuts down. The backup systems kick in, then those systems trip and shut down. The destruction of the Diablo Canyon Power Plant has wreaked havoc on California's electric grid. Demand is far outpacing supply. Computer servers and storage systems that process data begin to overload, and start shutting off, falling like dominoes.

Eighty. Then one hundred. Then 150 million of X's users log on all at once. The site buckles under the strain. Crashes in entirety. X is now permanently and forever down.

25 MINUTES, 30 SECONDS
Diablo Canyon, California

The nuclear bomb that struck the Diablo Canyon Power Plant was a 300-kiloton surface burst. Unlike an airburst, which is designed to kill the most people on the ground using blast, a surface burst kills fewer people in the immediate vicinity, but produces far greater amounts of fallout than if exploded in the air. Fallout got its name because it literally "falls out" of the sky after the explosion passes and the shock wave subsides.

The weapons technology involved in getting a KN-23 submarine-launched ballistic missile from a missile tube in an underwater vessel to a target on land has been decades in the making. The Americans and the Russians began working with sub-launched missile technology in the 1950s and have been at it ever since. North Korea is relatively new to the game, but thanks to theft and beginner's luck, the submarine-launched ballistic missile fired at the nuclear power plant in California missed the center point of its target by only a few football fields' distance.

The bomb struck the earth and detonated just below the power plant's southernmost employee parking lot, 100 feet back from the edge of the cliff. Countless effects have been calculated by defense officials, including ones that involve hitting a nuclear reactor with a missile. But what has happened here is almost beyond measure. In a fraction of a second, everyone at the Diablo Canyon facility has been incinerated. There is no one left alive to measure anything.

All nuclear power plants in the United States are built to withstand a direct hit from a fighter aircraft. In 1988, Sandia National Laboratories did a containment vessel integrity test, flying an F-4 Phantom fighter jet into a twelve-foot concrete wall of approximate construction, a slab designed to simulate a reactor containment vessel wall. Most of the jet was atomized; the wall suffered a 2.3-inch scar. But this remotely controlled aircraft was traveling nearly 500 miles per hour and its spare tanks were filled with water, not fuel.

Hitting a nuclear reactor's containment vessel with a nuclear bomb is another league of destruction. When a 300-kiloton nuclear bomb detonates, it releases 300 trillion calories of energy within one-millionth of a second, a ridiculous amount of force for the average human mind to comprehend. In dynamite, that is the equivalent of 600 million pounds of TNT, a figure equally incomprehensible. (A medium-sized pipe bomb has an explosive capacity of around five pounds.)

Historian Lynn Eden, scholar emeritus at Stanford University and an expert on nuclear firestorms, explains, "Because the early fireball would be so hot, it would expand rapidly. By the time the fireball approached its maximum size it would be more than a mile in diameter." A mile-wide nuclear fireball is enough to entirely destroy the 750-acre Diablo Canyon facility. And because roughly half that diameter area includes ocean, the entire nuclear power plant has now cratered into the sea.

Everything inside the fireball is obliterated.

Some of what used to be inside the crater gets deposited on the partial rim with the rest carried up into the air, to return to the earth as fallout. As Carl Sagan warned back in 1983, "High yield ground bursts will vaporize, melt, and pulverize the surface at the target area and propel large quantities of condensates and fine dust into the upper troposphere and stratosphere." And because this fireball vaporizes so much ground, its mushroom cloud contains an unprecedented amount of radioactive material.

In *The Effects of Nuclear Weapons*, the army's scientists did not mince words. "A nuclear explosion occurring at or near the earth's surface can result in severe contamination by the radioactive fallout . . . a gradual phenomenon extending over a period of time . . . Fallout can occur even when the cloud cannot be seen [with particles] approximately 100 micrometers in diameter . . . to pieces about the size of a marble."

But the army's description does not do justice to what is actually happening here. It does not include the cataclysmic effects that come with the dispersal into the atmosphere of the radioactive inventory from Diablo's twin 1,100-megawatt reactor cores and its 2,000 metric tons of intact spent fuel.

Seconds pass. What is happening inside the mile-wide bomb crater is precisely what nuclear physicist Ralph E. Lapp warned about in the Ergen Report back in 1971. What remains of the twin reactor cores burns, spewing radioactive lava now boring down into the earth. Diablo's decommissioning panel previously warned that if temperatures were to reach 1,652 degrees Fahrenheit (900 degrees Celsius), "the hot fuel rods will spontaneously combust."

And now they have.

All of the more than 2,500 spent fuel assemblies burn, transforming into a radioactive brew of poisonous fallout. Minutes ago, the plant's open-air, dry cask field of fifty-eight concrete canisters stood upright like giant chess pieces, each one bolted down to a seven-and-a-half-foot-thick concrete pad. The bomb blast shattered their concrete shells, knocked them over, and blew them apart, and now they too emit extraordinary amounts of highly radioactive waste.

Until the bomb struck, Diablo's reactor Unit 1 and Unit 2 were producing enough megawatts of electricity to deliver power to roughly 10 percent of all Californians, some 3.9 million people in 2024. Not anymore.

Power plants require electricity to function. The bomb explosion has destroyed the AC power systems that once kept Diablo online, and the power isn't coming back anytime soon.

The facility's six backup diesel generators were obliterated by the fireball, as were the fuel storage tanks and backup battery systems. The plant's on-site fire department—its two fire engines, water reservoirs, and the machines that pump seawater onto burning buildings—all have turned to ash. Five million gallons of emergency water have been dispersed in the infernal heat. The plant's auxiliary seawater snorkels, its cooling water intake systems, and its hot water discharge areas all have collapsed into the sea.

Emergency management helicopter crews will not arrive any

time in the near future to try to put the fires out, certainly not as Russian crews did during the Chernobyl disaster of 1986. The U.S. Army can't fly overhead and try to smother with sand and boron whatever might be left of the two exposed nuclear reactor cores. The high levels of lethal-dose radiation pouring out of the site make passage through the debris cloud instantaneously lethal for weeks or months to come.

Gordon Thompson, director of the Institute for Resource and Security Studies, describes the consequences of a spent fuel assembly fire. "The fire [can]not be extinguished at that point, simply because it [can]not be approached due to the extreme radioactivity." Thompson has studied nuclear fuel storage systems since 1978. His calculations indicate that up to 100 percent of the plant's radioactive fuel's elements would be released into the atmosphere.

"You're talking about an event that would force the long-term abandonment of an area roughly the size of New Jersey," Frank von Hippel tells us, then, confronted with this scenario, rephrases: "Two New Jerseys."

Los Alamos nuclear engineer Dr. Glen McDuff paints an even darker picture. "The situation would be far, far worse," he warns. "Spent fuel rods are radioactive. Hit by a nuclear bomb, they would shatter into a zillion pieces."

What this means, McDuff tells us, is that "you'd now have radioactive pieces of spent fuel rods seeded in your fallout. You'd have a situation where the middle of California is unusable forever. The land could be contaminated all the way to Nevada, perhaps even Colorado. Diablo Canyon would never recover. Ever."

26 MINUTES

National Defense Management Center, Moscow, Russia

The National Defense Management Center in Moscow. (www.Kremlin.ru)

Among the most significant people who managed to see, and to download, the cattle rancher's video before X went down are in Russia. They are the deputies serving the top generals in the Russian General Staff. This group of young officers in Moscow is now glued to electronic screens replaying the mushroom cloud video in a loop. Here on the icy banks of the Moskva River, inside Russia's National Defense Management Center, every last person—from the generals to the janitors—has stopped what he or she was doing and now scrambles to make sense of what the hell is going on in the United States.

The West Coast of America just got hit with a nuclear bomb.

This is shocking. This is catastrophic. But most of all, this is terrifying. Deterrence is a psychological phenomenon. A state of mind. Now that deterrence has failed, anything can happen. Anything at all.

It is 10:29 p.m. Moscow time. The night watch commander here at the National Defense Management Center quickly sets up an emergency teleconference for the senior commanders of the General Staff. Those who are already physically in the building rush into the control center of strategic nuclear forces, an auditorium-style, fortified command center, similar to the bunker beneath the Pentagon in Washington, D.C.

Russia had nothing to do with what just happened in the U.S., in this scenario. The ranking Russian generals signing into the teleconference one by one know this to be fact. They are the individuals in charge of the nation's nuclear forces. But conclusions drawn by others will be impossible to control.

Deterrence has failed. The theory that Mutual Assured Destruction keeps the world safe from nuclear weapons is no longer valid. In this moment of crisis, how will a decapitation event against the United States by a rogue third party impact decisions made by Russia's Nuclear Command and Control?

Former secretary of defense Leon Panetta provides us with his impression of what might be transpiring in such a moment. "I honestly don't think there's a great deal of thought given to the MAD chemistry at a time like this." Panetta fears that "when nuclear bombs start flying, there is not a lot of time to start thinking, 'Who the hell else is feeling threatened?' There's not a lot of thought given to who the hell else may be thinking about doing *what*. . . . Not at a time like this." Crisis mindset can be a dangerous thing.

The National Defense Management Center in Moscow is a nerve center of Russia's Nuclear Command and Control. Located two miles from the Kremlin, here is where Russia's top generals can coordinate all military action around the world, including nuclear missile launches. The command bunker was designed to emulate the one beneath the Pentagon, only more grandiose. A floor-to-ceiling screen displays real-time military action on an electronic system bigger than an IMAX 180-degree digital dome, according to the Kremlin. Tablet computers connect military officers to a supercomputer in the basement. With its 16 petaflops of speed and 236 petabytes of storage capacity, the Kremlin claims their computer outperforms the Pentagon's three to one. That, as Defense Minister Sergey Shoigu told TASS Russian News Agency, its "colossal" power allows it to run war games and make predictions about nuclear conflict with a human brain–like capacity, designed "to synchronize decision-making capabilities [with real-] world events." That it has the power to analyze the movements of other nations in near-real time and to advise the Russian president about military actions to take in response.

A Bolt out of the Blue nuclear attack levied against the United States is deeply troublesome to Russian Nuclear Command and Control. The night watch commander picks up the phone and calls the general he reports to.

Ваше присутствие срочно необходимо!! he says. *You must get here immediately!*

27 MINUTES

In Space

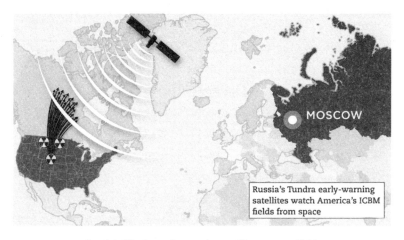

Russia's Tundra early-warning
satellites watch America's ICBM
fields from space

Russia's Tundra early-warning satellites are unreliable.
(Image by Michael Rohani)

U p in space, thousands of miles above the Earth's surface, a
technology-based disaster is underway. A Russian satellite at
the apogee of its highly elliptical orbit is monitoring the northern-tier
Minuteman ICBM fields in the Unites States, when the signals
intelligence it receives sets off a series of alarms. These classified
warnings are the Russian equivalent of:

BALLISTIC MISSILE LAUNCH, ALERT!

For early-warning missile launch detection from space, the U.S.
Defense Department relies on SBIRS, a satellite system so techno-
logically capable it sees the hot rocket exhaust on a single ICBM in
a fraction of a second after launch. In an attempt at parity, Russia
has built an early-warning satellite system known as Tundra, a
constellation of military satellites that claims to likewise be able to
scan the sky above U.S. Minuteman missile fields, and other places
around the globe, from space. To see, in close to real time, an

enemy's or adversary's ICBM launch that threatens Russia with nuclear attack.

But Tundra's capabilities are not anywhere near SBIRS capabilities, a weakness that Russia is loath to admit. Defense analysts generally agree that Russia's early-warning satellite system is deeply flawed, which, in a moment such as this, makes for a potentially deadly situation.

"Tundra is not great," says Pavel Podvig, the Western world's top expert on Russian nuclear forces, who works with the United Nations Institute for Disarmament Research.

Ted Postol is blunt. "Russian early-warning satellites don't work accurately," he says. "As a country, Russia doesn't have the technological know-how to build a system as good as we have in the United States." This means "their satellites can't look straight down at the earth," a technology known as look-down capability. And as a result, Russia's Tundra satellites "look sideways," Postol warns, "which handicaps their ability to distinguish sunlight from, say, fire."

Notably troublesome is how Tundra sees clouds.

"Their satellites can mistake cirrus clouds for missile plumes that aren't there," Postol explains.

And seeing missile plumes that aren't there opens the door for catastrophe.

In a moment of heightened alarm, "Moscow could think it's being attacked."

If Russia thinks it's being attacked, the consequences would be dire.

In a 2015 briefing on Capitol Hill (open to the public) called "Accidental Nuclear War between Russia and the United States," Postol told a group of congresspeople that Russia's "fragile early-warning system poses one of the greatest dangers of nuclear use [that is] currently facing the U.S." That if misinterpretation of satellite data were to happen, "Russia could engage in a gigantic, spasmodic launch of all its nuclear forces."

Former STRATCOM commander General Kehler warns us of what that could mean. "Russia is the only country that can destroy the U.S. in the next couple of hours."

28 MINUTES

Marine One, Airborne over Bethesda, Maryland

Marine One races away from D.C. airspace as fast as the machine can physically fly. For a Sikorsky VH-92A, this means over 150 miles per hour. Inside, the president remains on comms with the chairman and the STRATCOM commander.

With every minute that passes, the president's Marine One travels a little more than two miles farther away from the lethal proximity effects of the nuclear bomb that is rapidly descending on D.C.

Still at the top of the list of threats to the president's life in this moment is electromagnetic pulse, that fast burst of electric current that likely will destroy all of Marine One's electronic systems and cause it to crash.

The special agent in charge of the president's security detail has been focused on how to mitigate this threat, and now he has decided to take action. He instructs the three-man CAT Element to get ready to tandem jump the president out of the helicopter.

Scientists have known about natural EMP events since the 1800s. Richard Garwin wrote the first paper on nuclear EMP in 1954, at Los Alamos (its findings are classified). American defense scientists started paying more attention to its effects in 1962, after observing a nuclear weapons test in outer space called Starfish Prime. From post-blast measurements, it became clear that an

EMP weapon exploded at high altitudes has the capability of permanently destroying large-scale infrastructure on the ground.

"During the Cold War, Russia live-tested an EMP in space over Kazakhstan," the former CIA Russia analyst and later EMP Commission executive director Dr. Peter Pry tells us. And that this high-altitude EMP destroyed "all manner of electronics within an enormous footprint extending hundreds of miles" on the ground below. When a nuclear bomb detonates closer to the ground, EMP effects are localized. The president's Marine One helicopter is EMP-protected, but the equipment has only ever been tested in a chamber. No one knows what will actually happen in a real event.

The president is being taken to the Raven Rock Mountain Complex, the Pentagon's Alternate National Military Command Center, also known as Site R. The bunker was built during the Cold War. Its original plans were drawn by the Nazi engineer turned U.S. postwar Operation Paperclip scientist Georg Rickhey, whose credentials the American military admired, and who had built Hitler's underground bunker in Berlin during the war. The distance from the White House to Site R is roughly seventy miles. Marine One usually takes around thirty minutes to get there, depending on takeoff and landing times. The commander in chief has been in the air for a little over four minutes. Not for another four or five miles will the helicopter be outside the dangerous overpressure zone.

Marine One moves fast over Bethesda Hill, near where the interstate highway crosses Timberlawn Local Park. In the grass below, children playing on swing sets and slides get scooped up by terrified parents and babysitters as they receive word of a nuclear attack in California, everyone now racing to get home.

Inside Marine One, over satellite comms, the chairman of the Joint Chiefs of Staff presses the president into action. Five minutes remain on the Red Impact clock. The chairman of the Joint Chiefs is as certain as he is calm.

Chairman: *Sir. We need, from you, the universal unlock code.*

President: *What in hell is the universal unlock code?*

It is remarkable just how little a president of the United States knows about nuclear war.

STRATCOM commander: *The U.S. has been attacked.*

The Red Impact clock continues to count down. Explanations at a time like this seem absurd.

Chairman: *I advise you to provide STRATCOM with the universal unlock code, Mr. President. Sir.*

If there were time to explain, it would go like this. In the words of former launch officer Bruce Blair and colleagues Sebastien Philippe and Sharon K. Weiner: "If the president selects a limited nuclear option, a selective unlock code allows crews to fire specific missiles at specific targets, and only those missiles." The trio are citing a feature called right of launch, a critical component of nuclear command and control that guarantees the president, and only the president, can ever authorize nuclear use. The selective unlock code acts as a safeguard.

Unless, that is, the president overrides right of launch with the universal unlock code. "Just as the adjectives suggest, this code would allow intercontinental ballistic missile and submarine crews to launch all of their nuclear weapons," Blair, Philippe, and Weiner tell us.

STRATCOM commander: *We need the universal unlock code!*

America's ICBM crews have just launched fifty Minuteman missiles on the president's command. The submarine launch of another thirty-two nuclear warheads is underway. Should the president need to authorize a second nuclear strike, he must do so with new nuclear launch codes.

"Although the launch crews all have the keys necessary to fire additional nuclear weapons," the weapons experts explain, "they lack the unlock codes needed to arm, target, and fire those weapons." If a second launch needs to occur, "multiple different unlock codes would [have to] be sent to the launch crews."

And for that, the National Security Agency must create entirely new codes.

Right of launch ensures that if the president authorizes the use of eighty-two nuclear warheads, crews launch eighty-two warheads. Not eighty-three, and not eighty-four.

The STRATCOM commander tells the president that STRATCOM assumes the position that there will likely be additional missile strikes against the United States. And STRATCOM will need to respond.

The chairman is blunt: If the president dies, STRATCOM cannot launch additional missiles. Unless STRATCOM has the universal unlock code.

The president stares out Marine One's window.

In the middle of the mayhem, a thought occurs.

Where's the VP? the president asks.

If the president dies, authority transfers to the vice president, who, as second in the line of succession, is also accompanied 24/7/365 by a mil aide carrying a Football.

National security advisor: *The VP was at Arlington Cemetery laying a wreath on a grave. Movement is underway but—*

Chairman: *With line of succession in jeopardy, we need the universal unlock code.*

This is the razor's edge. Like the W. Somerset Maugham novel of the same name. The story of a World War I pilot so traumatized by the carnage of war, he rejects war in pursuit of the meaning of life.

"The sharp edge of a razor is difficult to pass over; thus the wise say the path to Salvation is hard."

Contemplating the reality of the universal unlock code, the president is incentivized. If he learned about any of this during his president-elect briefing, he doesn't recall. Now it seems profound. If the world is going to end in nuclear holocaust, he'd rather not be the one with a billion or more people's blood on his hands.

The president authorizes the universal unlock code.

In the event the president or his successor becomes unlocatable, nuclear launch decisions can be made directly by the STRATCOM commander now.

31 MINUTES
National Military Command Center, Pentagon

Inside the nuclear bunker beneath the Pentagon, 120 seconds remain until a nuclear bomb detonates over the building, obliterating everyone and everything with a violence and a permanence that is as catastrophic as it is absurd. All 27,000 personnel who work here are about to die. This includes all the headquarters command staff for the army, the navy, the air force, the Marine Corps, the Space Force, the Coast Guard, the eleven U.S. combatant commands, many of the seventeen intelligence agencies, and tens of thousands of other humans. And this is just at the Pentagon.

Unless, that is, North Korea's nuclear warhead fails upon reentry.

Which it could.

The Hwasong-17 has traveled 6,000 miles from Pyongyang. It has reached speeds of 15,000 miles per hour and a cruising altitude of 700 miles. It has gone through Boost and Midcourse Phases. All four U.S. interceptor missiles that tried to shoot it down missed. Now the nuclear warhead must reenter Earth's atmosphere. This is a critical time, one where failure is commonplace.

"Reentry is an area where so many different things can go wrong," Los Alamos weapons engineer Glen McDuff tells us. "It has to be precise. Spinning like a bullet. If the reentry vehicle gets off target, loses flight stability, it doesn't reenter. It burns up."

For years, the CIA remained convinced that North Korea's ballistic missiles did not have reentry capability. Then, in 2020, for reasons not made public, their assessment changed.

So many lives hang in the balance. Will reentry succeed or fail?

32 MINUTES
SecDef and Vice-Chairman in the Osprey

S eated inside the V-22 Osprey barreling toward Site R, the secretary of defense has been listening in on satellite comms. But his focus is on Russia. He is determined to speak with the president of the Russian Federation.

Beside him in the aircraft, the vice-chairman is on the line with an officer from the Defense Information Systems Agency, a critical special missions support unit. DISA is the combat support agency charged with connecting the entire force of Defense Department employees—over 4 million users—to the Defense Information System Network worldwide. Through its Joint Staff Support Center, DISA operates and maintains the National Joint Operations-Intelligence Center inside the Pentagon and at Site R. With the Pentagon just seconds away from complete annihilation, all emergency operations and communications have switched over to Site R. DISA's critical special missions support personnel are relaying everything they can, as fast as they can, to the vice-chairman and the secretary of defense.

The SecDef and vice-chairman have been in the air for fourteen minutes and they are already almost twice as far out of D.C. airspace as Marine One. The V-22 Osprey is a significantly faster aircraft, larger, and with a much greater wingspan. On each wingtip a thirty-eight-foot-diameter, three-blade composite rotor is attached to a rotating nacelle, each able to swivel up to ninety degrees (in the vertical direction, when the plane operates as a helicopter). This feature allows the Osprey to land and take off vertically, like a conventional helicopter, but also gives it the power to fly twice as fast as most other helicopters by rotating its nacelles forward and converting itself into a turboprop plane.

Because the Osprey left the Pentagon before the president left the White House lawn, and because the Osprey is faster, it is already out of the dangerous overpressure zone, which means the SecDef and the vice-chairman have a much greater chance of making it to the Raven Rock Mountain Complex alive than the president does.

So much has happened in the last thirty-two minutes. So much depends on what happens next. But the SecDef remains focused on one thing: getting the Russian president on the line. Like many who become the U.S. secretary of defense, the SecDef in this scenario has spent his life working within the military-industrial complex. This makes him uniquely aware of an existential peril that exists.

A terrifying flaw in Mutual Assured Destruction.

A kind of hole. Over the North Pole. A weakness that is well known to nuclear weapons experts like Hans Kristensen, but largely ignored by the rest of the world.

"The Minuteman III ICBM does not have enough range to target North Korea without overflying Russia," Kristensen explains.

Meaning fifty ICBMs launched from missile fields in Wyoming must travel on a trajectory that flies *directly over* Russia.

"The hole. It's very dangerous," former secretary of defense Leon Panetta confirms. "I don't think people give it enough thought."

At the time of this scenario, relations between the U.S. and

Russia—two nuclear-armed superpowers—are at an all-time low. Paranoia is high. In this scenario, the U.S. president is not on friendly terms with the president of the Russian Federation. And now nuclear weapons have been launched by the United States at North Korea in a counterattack—and they must fly over Russia to get there.

This is a recipe for disaster. In this scenario, the secretary of defense fears—with very good reason—that if he doesn't reach the Russian president immediately, as in now, a cascading series of new, nightmare events could unfold.

32 MINUTES, 30 SECONDS
Osan Air Base, Republic of Korea (South Korea)

In an underground bunker at Osan Air Base in South Korea, a U.S. Air Force colonel stares at a satellite image on a screen in front of her. Few U.S. military bases in the world remain on as permanent a high-alert status as Osan.

Their defense posture is, literally, "ready to fight tonight."

In the nuclear conflict now unfolding, South Korea is almost certainly a next target. The U.S. colonel watches the screen in front of her; beside her is her South Korean counterpart. Analysts have identified movement along the border with North Korea, less than fifty miles from the bunker here.

On Osan's tarmac, F-16 Fighting Falcons and A-10 Thunderbolts taxi down the runways as American and South Korean pilots prepare for combat. U.S. Army Black Hawk helicopters prep sling loads for disbursement to smaller, forward-operating locations. Everyone—from the pilots, to the maintenance crews, to the soldiers who pump gas—is suited-up in chemical, biological, and radiation protection gear.

*U.S. pilots in South Korea train in chemical, biological, radiological, and
nuclear incident gear. (Courtesy of Colonel Julian Chesnutt [ret.])*

The intelligence community estimates that, as of 2024, North
Korea has roughly fifty nuclear bombs. North Korea is also understood to maintain the largest chemical weapons stockpile anywhere
in the world—5,000 tons' worth—much of it preloaded onto
rockets.

Osan Air Base is always ready for combat. With its sister facility,
Camp Humphreys, located twelve miles to the south, the U.S. military maintains its mission in Korea of providing a ring of safety
around Seoul.

Seoul is one of the largest megacities in the developed world
and is situated just forty miles to the north of Osan Air Base. With
its 9.6 million residents, Seoul is among the most densely populated cities on Earth, with roughly 1 million more people than
New York City. The Seoul Capital Area has 26 million people.
Half the country lives here.

To protect the Osan Air Base from missile attack, the base relies
on the Terminal High Altitude Area Defense system—the

multibillion-dollar system designed to detect and shoot down incoming missiles. But every weapon system has holes. THAAD's weakness is that it cannot handle volume.

"THAAD systems are set up to engage several targets at a time," says military historian Reid Kirby, "not hundreds of them." Kirby consults for non-governmental organizations on North Korea's weapons of mass destruction capabilities.

The U.S. Air Force colonel in the bunker stares at the satellite images, eyes peeled for signs of movement along the border with the North.

For signs of a dreaded chemical weapons saturation attack.

32 MINUTES, 30 SECONDS
Marine One, Airborne

There is chaos in Marine One. Some of the individuals on board are shouting, others are praying, others texting their final goodbyes. The mil aide is focused on the Football. The special agent in charge and the three-man CAT Element are all focused on saving the president's life. In the cockpit, the pilot moves the helicopter into a steep climb, then indicates to the special agent in charge that the aircraft has reached the altitude required.

The SAC signals to the lead operator on the CAT Element.

The CAT operator grabs the president by his harness and clips the commander in chief to his own body. The mil aide stands, the Football secured to his chest. A second CAT operator slides open the helicopter door.

Wind rushes in.

The president and the CAT operator jump.

The SAC jumps.

The mil aide jumps with the Football.

The two remaining CAT operators jump.

From inside the aircraft, the presidential advisors watch them go.

The president, strapped to the CAT operator in tandem, falls through the air.

Riiippp. Riiippp. Riiippp . . .

Each CAT operator pulls his parachute's rip cord. The SAC pulls his rip cord. The mil aide with the Football pulls his rip cord. Six parachutes unfurl.

Seconds pass, the parachutes floating to Earth as designed.

There is a flash of nuclear light.

Followed by a fraction of a second of eerie and profound silence.

Then—

BAAM . . .

33 MINUTES

Ground Zero, the Pentagon

A 1-megaton thermonuclear bomb detonates in a live-action test in French Polynesia in 1970. (French Armed Forces)

In the first fraction of a millisecond, a flash of light superheats the air to 180 million degrees Fahrenheit, incinerating people, places, and things, and absorbing a once bright, once powerful, once vibrant city center in a holocaust of fire and death. The fireball from this 1-megaton nuclear weapon that strikes the Pentagon is thousands of times more brilliant than the sun at noon. People from Baltimore, Maryland, to Quantico, Virginia, see this flash of light. Anyone staring directly at it is blinded by it.

In this first millisecond, the fireball is a 440-foot-diameter sphere. Over the next ten seconds, it expands to 5,700 feet in diameter, more than one mile of pure fire—nineteen football fields of fire— obliterating the nexus of American democracy.

The edges of the fireball stretch all the way to the Lincoln Memorial to the north and into Crystal City to the south. Everything and everyone that existed in this space is incinerated. Nothing remains. No human, no squirrel, no ladybug. No plants, no animals. No cellular life.

The air around the fireball's edges compresses into a steeply fronted blast wave. This dense wall of air pushes forward, mowing down everything and everyone in its path for three miles out, in every direction. Accompanied by several-hundred-mile-per-hour winds, it is as if Washington, D.C., just got hit by an asteroid and its accompanying wave.

In Ring 1—a nine-mile-diameter ring—engineered structures change physical shape and most collapse. Piles of rubble left behind stand thirty or more feet high. The initial thermonuclear flash has set everything in the fireball's line of sight on fire. It melts lead, steel, titanium. It turns paved streets into molten asphalt.

At the outer edges of Ring 1, rare survivors become trapped in liquified roadways, catch fire, and melt. The X-ray light of the nuclear flash burns skin off people's bodies, leaving their extremities a shredded horror of bloody tendons and exposed bone. Wind rips the skin off people's faces and tears away limbs. Survivors die of shock, heart attack, blood loss. Errant power lines whip through the air, electrocuting people and setting new fires alight everywhere.

As tens of seconds pass, the fireball rises three miles up into the air. Its ominous cloud cap turns the light of day into darkness. Some 1 to 2 million people are dead or dying, hundreds of thousands more now caught in the rubble and the flames. "There will be virtually no survivors," the government's nuclear advisory panel has long warned of what will happen in the first ring around ground zero. "There will be nothing recognizable remaining. . . . Only foundations and basements remaining."

Never in the history of mankind have so many human beings been killed so fast. Not since a mountain-sized asteroid smashed into Earth 66 million years ago has so much global devastation been set in motion in a single strike.

The die has been cast.

The singular, haunting words from former STRATCOM commander General Robert Kehler come alive: "The world could end in the next couple of hours."

And now it is about to.

33 MINUTES
Serpukhov-15, Kaluga Oblast

Serpukhov-15 satellite control center in Russia.
(Ministry of Defense of the Russian Federation)

In the forest ninety miles southwest of Moscow, in rural Kaluga Oblast, the Serpukhov-15 satellite control has picked up a signal. Red lights flash. Alarms sound with shrill repetition.

"Attention. Launch." An automated voice instructs the crew.

An American ICBM launch has been detected.

The instruction is followed by the "First Echelon" command, Russian nomenclature indicating the highest level of nuclear alert.

Serpukhov-15 is Russia's western command center for incoming ICBM launch data. It is a component of the Russian Air and Space Forces, which itself is "a separate branch of Russia's armed forces, subordinated directly to the General Staff," Pavel Podvig explains. The radars here receive data from Tundra space satellites and it is the job of the Serpukhov-15 commander to relay that information up the chain of command.

The Russian Ministry of Defense has had officers stationed at the Serpukhov-15 facility for more than fifty years. As in America, there have been terrifying false alarms. Once, in 1983, a lieutenant colonel named Stanislav Petrov was the commander in charge when satellite data indicated there were five American ICBMs on their way to strike Moscow with nuclear weapons. For reasons having to do with human intuition, Petrov became suspicious of that attack information. Years later, he told *Washington Post* reporter David Hoffman what he was thinking at the time. "I had a funny feeling in my gut," Petrov said, asking himself, Who starts a nuclear war against another superpower with just five ICBMs?

In 1983, Petrov made the decision to interpret the early-warning signal as a "false alarm," he said, thereby not sending a report up the chain of command. For his well-placed skepticism, Lieutenant Colonel Stanislav Petrov famously became known as "the man who saved the world from nuclear war."

But in this moment of intense nuclear crisis in this scenario— with the U.S. under nuclear attack, and a slew of ICBMs having just launched from a missile field in Wyoming—the reaction of the present-day commander at Serpukhov-15 is different than Petrov's reaction was in 1983. It is not just that Tundra erroneously reports sunlight as hot rocket exhaust, or that it confuses clouds with missile plumes. Tundra misreports the number of things.

"Tundra can probably not accurately measure the number of ICBMs in a fifty Minuteman launch," Ted Postol maintains. "It could look like one hundred." Or more.

The commander at Serpukhov-15 stares at the early-warning data on the electronic screen in front of him. What are fifty Minuteman missiles heading over the North Pole, Tundra "sees" as more than 100 ICBMs.

That is a mother lode of nuclear warheads.

Enough for a preemptive, decapitation strike against Moscow.

The commander at Serpukhov-15 in this scenario does not have the same skepticism about intent that Lieutenant Colonel Petrov did some forty years before.

He picks up the phone and calls Moscow.

The Americans are attacking us with ICBMs, the commander says.

34 MINUTES
Hudson Yards, New York City

N ew York City lies roughly 2,500 miles east of Diablo Canyon in California, and 200 miles northeast of Washington, D.C., as the crow flies. Not close enough to either location to yet feel the physical effects from the detonation of the nuclear bombs. But from a psychological standpoint, New York City—America's largest metropolis—erupts into panic and chaos. With news of nuclear attack spreading across the world like wildfire, millions of New Yorkers fear their city to be a next target. At the Cable News Network studio in Hudson Yards, employees flee the building with an urgency not seen since World Trade Center employees tried desperately to escape the impending collapse of the Twin Towers on 9/11.

A few journalists have stayed behind in the newsroom in this scenario. Those remaining at their posts scour social media sites still functioning, furiously searching for content to share with the world. Engineers in the tech room copied the Point Buchon cattle rancher's video from social media and it plays in a loop on-screen. Like Jules Naudet's 9/11 video of the first airplane crashing into the North Tower, this image is an origin point for war.

No CNN reporter in D.C. answers his or her phone. Cell service is down. "Northern Virginia has well over 60 percent of the world's data centers," America's first cyber chief, retired brigadier general Gregory Touhill, tells us. No one from the White House press secretary's office can be reached. Messages for the CNN liaison at the Pentagon go directly to voicemail. Same with the army, navy, air force, Marine Corps, Coast Guard, Space Force, Department of Homeland Security, and FBI.

Before X buckled and crashed, cell phone videos were flooding social media platforms. Some of the visuals were screen-grabbed here at CNN. But with one fact-checker left in the building, authentication becomes an impossible job. How to discern images of reality from the horrifying AI movie clips flooding the internet?

The fact-checker stares at pictures of burned, blackened corpses. At people that do not look human, or even real. As it was in Hiroshima and Nagasaki in August 1945, so it is in America now: People without faces. People without skin. Naked people running, their clothes and bodies on fire. A man holding a dead child. A dead horse in the street. A teenager with a severed body part in hand.

The anchor who has stayed here in Hudson Yards reads from a teleprompter, trying to keep his composure while beginning to process what is actually going on.

Anchor: *We understand that a nuclear bomb has apparently struck a nuclear power plant in California 165 miles north of Los Angeles.*

His voice cracks.

Anchor: *And also apparently—we just don't know for certain—just seconds or minutes ago—we don't have confirmation—a second nuclear bomb struck Washington, D.C.*

An emotional Walter Cronkite almost cried on live TV after President John F. Kennedy was murdered. After the Hindenburg zeppelin exploded into flames, Herb Morrison screamed, "Oh, the humanity!"

How to process this?

The anchor looks down as a Wireless Emergency Alert appears on his cell phone. He looks back up at the camera.

Anchor: *FEMA has issued this warning.*

He holds up his cell phone to the camera. It reads:

U.S. UNDER NUCLEAR ATTACK

SEEK IMMEDIATE SHELTER

THIS IS NOT A DRILL

35 MINUTES
Diablo Canyon, California

A t the Diablo Canyon Power Plant, powerful updrafts suck radioactive dirt and debris up into the growing mushroom stem and cloud. Towering 30,000 feet high, this terrifying aberration is now visible from vista points up and down the California coast, including at Vandenberg Space Force Base—home to four of the forty remaining interceptor missiles. Vandenberg Space Force Base is located roughly thirty-five miles to the southeast of where the Devil's Scenario is underway.

The surrounding hills are on fire. Skyscraper-height flames devour forests, killing wildlife and subsuming everything in its path. Superheated winds from burning trees generate fire tornadoes with hundreds-of-mile-an-hour winds, knocking over trees and carrying car-sized burning debris into adjacent canyons, fueling new fires everywhere.

For tens of thousands of Californians, abject panic takes hold as Diablo Canyon's emergency sirens—stretching out more than a dozen miles in all directions—begin screeching alarm.

There is mayhem, everywhere.

Some 143,000 people reside in the ten-mile radius of Diablo Canyon's twelve Protective Action Zones, all now trying to evacuate, all at once. From Pismo Beach to Los Osos, everyone is desperate to escape death by smoke, fire, and radiation poisoning.

The outlook is grim.

They are all trying to escape by way of a historic highway that is almost 100 years old.

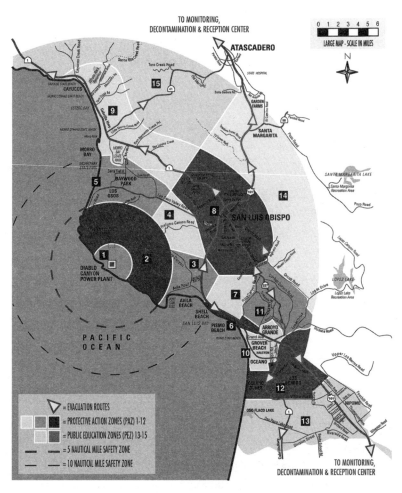

Diablo Canyon, nuclear accident escape routes.
(U.S. Nuclear Regulatory Commission)

HISTORY LESSON NO. 7

Proud Prophet War Game

In 1983, at a high point in nuclear stockpile insanity—when there were nearly 60,000 nuclear weapons ready to be launched (35,804 in Russia; 23,305 in the U.S.)—President Reagan ordered a simulated war game, code-named Proud Prophet, to explore the outcome and effects of a nuclear war. The Proud Prophet war game was designed by a man named Thomas Schelling, a Cold War intellectual with economics degrees from Harvard and Berkeley. Schelling was a faculty member at the New England Complex Systems Institute, a think tank dedicated to the study of "complex systems." Some complex systems exist in nature. Earth's global climate, the human brain, a living cell are examples of complex systems. Others are made by humans, and contingent upon machines—like the power grid, the internet, and the U.S. Department of Defense.

Thomas Schelling's specialty was applying game theory to complex systems. He used mathematical models to discern and predict outcomes. He was taken very seriously. In 2005, when Schelling was in his eighties, he was awarded the Nobel Memorial Prize in Economic Sciences (with Robert J. Aumann) for "having advanced our understanding of conflict and cooperation through game-theory analysis."

"The power to hurt is bargaining power," Schelling famously wrote in his book *Arms and Influence*. "To exploit it is diplomacy—vicious diplomacy, but diplomacy."

The goal of the classified Proud Prophet war game was to demonstrate what happens when diplomacy fails—when deterrence fails. To demonstrate to the highest-ranking officers in the U.S. Nuclear Command and Control system the various ways in which nuclear war could, and would, unfold after it began. Every day for two weeks in

1983, more than 200 people gathered at the National War College in Washington, D.C., to play the game, cloistered away inside a secure location to prevent leaks.

The National War College is located inside the National Defense University, which is located just across the river from the Pentagon. Each day, to play the game, the secretary of defense would pick up a red phone and call the chairman of the Joint Chiefs of Staff to discuss various ideas in the different nuclear war scenarios put forth by Schelling. Schemes included everything from tactical nuclear strikes in a so-called limited nuclear war, to massive decapitation-event scenarios. There were exercises with NATO and without NATO nuclear forces getting involved. There were scenarios where the U.S. launched nuclear war preemptively, beginning with everyone at the Pentagon in a state of focused calm. There were exercises where nuclear war was launched in crisis mode. In full-on panic mode. With and without China entering the conflict. With and without the UK involved.

Paul Bracken, a professor of political science at Yale, was one of the civilian individuals invited to participate in playing the classified nuclear war game. The results were horrifying, Bracken says. Over the course of two weeks, in every simulated scenario—and despite whatever particularly triggering event started the war game—nuclear war always ended the same way. With the same outcome. There is no way to win a nuclear war once it starts. There is no such thing as de-escalation.

According to Proud Prophet, regardless of how nuclear war begins, it ends with complete Armageddon-like destruction. With the U.S., Russia, and Europe totally destroyed. With the entire Northern Hemisphere uninhabitable from fallout. With the death of, at minimum, a half billion people in the war's opening salvo alone. Followed by the starvation and death of almost everyone who initially survived.

"The result was a catastrophe," Bracken recalls. A catastrophe "that made all the wars of the past five hundred years pale in comparison. A half billion human beings were killed in the initial exchanges . . . NATO was gone. So was a good part of Europe, the United States, and the Soviet Union. Major parts of the northern hemisphere would be uninhabitable for decades." Everyone left very upset.

The results of Proud Prophet remained unknown to the public for almost three decades, until 2012, when the war game was declassified. If you can call it declassification. Most pages looked like this:

The 1983 Proud Prophet-83 nuclear war game was "declassified" in 2012.
(U.S. Department of Defense)

There was an upside. Proud Prophet's declassification allowed people like Paul Bracken to discuss parts of it without violating the Espionage Act of 1917, even if in very general terms. From Bracken, we learn firsthand that military leaders at the time were wholly unprepared for the decisions they were going to have to make—from the initial spark of nuclear war, to the last breath any of them would take.

Fourteen years later, Vice President Al Gore asked Professor Bracken to lead a different kind of war game simulation, not a nuclear war game, but one involving a cyberattack on Wall Street. In the late nineties, VP Gore was worried the newly popular internet was making America's banking system vulnerable to terrorist attack.

"His people asked me to set up a game," Bracken recalls of the Gore request, one that involved seventy-five military and civilian personnel, including bankers from Wall Street.

The cloistered, classified room at the National War College was not available at the time. Someone from the financial firm Cantor Fitzgerald arranged for a banquet room at the World Trade Center, Bracken explains, in the top-floor restaurant with its magnificent, city-wide view. A restaurant known as Windows on the World. For three days in 1997, the group engaged in a highly classified, simulated war game. A cyberterror attack.

Their conclusion—drawn from the war game—was basic, Bracken contends. "Move data storage away from Manhattan. The Wall Street firms accelerated the movement of data storage to New Jersey and Long Island." Cheaper. Safer. Great. Except: "What we didn't figure out was the actual attack," Bracken laments. "We didn't think of driving an airplane into [the] building" where the game was being played. That is, flying a commercial airplane into the World Trade Center.

Four years later, fifteen of the people who were playing that simulated war game were killed in the 9/11 terror attack at the World Trade Center, when two commercial airliners were flown into the two tall towers there. The Windows on the World restaurant, and both of the towers, were reduced to rubble and ash.

After nuclear war, much of twenty-first-century humankind will be just the same. There one moment, then gone.

36 MINUTES
U.S. Strategic Command Headquarters, Nebraska

Thirty-six minutes have passed in this scenario. The STRATCOM commander is out the door, running toward the Doomsday Plane—officially called the E-4B Nightwatch—a militarized, retrofitted Boeing 747 idling on the tarmac. The Doomsday Plane is always ready for takeoff—ready 24/7/365 to orchestrate a commander's airborne escape. This is because the Doomsday Plane fights nuclear war from the air.

It is springtime in Nebraska. The tarmac here is clear. No flooding, no hurricanes. The Safe Escape clock inside the underground bunker zeroed out minutes ago, but the STRATCOM commander had to get the universal unlock code from the president of the United States. And now he has.

The amount of time it takes to exit the Global Operations Center, run across the tarmac, and sprint up the jet bridge stairs of the Doomsday Plane and into the Defense Department's war room in the sky is well-rehearsed. "I have a certain amount of minutes to get on that plane and for that plane to get off [the ground] and to a safe distance before a nuclear weapon [goes] off here," STRATCOM Commander General Hyten told CNN in 2018.

Inside the conference room on board the Doomsday Plane, the commander straps himself in and rejoins the satellite comms with the Nuclear Command and Control System commanders who remain alive.

Still no word from the president. Still no word from the VP.

The mil aide has the Football, STRATCOM knows this, and they know where the Football is. Contained inside the satchel is a classified tracking system engineered to defeat EMP effects. The

Football is lying on the ground in a forested area in rural Boyds, Maryland. A quick reaction force has been dispatched from Camp David to locate and retrieve the Football, and hopefully the president, but the QRF helicopter is still in the air and no one knows if the president is with the mil aide, or if he and the CAT operator he is with got separated by bomb blast and wind drift.

The tracking systems on Marine One ceased transmission three minutes ago. All cell signals from the passengers on board, and those who parachute-jumped, ceased transmitting when the bomb detonated over D.C. Localized EMP zeroed out everything in the overpressure zone.

The secretary of defense and the vice-chairman of the Joint Chiefs of Staff were far enough out to remain flying. Now they are just minutes away from landing at Site R. The vice-chairman is on the call with STRATCOM, via satellite phone. She waits for the commander to get oriented inside the war room on the Doomsday Plane.

The Doomsday Plane got its name because it is the location from where the STRATCOM commander (or whoever is acting as such) will execute emergency orders during nuclear war. Each jet is hardened against electromagnetic pulse, and with mesh over the windows to prevent against potential breakage by shock wave. The satellite-based communications system on the E-4B Nightwatch is designed to provide worldwide communications between senior military leaders and the Joint Force. The aircraft can fly in circles over the country for twenty-four or more hours at a time without refueling, dispatching nuclear launch codes to any leg of the triad, anywhere in the world. If its satellite comms go down nationally or globally, the Doomsday Plane will use extremely high frequency (EHF) and very low frequency/low frequency (VLF/LF) links with other aircraft in its fleet. This includes the E-6 Mercury aircraft, officially called the Take Charge and Move Out platform—a Cold

War–designed system that also functions as a last-resort command center in the sky.

Doomsday Planes have equipment that allows the commander to launch (remotely from the air) all weapons in all three legs of the nuclear triad—submarines, bombers, and ICBMs—even after the systems' individual launch control centers have lost the ability to do so from the ground.

The Doomsday Plane takes off from the tarmac here at Offutt Air Force Base at a maximum climb angle. The STRATCOM commander is briefed on the strike against the Pentagon, given bomb damage assessment and death toll and casualty estimates. He is briefed on the time to target for the fifty Minutemen III ICBMs. He is briefed on the remaining time to launch for the Trident SLBMs.

The commander is shown high-resolution images of Washington, D.C. These are digital composites being assembled in real time by advanced sensor systems on board unmanned aircraft flying over ground zero around Washington, D.C. For decades, starting in the late 1940s, the air force practiced flying through nuclear mushroom clouds, using decorated combat pilots like Colonel Hervey Stockman to develop tradecraft. Now drones do this job, unmanned vehicles controlled from a joint NSA-NRO facility (not in D.C.)—an installation so highly classified, sharing its location would be a violation of the Espionage Act.

The sensor systems on board include the DARPA-conceived Autonomous Real-Time Ground Ubiquitous Surveillance–Infrared system, designed to provide battlefield commanders with situational awareness on the ground. In 2013, the ARGUS infrared system could identify a person wearing a wristwatch from over two miles away, its name an homage to the ancient Greek beast Argus Panoptes, an all-seeing monster with 100 eyes.

The STRATCOM commander stares at ghastly images of where the mighty U.S. Pentagon once stood. The visuals are devastating. At the dawn of the nuclear age, the Joint Chiefs of Staff were forewarned that nuclear bombs were "a threat to mankind and to civilization." That if used against cities, they could "depopulate vast areas of the Earth's surface."

And now, the STRATCOM commander is one of the first Americans to see this prediction come true.

He sees it from above, with his own eyes.

37 MINUTES
Undisclosed Location, Pacific Ocean

Thousands of miles from Washington, D.C., in the middle of the Pacific Ocean, in an undisclosed location known only to its commander and crew, sirens on the USS *Nebraska* blare. All 155 submariners on board this vessel remain intensely focused on one thing and one thing only: nuclear launch.

The USS *Nebraska* is a nuclear-powered, nuclear-armed submarine singularly capable of unleashing twenty times more destruction than all the explosives used in World War II, including both atomic bombs dropped on Japan. Like all Ohio-class submarines, the *Nebraska* is silent, undetectable, and always ready for launch. In this moment, launch is seconds away. "We have the power to destroy an adversary's military, infrastructure, and everything in between," submariner Mark Levin told listeners in a Defense Department podcast. "A survivable system for carrying out a retaliatory nuclear attack."

"Survivable," meaning the submarine survives.

The crew on the USS *Nebraska* is highly skilled and uniquely trained. They are accustomed to traveling deep underwater for

A Trident submarine-launched ballistic missile (SLBM) launches from the
USS Nebraska. (U.S. Navy, Petty Officer 1st Class Ronald Gutridge)

seventy days at a time. No texts, no emails, no radio contact, no
radar signature. U.S. Ohio-class submariners pride themselves as
being the ultimate nuclear deterrent; only an insane person would
want to be on the receiving end of its wrath.

When the crew gets the order to launch nuclear weapons, it
follows those orders precisely as rehearsed. The launch order from
the president was authenticated and decoded by two junior officers.
This string of coded data includes information about plan of action
and timing of action. About which targets to strike, the precise
coordinates involved—and when.

The action begins. Of all the complex, multistep protocols and
procedures in U.S. Nuclear Command and Control, the firing of
Trident nuclear missiles is designed to be simple and fast.

The crew moves the 18,750-ton submarine into position. To its
subsurface launch depth of around 150 feet.

The commanding officer, the executive officer, and two junior officers each individually authenticate the president's order one last time.

The captain and his executive officer open the onboard double safe.

The two individuals retrieve two items from inside the safe. A Sealed Authenticator System card and a fire-control key are each removed.

The key is inserted in its requisite slot, then turned. The missiles are armed and ready to fire.

There are twenty active missile tubes on each Ohio-class nuclear submarine. Each tube contains a Trident II D5 missile. Eight of the twenty missiles will fire.

Each of the eight missiles is armed with four separate nuclear warheads in its nosecone.

Each warhead carries a 455-kiloton nuclear bomb.

The commanding officer authorizes the launch of the eight Trident missiles.

The weapons officer pulls the trigger that launches the first missile.

An explosive charge flash-vaporizes a tank of water at the base of the missile tube.

The pressure of the expanding gas drives the missile out of the submarine through a diaphragm at the top of the launch tube, jettisoning the rocket out the tube, out the body of the submersible, and away from the submarine with enough momentum to reach the surface.

A little more than one second after launch, the first Trident missile breaches the waterline. As it clears the surface of the Pacific, its first-stage rocket motor ignites. Rising up into the air, Boost Phase begins.

Fifteen seconds pass. The second Trident missile emerges from its tube. And the next one comes fifteen seconds after that. The fittingly simple order goes like this:

Missile 1.
Missile 2.
Missile 3.
Missile 4.
Missile 5.
Missile 6.
Missile 7.
Missile 8.

Eight missiles, each carrying four 455-kiloton nuclear warheads, for a total of thirty-two warheads that will soon destroy multiple targets across North Korea.

The first stage on each rocket will burn for sixty-five seconds, followed by another fourteen minutes of travel time to target.

As is the case with an ICBM, an SLBM cannot be recalled. What is done is done.

37 MINUTES, 30 SECONDS
Joint Operations-Intelligence Center—
Raven Rock Mountain Complex, Pennsylvania

Deep inside the belly of the Raven Rock Mountain Complex, officers working nuclear support operations in DISA's Joint Operations-Intelligence Center fire off emergency action commands.

FPCON Delta, Force Protection Condition 1, the highest alert level for an attack against a military installation, is now officially in effect. This is enacted separately from DEFCON 1, which presumes an attack on the civilian population. Department of Homeland Security instructs Customs and Border Protection, the Department of Transportation, and the Coast Guard to close all U.S. borders. The Federal Aviation Administration issues SCATANA, the Plan for the Security Control of Air Traffic and Air Navigation Aids under emergency conditions, grounding all aircraft.

At all military installations around the nation, garrison gates close. Base security forces initiate 100 percent ID card check protocols. Rapid base containment by local military and civilian forces begins.

At U.S. military installations around the world, geographic combatant commanders enforce FPCON Delta measures, in a futile attempt to secure and protect their areas of responsibility from attack. Futile because nuclear attacks are impossible to defend against. Still, lockdown has begun around the world.

America is at nuclear war with North Korea.

38 MINUTES
Ground Zero, Ring 1 and Ring 2

In Washington, D.C., Ring 1 is a holocaust. Ring 1 is that nine-mile diameter area around ground zero where engineered structures have changed shape and collapsed. Casualties near 100 percent, everyone is dead or dying.

Buildings that once stood upright herein—the White House, the Capitol, the Supreme Court, the U.S. Departments of Justice and State, the Federal Bureau of Investigation, the U.S. Treasury, the Library of Congress, the National Archives, the Metropolitan Police Department, the U.S. Departments of Agriculture, Education, Energy, Health and Human Services, the National

Academy of Sciences, the American Red Cross, Constitution Hall, to name but a few—they have been obliterated, shattered, blown apart, cracked open, knocked down, and set alight. All of the human beings who were standing, sitting, walking, waiting, or working in each and every one of these buildings just a few minutes ago—are no more.

The iconic structures built of chiseled granite and marble, of steel and stone, with Parthenon-styled columns and neoclassical facades, if they once seemed indomitable, they are now just piles of rubble and debris. Wreckage of war. Shavings and fragments of things that once were.

Consider the tiny sliver of land that was the National Mall, the long grassy park known as America's Front Yard. A park visited by over 25 million people each year. A once popular place for music concerts and festivals, for picnics and protests, for joggers and tourists and newlyweds. It represents an infinitesimal amount of what is now gone. Five minutes ago, this landscaped park was lined with history museums and curious visitors. Now everything in all the Smithsonian museums—the dinosaur fossils, the botany and book collections, the paintings in the National Portrait Gallery, Muhammad Ali's robe, all the people gazing curiously at these collections—they were there one minute, and a second later violently transformed into millimeter-sized pieces of ash.

Ground zero's Ring 2 is ablaze. Ring 2 is the fifteen-mile-diameter ring, an area where a vast majority of those not already dead are in the process of dying from third-degree burns. The nuclear bomb's 180 million degree Fahrenheit flash of X-ray light has ignited a mass fire that now begins to consume everything in this ring, and beyond. Millions of flammable items in Ring 2 have been set alight, all at once, like millions of matches dropped in dry grass.

"Ignition is complicated," Dr. Glen McDuff tells us. Los Alamos scientists have spent decades calculating "ignition thresholds" for natural and man-made items in the vicinity of a nuclear detonation. Pine needles and black rubber can spontaneously ignite 7.5 miles from the center point of a 1-megaton detonation, as does most car upholstery, whereas plastics are more likely to emit "jets of flame." These mini-torches of fire start new fires, which start new fires. Buildings not yet ablaze soon will be. This includes most of everything south to Alexandria, west to Falls Church, north to Chevy Chase, east to Capitol Heights, and all the neighborhoods in between.

Just five minutes have passed since a nuclear bomb hit the Pentagon. The fire that is burning down Ring 2 will kill more people than the bomb itself. Stanford scholar emeritus Lynn Eden explains, "The energy released by this mass fire would be fifteen to fifty times greater than the energy produced by the [original] nuclear detonation [with] winds powerful enough to uproot trees three feet in diameter and suck people from outside the fire into it." Human beings will be physically drawn up from one space into another, as if caught inside some monstrous, colossal vacuum or pump.

Ted Postol describes how this happens from a physicist's point of view. "A counter-intuitive process begins," he says. "The fireball will rise buoyantly to an altitude of maybe five miles before it stabilizes. During the process of rising, it creates gigantic afterwinds on the ground of roughly 200 to 300 miles per hour, *internal*, just from the sucking action of this rising fireball that move inward rather than outward." As this whipping, whirling cyclone of fire grows more vicious by the second, it begins to create its own weather as it burns out of control. In the next few hours, it will consume all of greater Washington, D.C., and the suburbs beyond. It will destroy everything and everyone in the city until there is nothing left to burn.

Meanwhile, the bomb's electromagnetic pulse has knocked out

electricity. Without power, there are no water pumps. Without water, there is no way for humans to put out these raging fires. No emergency crews will arrive. Lethal-level radiation after a nuclear explosion means first responders wait twenty-four to seventy-two hours before going into regions at the outer edges of the vast fire zone. In the time that passes, everything in a 100-square-mile (or more) radius around ground zero will burn. FEMA's own head-quarters, located 2.1 miles northeast of the Pentagon, at 500 C Street SW, has been flattened. FEMA's ten regional offices around the country are already overwhelmed.

Across the landscape of Ring 2, parts of buildings that survived the initial blast collapse, adding more fuel to the fires. Gas lines explode. Tankers carrying hazardous materials explode. Chemical factories explode, setting new fires. In pockets of places not yet physically ablaze, superheated winds of hurricane force bring air temperatures in excess of 1,220 degrees Fahrenheit, melting lead and aluminum. In the outer edges of Ring 2, survivors in subway tunnels and basement bunkers gasp for air. If the carbon monoxide hasn't already killed them, it will soon. In secret tunnels beneath the Capitol Building and the White House, statesmen and staffers bake to death as if inside a broiler oven. Like firefighters caught in a raging wildfire, there is no way to escape. No way to survive.

In Washington, D.C., all is lost.

38 MINUTES
Raven Rock Mountain Complex, Pennsylvania

I t is 3:41 p.m. local time when the Osprey touches down on the helipad near Site R's west gate. The nuclear command post is on lockdown. Soldiers armed with assault rifles man the guard towers, eyeing the tree line for possible breach or attack. With FPCON

Delta in effect, all area personnel have been called to arms; everyone at the Raven Rock Mountain Complex in the Blue Ridge Mountains is on the highest level of threat alert.

The secretary of defense and vice-chairman will be taken in through portal B, a double-doored entrance shaft near the fortified east vent. But getting out of the helicopter in this scenario is taking longer than it should. The secretary of defense has been blinded by thermonuclear flash.

Because he cannot see, he cannot walk without someone guiding him. The visual impairment is likely nonpermanent. Nuclear flash can temporarily blind people and animals who happen to be looking in the direction of a nuclear explosion when it occurs—even if they are as far as fifty miles away.

The secretary of defense was looking out the helicopter window in the direction of the Pentagon when the bomb detonated. The transparencies on the Osprey are among the most sophisticated in the world, but they'd never been put through an actual nuclear bomb test. The SecDef knew better than to look in the direction of the bomb when it exploded, but like a moth drawn to a flame, he had to see deterrence fail with his own two eyes. He had to see it to believe it, and now he's blind.

There is still no word from the president. This is not good. The vice president, the speaker of the House, the president pro tempore of the Senate, the secretary of state, and the secretary of the treasury have all been unlocatable since the bomb struck the Pentagon minutes ago. With these five individuals now presumed dead, the secretary of defense is the next in line for presidential succession.

Someone needs to be sworn in as commander in chief, and fast. Now is not the time for the nation to be without a leader. But a suddenly blind secretary of defense—addressing a terrified nation to announce he's the acting president in an unfolding nuclear catastrophe—is far from ideal.

Aides help the sightless SecDef disembark from the helicopter. The group passes through security and into portal B. Into an elevator that takes them down 650 feet into a series of cavernous tunnels and bunkers and office-style rooms. Raven Rock was built to hold 3,000 people inside its original 265,000 square feet of space, including leaders of the military branches and the chairman of the Joint Chiefs of Staff. But a nuclear strike against D.C. is a decapitation event. Only a handful of people got out of Washington before the bomb hit. The marine helicopters carrying the president's executive staff have also been radio silent since detonation.

The secretary of defense and the vice-chairman of the Joint Chiefs of Staff discuss the most pressing issue at hand.

Vice-chairman to SecDef: *We need to get Moscow on the line.*

Each has been trying to reach their Russian counterpart, without success. They are in agreement that nothing is more imperative than to get the Russian president on the phone. As the pair moves through the underground command center, DISA continues to work to connect with the Kremlin. Aides scramble to locate a Bible or any kind of book for the potential swearing-in ceremony for a new commander in chief (Lyndon B. Johnson was sworn in as president with his hand on a three-ring binder).

The SecDef and vice-chairman debate their approach with Moscow. Do they tell the Russian president that the American president is missing and presumed dead?

SecDef: *We should wait.*

Vice-chairman: *There's no time to wait. We tell Moscow now.*

SecDef: *Without a president we look weak.*

Vice-chairman: *Miscommunication comes with too great a risk.*

DISA: *You're connected with Moscow.*

The vice-chairman takes the call. She is greeted by a member of the Russian General Staff.

Vice-chairman: *We need to speak to your president immediately. We're under nuclear attack. We mean no harm to Russia.*

The Russian general responds: *The Russian president is available for the president of the United States.*

Vice-chairman, repeats: *The U.S. is under nuclear attack.*

It's like he didn't hear her.

Russian general: *Да.*

Which means "yes."

The vice-chairman tells the officer of the General Staff that Russia must refrain from any military action until the two nuclear-armed adversaries can get their two presidents on the phone. This is nonnegotiable. She is firm.

The officer says in Russian: *Ваш президент уже должен был нам позвонить.*

Which translates as: *Your president should have called us by now.*

And the line goes dead.

39 MINUTES
NATO Headquarters, Brussels, Belgium

I t is 9:42 p.m. local time at North Atlantic Treaty Organization headquarters on Boulevard Léopold III in Brussels, Belgium. Inside the glass-faceted building, designed for the Belgian Ministry of Defense to represent interlocking fingers, NATO moves swiftly into action.

The function of NATO is to further democratic values and peacefully resolve disputes. NATO's mission is to promote unity and cooperation, but NATO also promises lethal action if any one of its members is attacked. Now that the U.S. has been hit by nuclear weapons, NATO invokes Article 5, its provision that states an attack on one member is an attack on all members. That each member of the alliance will come to the aid of the attacked party, and with nuclear force if necessary. NATO does not own nuclear weapons, but the U.S. keeps 100 nuclear bombs deployed on NATO bases in Europe. These 100 tactical nuclear weapons are part of a so-called nuclear sharing program between NATO and the United States. This means that U.S. nuclear equipment has been installed on jet aircraft fleets at six military bases in five NATO member countries; each country's air force is assigned to carry out NATO strikes using U.S.-owned nuclear bombs kept on each base. But before any of these nuclear missions can occur, before any nuclear bombs can even come out of their WS3 vaults and get loaded onto jets, NATO's Nuclear Planning Group must receive authorization from the president of the United States. According to the NATO press office, the UK prime minister must also authorize this action.

But no one knows where the U.S. president is. Or if he is even alive.

Cars squeal down Boulevard Léopold III. Local leaders are deposited at NATO headquarters' front gates and run inside. They hurry into the headquarters conference hall, where the Nuclear Planning Group members assemble on electronic teleconference, on a massive television-style screen. NATO translators speaking more than a dozen different languages place headphones over their ears, listen, and wait. Every member of the NATO Nuclear Planning Group waits for word from, or of, the American president. And while they wait, aircrews at six air bases across Europe receive Emergency Action Messages to prepare for war. At bases in:

- Belgium
- Netherlands
- Germany
- Italy (at two bases)
- Turkey

All airmen and soldiers at each of these bases get ready for combat, each base already at DEFCON 1. Pilots and crews rush into hardened aircraft shelters—concrete igloo-type structures that are able to sustain a hit from a 500-pound bomb, and where nuclear-capable bomber aircraft are kept. Everyone is now waiting on word from the chain of command.

39 MINUTES

National Defense Management Center, Moscow, Russia

Inside the war room at the National Defense Management Center in central Moscow, members of the Russian General Staff focus on video screens. They are watching real-time actions at NATO bases across Europe, thanks to a network of surveillance systems and other assets in place.

In Belgium, in the Netherlands, in Germany, in Italy, and in Turkey, NATO bases equipped with nuclear-capable jet fighters idle on runways, awaiting orders. From the Russian point of view, this movement—and there is lots of it—sets off a series of cascading alarms.

Using signals intelligence intercepted from NATO communications systems, and algorithms run by the supercomputer in the basement of the National Defense Management Center, Russian analysts interpret what they believe is happening in nearby Europe.

Their conclusion is that NATO is preparing nuclear strikes.

Russia considers NATO a primary adversary. For decades during the Cold War, Russia had its own alliance, the Warsaw Pact, aimed at countering NATO and the West. Newly declassified documents show that the Warsaw Pact countries—Albania, Bulgaria, Czechoslovakia, East Germany, Hungary, Poland, Romania—maintained their own nuclear attack strategy against the West for decades, this despite Russia still claiming today not to have had a Launch on Warning policy during Soviet times.

Despite intense animosity and name-calling over the decades, NATO and the Warsaw Pact countries never engaged in direct military conflict. There was posturing and skirmishing, but no live-fire battles. When the Soviet Union dissolved in December 1991, the Warsaw Pact ceased to exist. And then, one by one, lands formerly controlled by Russia began shifting their allegiance to the West.

For many in Russia, it was a slap in the face. By 2014, the Russian Federation officially reinstated its anti-NATO position. The expansion of NATO into Russia's old neighborhood was "undermining global stability and violating the balance of power in the nuclear-missile sphere," official Russian military doctrine declared.

Now in this scenario, generals inside the Russian National Defense Management Center watch activity swirl around nuclear-capable jet fighters at air bases including Aviano in Italy and Kleine Brogel Air Base in Belgium. These NATO bases are considered within striking distance of Moscow, some 1,300 miles away—roughly the same distance as from Boston to Miami.

Inside the war room at the National Defense Management Center in Moscow, contingency plans come to the fore. The missile attack early-warning information from Tundra satellites, confirmed by Serpukhov-15, has activated the Kazbek communications system. Pavel Podvig tells us that this kind of early-warning notification confirmation would initiate a nuclear high-alert status known as "preliminary command."

"Once this is done," Podvig clarifies, "everyone waits. And they wait. . . . They wait until they actually have an actual [instruction] to launch."

The Russian generals begin sharing their opinions about what is happening in the United States, and what should happen next.

The future of Europe hangs in the balance.

The consequences of a nuclear conflict between Russia and NATO are cataclysmic. A 2020 computer simulation by nuclear weapons scholars with Princeton University's Program on Science and Global Security found that a nuclear exchange between Russia and NATO would almost certainly escalate quickly, leading to the death and injury of nearly 100 million people in the first few hours.

The Russian generals talk among themselves. They prepare what they are going to say to the Russian president.

40 MINUTES

Cheyenne Mountain Complex, Colorado

The U.S. military has fired eighty-two nuclear warheads at North Korea with the goal of decapitating the country's leadership before it launches any more nuclear strikes against the United States. This action is based on military doctrine called restoring deterrence.

Nuclear war is not supposed to happen. Deterrence is supposed to hold. But if it doesn't, restoring deterrence is what happens next. "Changing an adversary's decision calculus regarding further [nuclear] escalation" is how a 2020 White House briefing document described it.

In the words of STRATCOM commander Admiral Charles A. Richard (two years later), "Deterrence day-to-day is different from deterrence in crisis. It's different from deterrence in conflict. It's different from deterrence after first nuclear use, when you're attempting to restore deterrence."

Restoring deterrence after first nuclear use in this scenario involves STRATCOM using overwhelming nuclear force in an effort to pressure the attacker to capitulate. To render them incapable of further attack. To change their decision calculus. But will it succeed?

According to the U.S. Army, this task—on a scale of military hardship—ranges from difficult to impossible. North Korea's supreme leader has almost certainly disappeared into one of the nation's many underground facilities. Into a deeply buried bunker system, a labyrinth of tunnels and command centers that has been carefully engineered over decades to hide the leadership before, during, and after a nuclear war.

"North Korea is known to have an extensive network of tunnels and underground facilities used for suspicious purposes," says the army through a spokesman, "including infiltrating the South, protecting the reclusive regime, and conducting nuclear tests."

Using defector accounts, the South Korean military has mapped out some of the North's underground system and believes as many as 8,000 bombproof bunkers presently exist. But because Western intelligence assets in North Korea are rare, the U.S. remains mostly blind to the details. "It is one of the hardest, if not the hardest, collection nation that we have to collect against," Director of National Intelligence Daniel Coats told Congress in 2017. "We do not have consistent ISR [Intelligence, Surveillance, and Reconnaissance] capabilities. There are gaps. The North Koreans know about these." And as Bruce Blair wrote in 2018, "The possibility of intelligence gaps and hidden North Korean nuclear weapons and command bunkers would vex the U.S." in any future warfighting campaign. This includes where the North Korean leader might go to hide after launching a preemptive salvo in a nuclear war.

To stop North Korea from launching more missiles, STRATCOM must destroy North Korea's leadership *and* its Nuclear Command and Control. This poses an even more challenging problem, according to intelligence analysts in Washington think tanks. The country is run by a small group of loyalists called the Personal Secretariat, a majority of whom remain with the leader at all times. This unusual cadre of men and women includes his political and military advisors, but also his bodyguards, bankers, assistants—even his children's nannies.

Michael Madden, director of the North Korea Leadership Watch at the Stimson Center, explains. "The Personal Secretariat manages everything. His schedule, his haircuts, what he wears, his billions of U.S. dollars in foreign bank accounts. One unit assassinates people. Another issues military commands. And another has command and control over all of North Korea's security and military forces, including its nuclear weapons and other weapons of mass destruction."

How to target a group of people holding the reins of power, when almost nothing is known about who they are, and even less about where they are? North Korea doesn't produce public reports. They have no independent newspapers or magazines. Most intelligence community information comes from satellite images and defector reports. Which means the first thirty-two submarine-launched nuclear warheads will strike "counterforce targets," to include:

- North Korea's nuclear launch facilities
- North Korea's Nuclear Command and Control facilities
- North Korea's nuclear weapons production facilities

In its attempt to decapitate North Korea's leadership, the Defense Department will have to kill millions, or tens of millions, of North Korean civilians. Some argue this violates the United Nations Charter as well as the *Jus Ad Bellum* principles of international law. That it violates the two fundamental principles of "humanity and military necessity," including three long-standing requirements regarding "distinction, proportionality, and avoidance of unnecessary suffering." But as humans around the world are collectively about to learn, the first rule of nuclear war is that there are no rules.

The Defense Department's logic in destroying the North Korean capital city of Pyongyang, as well as large swaths of the countryside, is that it will put an end to one decision-maker's madness. The presumption here is that killing millions of North Koreans with a barrage of nuclear warheads offers the best chance of stopping North Korea's leader from killing millions more Americans.

That killing more people can prevent killing more people. That it can restore deterrence. But will it?

40 MINUTES, 30 SECONDS
Hoejung-ni (회중리) Underground Facility,
Hwapyong County, North Korea

In an isolated mountain valley in northern North Korea, roughly twenty miles from the border with China, a heavy steel door in the side of a mountain swings open wide. This is the clandestine Hoejung-ni missile operating base, which includes a secret city underground.

From decades of archival satellite imagery, the CIA has determined there to be more than twenty aboveground structures here, including a greenhouse to grow food and a lawn for a parade. That the complex includes at least two underground facilities and can house at least one regiment-sized missile unit, exact numbers unknown. "The mountaintop here is covered with soil and has mature vegetation growing tall, designed to disguise itself from satellite detection overhead," imagery analyst Joseph Bermudez Jr. explains. But almost nothing is known about what goes on inside the facility. "North Korea has never acknowledged its existence, and its national designator is not known."

Seconds after the steel door in the side of the mountain swings open, out rolls a Korean People's Army ballistic missile transporter-erector-launcher with a Hwasong-17 ICBM lying horizontal on its 22-wheeled flatbed.

The launcher drives several hundred feet down a dirt mountain road lined with a protective berm. The vehicle stops. Soldiers jump out, make adjustments, step to the side.

The missile is armed. It is readied. It fires.

In a plume of explosive rocket exhaust, the Hwasong-17 ICBM ascends from its launchpad and into the sky, moving above the wooded forest in Boost Phase. Its flames ignite the pine trees on the ground and send large boulders rolling downhill. The total number of North Korean nuclear bombs targeting the United States in this scenario has now risen to three.

Thousands of miles overhead, the Defense Department's mighty SBIRS satellite system sees the launch from space and notifies command. The likely targets for this second ICBM will take another several minutes to discern.

With the Pentagon destroyed, track data flows to NORAD, NORTHCOM, and STRATCOM via the command center in the sky, the Doomsday Plane, to Site R beneath Raven Rock Mountain, and to the two nuclear command centers that remain:

- The Missile Warning Center in the Cheyenne Mountain Complex, Colorado
- The Global Operations Center below Offutt Air Force Base, Nebraska

40 MINUTES, 30 SECONDS
National Defense Management Center, Moscow, Russia

Watching satellite TV inside his Moscow office, a colonel with Russia's Main Intelligence Directorate, the GRU, is so enthralled with the mayhem in America that he neglects checking his voicemail. He has not heard the message that came in fifteen minutes ago from a source he runs in Wyoming, USA.

The job of the GRU is to gather human intelligence for the Russian military through military attachés, foreign agents, and spies. This includes spies in America, like the old man who keeps an eye on the Echo-01 Minuteman III ICBM launch facility in Wyoming.

In Moscow, the GRU officer checks his voicemail.

He listens to a short, numerically coded message, one that follows previously authorized reporting protocols.

The message includes numbers and letters in the Russian alphabet, in Cyrillic, that verify content and authenticity.

Translated into English, the message is succinct: *The ICBMs have launched.*

Phone in hand, the GRU officer picks up a secure telephone and begins making calls.

40 MINUTES, 30 SECONDS
Hudson Yards, New York City

In New York City, at the Cable News Network studio in Hudson Yards, workers continue to flee the building in droves, including the anchor who, until just a few minutes ago, was reporting breaking news live on air.

In this scenario, a younger journalist now sits down in front of the camera. Working to keep her composure, she explains to whoever may still be watching that access to social media platforms across much of the country is mostly down. That the ability for viewers to watch this CNN broadcast is likely hit or miss, depending on where it is you live.

Many American TV and radio stations are not functioning—the result of data center failures, carrier failures, and workers straight up abandoning their jobs. With information sharing in a state of utter chaos, the journalist says she will now read out loud instructions downloaded from FEMA's Region 4 office in Atlanta, which is still functioning at this time.

Journalist: *I'm going to read from "Be Prepared for a Nuclear Explosion."*

Behind her, an electronic screen displays an image screen-grabbed from the California Department of Public Health.

The U.S. government regularly issues warnings about what to do in a nuclear explosion. (California Department of Public Health)

The terrifying photograph is a decades-old image of an actual nuclear mushroom cloud and stem. The photograph is real, a nuclear bomb captured on film during a Cold War bomb test—back when atmospheric nuclear testing was legal. The image has been touched up. Someone has added orange and red hues. It looks sinister and malevolent because it is.

Journalist: *People are supposed to "Get Inside, Stay Inside, and Stay Tuned." According to the federal government.*

Reading from FEMA's website, the young journalist gets interrupted by a colleague who hands her an official federal tome, a highlighted copy of a 135-page guidebook developed by the Executive Office of the President titled "Planning Guidance for Response to a Nuclear Detonation."

Journalist: *FEMA and the Office of the President say this is what people should expect from a 10-kiloton nuclear detonation in their city or town.*

She has no way of knowing the bomb that just struck Washington, D.C., was 1 megaton, which is one hundred times the yield. Skimming over the document, she reads aloud:

"Humans . . . incinerated
blast, thermal, and radiation injuries
beta burns to the skin
lethal radiation doses . . . 20 miles . . . from ground zero . . .
    even with medical care . . . not . . . expected to survive
blast and electromagnetic pulse . . . [will] damage
    communications infrastructure
Stalling of vehicles
infrastructure . . . completely destroyed
communications equipment (cell towers, etc.) . . . destroyed
Computer equipment . . . destroyed, control systems . . .
    destroyed
water and electrical system[s] . . . destroyed
Few, if any, buildings . . . structurally sound
Rubble in streets . . . rubble . . . 30 feet deep

Blast injuries . . . overshadowed by injuries [from] collapsing
   structures
Blast injuries . . . from flying debris and glass
Unstable structures, sharp metal objects . . . ruptured gas
   lines
Hazmat teams . . . thwarted . . . [by] stalled and crashed
   automobiles
Downed utility lines . . . overturned automobiles . . .
   completely block streets
Raging firestorm[s] . . . beyond the abilities of firefighters to
   control
Hazardous chemicals . . . medical triage . . . contamination
   from fallout . . . widespread . . . death."

And then the journalist comes upon a line so jarring, it causes
her to stop reading and to shake her head in disbelief. She takes a
breath and reads on:

"After a nuclear detonation, priorities are likely to change."

Her cell phone pings. FEMA has issued another Wireless
Emergency Alert.
She reads aloud:

U.S. UNDER NUCLEAR ATTACK

SEEK SHELTER BELOW GROUND

EVACUATION MAY BE NECESSARY TO AVOID FIRE RISKS

Turning back to the camera, she starts to say something, but
then stops. She loses her composure on-screen.
Journalist: *What in hell?*

She asks aloud, to no one in particular and everyone all at once:

Are we supposed to stay where we are? Or evacuate?

She holds her smartphone up to the camera and points.

Journalist: *These two sets of instructions from FEMA contradict one another.*

She stops speaking.

What is there to say?

40 MINUTES, 30 SECONDS
Los Osos, California

In the California beach community of Los Osos, a little over six miles north of Diablo Canyon, residents are in a state of absolute terror. The tall, rugged peaks between the nuclear power station and the town shielded many local residents from getting third-degree burns or carbonizing limbs. It protected them from getting impaled by flying objects, or being crushed to death under buildings mowed down by blast wave. But geography can't spare anyone in the area from an excruciating death by radiation that is inevitable, and will soon follow. If the radiation spewing out of the exposed reactor cores at the power plant doesn't kill them soon, the fallout from a mushroom cloud seeded with shattered spent fuel rods surely will.

Pocket dosimeters and ion chamber electroscopes carried by some area residents, to monitor accumulated radiation doses in emergency situations, have maxed out. These field-readable dosimeters are designed to aid in tactical decisions after an unforeseen radiological release. Residents of Los Osos who are prepared enough to be in possession of one of these dosimeters collectively realize the dire situation at hand. If they don't leave the area immediately, they will die.

The power is out. Television and FM radio not available any-where in the area. Even the NOAA Weather Radio All Hazards nationwide network—long considered a stalwart news source in a disaster—has collapsed from overload, with an eerie "unknown warning/unknown statement" error code broadcasting in a loop. Boats at sea tune in to Channel 16 (the VHF frequency for com-munication with other boats and the U.S. Coast Guard), but hear only indiscernible sounds.

The nuclear reactor oversight telephone line is down. Pacific Gas and Electric, which runs the power plant, has a troubling safety history that includes a $13.5 billion settlement of claims linked to California fires. The tragic irony here is that this catastro-phe is not their fault.

Cell phones and computers that were plugged into wall sockets when the bomb exploded have had their microprocessors destroyed. The battery-powered emergency sirens are, for the most part, func-tioning as designed. Pole-mounted horns screech ear-piercing wails, an ominous, steady three- to five-minute-long siren that sounds without interruption. A warning many residents know to mean:

NUCLEAR EMERGENCY!

Beyond the local beach towns, some half a million people reside within fifty miles of Diablo Canyon. Word spreads rapidly among residents here that across the country, Washington, D.C., is also under nuclear attack. That what is happening is not a localized nuclear accident, but nuclear war.

In coastal communities across San Luis Obispo County, cars back up out of driveways—windows up, noses and mouths cov-ered with pieces of clothing or masks they had left over from COVID times.

It is 12:43 p.m. local time.

Everyone's kids are still in school.

Every second matters.

The only way to stay alive is to evacuate.

But which way to go? Fallout moves with wind.

Beyond residents' driveways, a new horror presents itself in every town, at every turn, in every small and large community along the central California coast. Cars. Cars everywhere. Separating the Diablo Canyon Power Plant from most towns is a 1,800-foot-tall peak known as Mount Buchon. This hilly range of earth and stone buffered much of the bomb's localized electromagnetic pulse effects, sparing many cars from having their microprocessors fried. But the streetlights are out. Traffic is in a snarl. Residents in existential panic drive their cars over berms and across lawns in violent, desperate attempts at escape. Vehicles race down the wrong sides of the roads, smashing into other vehicles like bumper cars. It is bumper to bumper everywhere.

Eighteen minutes have passed since the Diablo Canyon Power Plant was hit by a 300-kiloton nuclear bomb. A radioactive forest fire has set the surrounding mountains on fire, a mega-inferno tearing its way down Mount Buchon on all sides, threatening people and entire towns. Radioactive ash fills the air. Marble-sized pieces of pulverized nuclear reactor concrete rain down from above. Dead seagulls fall from the sky, their wings on fire. People begin to lose control of their bowels. Start vomiting blood.

As the mushroom cloud rises, the sky goes dark.

Every second matters. People get out of their cars and begin running.

40 MINUTES, 30 SECONDS
Undisclosed Location, 700 Miles above the Pacific Ocean

High above the Pacific Ocean, eight Trident missiles arc over the Earth, traveling at 13,600 miles per hour, or Mach 18. Their flight began just minutes ago, from an undisclosed point in the middle of the Pacific Ocean, somewhere north of the island of Tinian. Their targets are in Pyongyang. The total distance to target is 1,800 miles. With a range angle of 38.26 degrees, the total travel time from launch to target is fourteen minutes; missile expert Ted Postol did the math.

Guiding the Tridents on their high-speed transit through the atmosphere is an unusual form of navigation in the modern era. The U.S. Navy's most powerful, most expensive, most accurate nuclear-armed missiles get where they are going by an astronavigation technique invented specifically for the Trident missile system: star sighting.

Long before humans figured out how to write language down, how to record their own histories into stone and clay, people figured out how to get from point A to point B with the help of the heavens. Celestial navigation involves the practice of fixing an object's position using the stars, the sun, and other celestial bodies.

"The submerged submarine has no ability to know exactly where it is at the time of launch," Trident missile guidance systems manager Steven J. DiTullio explains. There's a shipboard navigator, a human, to assist, "but even that isn't precise enough."

The solve—to usher in Armageddon—DiTullio says, is in the stars.

"The way that we handle [geolocation] uncertainty is by taking a star sighting during missile flight, to then effectively correct for the initial position error." Conceptually, this is the same system that has been used since the early days of the Cold War. The primitive technology prevents hacking. For this same reason, there is no remotely controlled kill switch on a ballistic missile. If there were, an enemy could ostensibly hack into a ballistic missile's guidance system and assume control of it.

Eight Trident nuclear missiles, each with enough combined explosive power to turn Pyongyang into a fireplace, continue on course. On a suborbital trajectory, guided by the stars.

41 MINUTES
Central Command Center, Komsomolsk-on-Amur, Russia

Russia's eastern counterpart to the Serpukhov-15 early-warning radar facility is a central command center without a known Western reporting name. Located near Komsomolsk-on-Amur in the Russian Far East, the facility sits on the banks of the Amur River, along an unnamed road, in Khabarovsk Krai. This location is roughly 175 miles from the border with China, and 600 miles from the border with North Korea. The facility's purpose is to interpret information from Tundra's constellation of early-warning satellites in space. To see attacking nuclear missiles that are coming in from the United States by way of the Pacific Ocean to the south. Launched, as they would be, from a U.S. Ohio-class nuclear-powered, nuclear-armed submarine.

Komsomolsk-on-Amur is a backwater city, isolated from the modern world. A regional center of metallurgy, aircraft manufacturing, and shipbuilding. It is also the former home to a notorious over-the-horizon radar transmitter facility called DUGA-2, but more famously known as Woodpecker. The radar system was named, as such, for the mysterious and repetitive tapping noise it transmitted over shortwave radio bands around the world for more than a decade during the Cold War. The steel and wire DUGA structure was a massive half-mile-long and 500-foot-tall monolith. NATO military intelligence monitored the site obsessively and gave it the reporting name Steel Yard. The DUGA transmitter in Komsomolsk-on-Amur was dismantled in the 1990s after the Soviet Union was dissolved, but its more notorious counterpart still stands, in Ukraine, inside the Chernobyl Exclusion Zone.

At 5:44 a.m. local time, the commander here at Komsomolsk-on-Amur is waiting for additional incoming information from Tundra space satellites. Across the Russian military, the Kazbek communications system has been activated. Every military facility in the country is on the highest-alert status, on so-called preliminary command. Just seconds ago, Komsomolsk-on-Amur received word from its sister stations in Barnaul and in Irkutsk.

"The Russian Aerospace Force has four types of ground-based early-warning radars potentially capable of detecting ballistic missile salvos," Dr. Thomas Withington tells us. An electronic warfare expert and military radar analyst with the Royal United Services Institute in England, Withington calculated how Russian track data in this scenario might come in. "Three minutes and nine seconds after the Tridents launched, the 77YA6DM Voronezh-DM radar system in Barnaul began tracking the submarine-launched ballistic missile salvo. Fifty seconds later, the 77YA6VP Voronezh-DP in Irkutsk began tracking [it, too]."

And now Komsomolsk-on-Amur gets alerted by the Tundra satellite system of an incoming missile attack from the Pacific. Early-warning space satellites "see" hundreds of objects coming at Russia—or what the commander *thinks* is at Russia—from the south. The same salvo seen by Russian ground radar stations in Barnaul and Irkutsk.

The Tundra system "sees" hundreds of objects at this point in time, not because Tundra is misperceiving sunlight or clouds for rocket exhaust. Rocket exhaust only happens in a ballistic missile's Boost Phase. The Tridents are now in Midcourse Phase, where a new misperception by Russian early-warning radar systems can occur. Trident missiles contain hundreds of objects inside every warhead bus. These objects are decoys, designed to fake out Russian interceptor missiles.

"These decoys are constructed from thin pieces of crossed wire, and shaped like jacks, the kids' toys," Ted Postol explains, and, to a radar system like the one at Komsomolsk-on-Amur, "these wires look like hundreds of additional warheads."

The commander picks up the phone and notifies Moscow that his early-warning system sees a massive barrage of warheads attacking Russia from the south.

41 MINUTES, 1 SECOND
Inside the Doomsday Plane, over North Dakota, USA

Inside the airborne command center in the Doomsday Plane, the STRATCOM commander opens the Black Book. With a third attacking ballistic missile on its way to the United States, additional nuclear counterstrikes against North Korea are under his review. The secretary of defense and the vice-chairman are also on the call, on Advanced Extremely High Frequency satellite comms, from Site R.

It has been eight minutes since DISA lost contact with Marine One. No one knows where the president is.

The quick reaction force has located the Football and is bringing it back to Raven Rock. The mil aide is dead, his parachute ripped apart by blast wave. The special agent in charge of the president's detail, the CAT operators, and the president are all still missing, presumably separated from one another by wind drift.

With the chairman of the Joint Chiefs dead, the vice-chairman is now the highest-ranking officer in the military, whose job it is to advise the president and the secretary of defense. As acting chairman, she outranks all other officers in the military, but she cannot command the military. That is the job of the president.

Vice-chairman: *SecDef needs to be sworn in as acting president. Now.* Everyone on satellite comms agrees.

But executive branch people at Site R are fighting over line-of-succession protocols from Article II, Section 1, Clause 4 of the Constitution. At issue is the still-unresolved, post-9/11 piece of congressional legislation about what to do after a "mass decapitation" event. The president pro tempore of the Senate is, in this scenario, apparently still alive. DISA received a message from one of his staffers just a few minutes ago. The second-highest-ranking member of the Senate was home sick when the bomb detonated over the Pentagon and now he's on his way to Site R—driving himself from Maryland in his own car—to assume his line of succession role as commander in chief.

National security advisor: *Forget that. We invoke the bumping procedure and swear in SecDef.*

He cites Title 3, Section 19 of the Succession Act of 1947. *People's choice.*

STRATCOM has a different focus.

STRATCOM commander: *We need to respond in force to incoming missile number three.*

Vice-chairman: *SecDef needs to be sworn in as acting president, now.*

STRATCOM commander: *We need to choose strike options.*

SecDef: *We can't do anything until we have the Russian president on the line.*

Everyone on the satellite call knows the STRATCOM commander is in possession of the universal unlock code, meaning he has the ability—and arguably the authority—to launch additional nuclear counterstrikes.

STRATCOM commander: *The Russian president refusing your call is not good.*

SecDef, upset: *He won't take my call because I'm not the acting president of the United States.*

Vice-chairman: *We need to swear in SecDef.*

SecDef: *I'm blind.*

As rapid-fire discussions ensue, and as decisions are being made about what looks strong and what looks weak, so are they being made in Russia—in a nuclear bunker underground.

42 MINUTES
Boyds, Maryland

No one has heard from the president because when the nuclear bomb hit the Pentagon, Marine One experienced a system failure from localized electromagnetic pulse and crashed into the ground. As we know, seconds before the crash, a member of the Secret Service CAT Element tandem-jumped the president out the open door of the Sikorsky, in an attempt to save his life.

The two men landed violently in a forested area in Boyds, Maryland, near Little Seneca Lake. The CAT operator had his neck broken. The president was cushioned by the CAT operator's body and kept alive by a stroke of luck.

Now the president unclips himself from the dead man's body and wriggles free. There's a deep gash on his forehead. His left arm and right leg have compound fractures. He can see the bloody, torn tendons and the gray-white exposed bone pushing through his skin. There is blood. Lots of blood.

The president lies here in this wooded area, listening to the trees sway in the early spring wind. He is terrified that he will die. He is helpless. He can't walk or even crawl out of here, not with the damage to his arm and leg. He is losing blood fast. He feels faint. He is the commander in chief and America is at nuclear war.

Will anyone find him?

The president's iPhone got lost in the mayhem. He tries using the dead CAT operator's radio, but it doesn't work. He is unsure where he physically is. There's a quick reaction force looking for him, he surmises. But without any communication devices working, how will they find him before he bleeds out?

42 MINUTES
Ground Zero, The National Zoo

In the Rings around ground zero in Washington, D.C., the horrific pain and suffering is not limited to humans. At the National Zoo, four miles north of the Pentagon, a majority of the animals are dead, but some are still alive, blinded, with third-degree burns, and in a complete state of shock. Asian elephants, western lowland gorillas, and Sumatran tigers writhe and bellow in their cages and their pens. Most have charred skin hanging off their bodies, their hair on fire.

Animals instinctively go to water when on fire, in a futile attempt to put out the flames. This includes humans, whose bodies now fill the waterways all across the city. The Potomac is clogged with untold numbers of dead, similar to what happened in Nagasaki, Japan, in August 1945. "Thousands of bodies bopped up and down in the river, bloated and purplish from soaking up the water," survivor Shigeko Matsumoto later recalled. Here in the waterways around D.C., large metallic-colored blowflies (carrion insects) land on the floating dead bodies and begin laying eggs.

The animals in their cages will all, almost certainly, die. There is no one left to feed them, or to free them—to let them try and survive on their own. Any human survivors near the National Zoo face insurmountable hurdles. Burned and bleeding, their lungs fill with toxic gases and smoke. They are desperately trying to leave the disaster area before the ensuing mega-fire burns them alive. But massive piles of rubble make the terrain near-impossible to traverse. Unsound buildings collapse all around.

Lethal radiation in the air silently sentences survivors to death.

HISTORY LESSON NO. 8

Radiation Sickness

Defense scientists have known what acute radiation sickness does to the body since the Manhattan Project years. Consider the May 1946 accident at Omega Site, at a secret laboratory hidden in the Los Alamos woods, the details of which remained classified for decades.

It was a cool spring day, three miles from the main lab, when a group of scientists stood hovering over a table, concentrating. The men were working on a plutonium bomb core, the first atomic test since Hiroshima and Nagasaki were destroyed. The U.S. nuclear stockpile at the time was around four. The future of the nuclear arms race depended on this moment. The Los Alamos scientists, upon whom many jobs and fortunes depended, were under great pressure to get this plutonium core experiment correct.

The physicist handling the plutonium that day was a man named Louis Slotin. There were seven other scientists in the room. Slotin had recently decided to leave the Manhattan Project for moral reasons, he told friends. The war was over and he was done working on atomic bombs. Los Alamos officials said fine, but required Slotin to train someone to take his place. That someone was a scientist named Alvin C. Graves.

During this dangerous experiment—dangerous enough to be known as "tickling the dragon's tail"—Slotin dropped one of the nuclear spheres he was handling, causing the material to go critical. Knowing the risk to himself, but hoping to save the others in the room, Slotin thrust himself in front of Alvin Graves, who was standing beside him. Eyewitnesses described a quick flash of blue light—a "blue glow," others said—and a wave of intense heat.

People began screaming. The security guard assigned to protect the nuclear material fled the room, raced outside, and ran up into the New Mexico hills.

Someone called for an ambulance to come quick. The laboratory was evacuated, but Louis Slotin stayed behind, to begin sketching out a diagram where he and everyone else had been standing, for future study and use. So defense scientists could understand how radiation poisoning works. How it kills.

Slotin's sketch was remarkably detailed for a man whose death by acute radiation syndrome had already begun. Years later, the laboratory made a mock-up of where Louis Slotin was when the accident happened. He was just thirty-five years old.

Louis Slotin's Los Alamos badge (left) and a laboratory mock-up of the experiment that killed him (right) at Los Alamos in 1946. (Los Alamos National Laboratory)

In the ambulance, Slotin vomited. His left hand, the one closest to the nuclear material when the accident happened, went numb. His groin began swelling. He had explosive diarrhea and vomited again, and again. At the Los Alamos hospital, more vomiting. More watery diarrhea releasing from his bowels. Prostrate and weak, watery fluid began collecting in his hands, which expanded like balloons. Horrible and painful blisters formed under his skin, then burst.

Doctors dressed the pustules on Slotin's hands with Vaseline and gauze. They tried debridement (scrubbing the skin with a wire sponge) to remove damaged tissue. They plunged Slotin's extremities in ice. Pumped his body with fresh blood. The days wore on. More ice baths. More blood transfusions. But nothing could alleviate the intense pain. A lethal dose of high-energy X-rays, gamma rays, and neutrons had penetrated Louis Slotin's organs. His body was now failing to oxygenate its own blood. Cyanosis set in, bluish discoloration that spread across his chest, arms, groin, and legs. The purple patches covering his body split open and hemorrhaged blood. The same thing happened to the open sores in his mouth. With thick pieces of skin now peeling off Slotin's hands, doctors considered amputation, but administered blood transfusions instead—one after the next, after the next.

As the end drew near, Louis Slotin was experiencing necrosis. Death of the limbs. All the bone marrow stem cells throughout his body were now dying or dead. He was experiencing necrosis of the blood vessel walls; jaundice; acute thrombosis in the small and large blood vessels; severe epithelial damage in the intestines. As his body began losing its ability to form antibodies, the cell lining in Slotin's gastrointestinal tract began giving off products that began moving into neighboring tissues. Louis Slotin's body was being invaded by bacteria in his own intestines. His adrenal glands were malfunctioning. Acute sepsis was setting in. He began experiencing extensive gangrene due to interruption in his blood supply. Then organ system damage. Tissue death. Circulatory collapse. Liver failure. Finally, complete organ failure. On day nine, Louis Slotin died from acute radiation poisoning.

Not long after Slotin took his last breath, Los Alamos doctors began slicing him open, eager to learn how radiation kills a human. Before 1945, the science of radiation poisoning did not exist. Now, in the spring of 1946, the very concept was less than one year old. With the first cut of the scalpel, doctors came upon a horror not observed in a world before the invention of the atomic bomb. The mess inside Slotin's dead body was like a sea of rotten soup. His "blood was uncoaguable at autopsy," one of the doctors wrote in a classified postmortem report.

The radiation poisoning had caused the near complete loss of tissue that once separated one of Slotin's organs from the next. Without this lining, his organs had merged into one. And to think, just a few months prior, Manhattan Project chief General Leslie Groves had assured the public and Congress that death by radiation poisoning was "a very pleasant way to die."

43 MINUTES AFTER LAUNCH
Underground Bunker, Siberia, Russia

The president of the Russian Federation is in an undisclosed location in Siberia, in a nuclear command and control facility hidden away from the rest of the world. The location could be beneath Mount Yamantau, in the Urals, or Mount Kosvinsky, near Sverdlovsk, or in the Altai Republic, near a snake turn in the Katun River. Either way, in this scenario he is several floors underground, inside a bunker designed to ride out nuclear war.

It is the middle of the night in Russia. It is cold. There is snow on the ground.

The Russian president has been awakened from sleep and now he is on a video conference call. With him are Russia's two top generals. The defense minister and the chief of the General Staff of Russia's armed forces. These three individuals are understood to each have beside them, at all times, one of Russia's three nuclear briefcases that transmits orders for a nuclear strike. The briefcase is called the Cheget. Russia's Football.

In November 2020, the Kremlin released a rare transcript of a meeting between President Vladimir Putin and his top generals in which the president outlined the importance of command and control bunkers, and their communications systems, in a nuclear war. "We are aware that a lot depends on the survivability of these systems and their ability to continue operating in a combat environment," he said. And he emphasized how "all equipment, hardware and communication systems of the nuclear forces control systems" had been recently upgraded. At the same time, Putin said, they "remain as simple and reliable as a Kalashnikov rifle." In this scenario, Russia's president and his family have been residing in a bunker, off and on, since the winter of 2022, when the

Russian military attacked its neighbor Ukraine and Russia's leadership became pariahs of the West.

Down in the bunker, the Russian president flips through Western news channels on satellite TV. From reports on still-functioning cable news stations, it is clear the U.S. has been hit by nuclear attack. Big cities are experiencing mass exodus the likes of which have never before been seen. In New York City, Los Angeles, San Francisco, and Chicago, helicopters flying overhead capture the mayhem as millions of people try to leave these cities, all at the same time. Widespread chaos, violence, and anarchy have begun.

The Russian president eyes the terror unfolding across the United States and wonders who is in control. Nuclear war planners in the U.S. and in Russia have long wondered what will happen to society were nuclear war to begin. And what about military command and control?

Who is in charge?

Defense departments run on hierarchy. A follows B follows C in a pyramid of power. In a time of nuclear crisis, a central question remains. Who will perform their job dutifully and who will ditch their post and run? Will those in the military chain of command choose country over family, or family over country? Can anyone predict such things? Will fate and circumstance play a role?

In this scenario, news reporters in smaller cities like Des Moines, Iowa, and Little Rock, Arkansas, continue to broadcast information, removed as they are by a thousand miles' distance from the nuclear attacks. Many big-city headquarters' facilities are down, or unable to broadcast anymore. Internet is hit or miss. Tens of millions of people in America cannot access the news.

The Russian president's nuclear bunker, like Site R, presently has electricity, internet, and hardwired telephone service. Underground bunkers are built for redundancy, their critical infrastructure components—including air, heat, and water—duplicated for resilience in emergencies and crises. Multiple high-capacity fiber-optic lines provide uninterrupted communications systems. The backup generators have backup generators.

In nuclear war, measurable distance from ground zero is everything. But when you are in charge, nothing is more important than speed. As Ronald Reagan once lamented, the U.S. president has only six minutes to respond after being notified by his advisors of an incoming nuclear attack. Now the Russian president faces the same insanely small window of time in which he must act.

In 2022, Vladimir Putin promised a "lightning fast" response to notification of any "oncoming strikes" against Russia, a threat widely interpreted as referring to Russia's nuclear triad. Two years before that, in 2020, he referred to upgrades in Russia's nuclear forces as being marked by incredible speed. "Not . . . Formula 1 fast," Putin said, "supersonic fast."

This is the moment. The time to act fast.

Several minutes have already been wasted watching satellite TV. The Russian president has just a few minutes remaining in which to decide what to do. An either/or paradox confronts Russia's president.

- Either the U.S. believes Russia is responsible for the nuclear strikes against the U.S.
- Or the U.S. knows Russia is not responsible for the nuclear strikes against the U.S.

For nuclear attack options, the U.S. has the Football. Russia has the Cheget, a small, similarly-styled briefcase kept close to the president (and two others) at all times. The Cheget is the centerpiece of Russia's president-centric Nuclear Command and Control, same as the Football is the centerpiece of America's president-centric Nuclear Command and Control. Inside the Cheget is Russia's version of a Black Book, a dinner menu–like list of nuclear strike options to choose from—and fast.

The Cheget connects its possessor to the Russian General Staff, the military officers at the command center in central Moscow. These are the generals and the admirals who control the physical launch mechanisms for Russia's nuclear triad. Its sea-land-air-based nuclear arsenal, which is almost identical in size to that maintained by the United States. Russia has 1,674 nuclear weapons deployed, a majority of which are on ready-for-launch status. On Hair-Trigger Alert.

With the president here in the underground bunker is the secretary of the Security Council, a most hawkish advisor in the inner circle. The secretary is a man with profound influence over the Russian president, a member of the so-called *siloviki* (the enforcers). No fan of the West, the secretary has stated publicly his belief that the "concrete goal" of America and her allies is the breakup of Russia, going so far as to accuse the U.S. military of preparing for "biological war" against the Russian people, adding neither context nor details.

In this moment of intense crisis, the secretary of the Security Council reminds the Russian president that he is running out of time. That he must make a decision about how he will act. The president asks his advisors to review what Moscow has confirmed as fact—what Russia's early-warning system has revealed to them.

For decades, the Soviet Union claimed not to have a Launch on Warning posture. Pavel Podvig tells us the Russian policy was (allegedly) to "first absorb attacking warheads" before launching a counterattack of their own. If this was Soviet propaganda, or was true, remains subject to debate.

What is clear is that, recently, Russia's official posture changed.

In a 2018 interview at the Kremlin, President Putin was asked if he would use nuclear weapons on early-warning notification alone. "The decision to use nuclear weapons can only be made if our missile attack warning system not only recorded the launch of missiles," Putin said, "but also gave an accurate forecast and flight trajectories, and the time when they fall on Russian soil." In other words, if Tundra satellites see missiles on their way, and a secondary early-warning system confirms flight trajectories and estimated attack times, Russia can—*and will*—launch nuclear weapons in response. It will not wait to absorb a nuclear blow.

It is along the razor's edge that the Russian president's advisors must now walk. The defense minister, the chief of the General Staff of the armed forces, and the secretary of the Security Council must report missile-attack warning information to the president with the authority of inner-circle advisors, while balancing technological uncertainties *that exist.*

The limitations of Russia's early-warning Tundra satellite system—its flaws and its weaknesses—are well known to scientists in the West, and likely to scientists in Russia as well.

But do the advisors know? Or have they been kept in the dark? The advisors brief the Russian president on what they know—or think they know.

- Twenty minutes ago, a nuclear power plant in California was hit by a nuclear bomb.
- Ten minutes ago, the Pentagon, the White House, the Congress, and all of Washington were destroyed by a second nuclear bomb.
- A few minutes later, Russia's Tundra satellites recorded launch of 100 or more Minuteman ICBMs from silos in Wyoming.
- A GRU asset near one of these ICBM sites confirmed launch with his eyes.
- Serpukhov-15 radars confirm 100 or more ICBMs coming over the North Pole.

- Three minutes ago, Voronezh radars in Barnaul and Irkutsk reported a submarine-launched salvo of missiles coming in from the south.
- Two minutes ago, Komsomolsk-on-Amur confirmed these warheads. There are hundreds of them.
- The situation is this: The warning system has recorded the launch of U.S. missiles. There are hundreds of warheads attacking Russia—from two sides. The forecast is that they will fall on Russian soil starting in about nine minutes' time.

On a satellite television station playing inside the Russian bunker, an American newscaster in Truth or Consequences, New Mexico, breaks the Russian president's reverie. The anchorman tells the audience that no one in the U.S. seems to know who is attacking the United States, what is really going on, or who—if anyone—is actually in charge. That the U.S. president has not addressed the nation, which is terrifying and troubling. He uses the word "surreal."

And then, the anchorman asks, *Is it Russia?*

He asks this out loud, on air, to no one in particular.

Who else would dare do this? Is capable of such brutality?

Down in the Russian bunker, six floors underground, the secretary of the Security Council tells the president he has ninety seconds remaining to decide what actions to take.

The Russian president asks if the American president has called him.

The answer is *nyet.* No.

The Russian president asks who from the White House has called. An aide steps forward and reads from a time sheet.

- The U.S. national security advisor called.

- The U.S. secretary of defense called.
- The vice-chairman of the Joint Chiefs of Staff called.

Russia's president considers a second set of either/or facts.

- Either hundreds of warheads approaching Russia on ballistic trajectories are targeting Russia
- Or hundreds of warheads approaching Russia on ballistic trajectories are not targeting Russia

Everyone here in the Russian bunker, and on the satellite video conference from the command center in Moscow, knows Russia did not attack the U.S. with nuclear bombs. And they know U.S. early-warning radar systems are enviably accurate, which makes them all reasonably sure that the U.S. president and his generals know the nuclear attack did not originate on Russian soil. But they also know the U.S. president—and possibly every leader in the Western world—despises the Russian leadership. And that when the U.S. wants regime change, history shows the U.S. will lie.

Everyone in the bunker is now thinking about the same historical event. Words emerge from thoughts and a brief discussion ensues. How, back in 2003, when President George W. Bush and Vice President Dick Cheney wanted to get rid of the president of Iraq, they put forth a narrative about Saddam Hussein having weapons of mass destruction, a story full of colorful details like yellowcake uranium from Africa, and got the entire United States Congress to go along with the lie. The result was an all-out attack against, and invasion of, the sovereign nation that is Iraq.

The defense minister tells the Russian president he has thirty seconds remaining to make a decision.

To launch or not to launch nuclear weapons against the United States.

As in America, launching nuclear weapons is the Russian president's call. It is his and his alone. The chief of the General Staff reminds the president that the Launch on Warning condition has been met. And he reminds the president of his position on nuclear use, from his interview in the Kremlin in 2018.

The president of Russia is furious. The president of the United States has not reached out to him. He sees this not just as an insult, but as a sign of something else. Like many leaders, the Russian leader in this scenario is also prone to paranoia. He now believes Russia is being targeted by America for a decapitation strike.

This fear is deep-seated, going back to Soviet times.

Former *Washington Post* Moscow bureau chief David Hoffman provides a chilling example of just how serious this paranoia was during the Cold War. How fearful Soviet leaders believed America intended to launch a massive, preemptive nuclear strike against Russian Nuclear Command and Control, and to counter that potential, decapitation-style attack, the Soviets developed a system known as the Dead Hand. A system to ensure that if Moscow gets preemptively attacked, nuclear war will not end until Russia's entire arsenal is emptied—to zero.

Officially called Perimeter, the Dead Hand works as an automatic control system made up of seismic sensors capable of detecting a nuclear strike on Russian soil. Should the system perceive it has lost communication with Russia's commanders, the Dead Hand can allegedly launch nuclear weapons on its own. The original blueprint was a "sort of doomsday machine that would launch without any human action at all," Hoffman says. A mechanized system preprogrammed for a final, Armageddon-like series of retaliation strikes. These blueprints have reportedly been refined, but the system is still in use. Whether or not it can launch without an actual human hand remains unknown. But it demonstrates how paranoid a leader in possession of a world-ending arsenal can be.

Après moi, le déluge.

Paranoia is a psychological phenomenon, same as deterrence. The consequences of a paranoid leader's fear of a preemptive decapitation strike are as real as the nuclear weapons themselves. True in this scenario. True in real life.

In this scenario, we don't know why the North Korean leader chose to launch a Bolt out of the Blue attack against America, but paranoia almost most certainly played a role. And now paranoia fuels the Russian president in his decision, one that must be made under threat of a ticking clock.

Faced with what he believes are hundreds of nuclear warheads bearing down on Russian soil—launched by the opportunistic Americans in a preemptive sneak attack—the Russian president chooses to launch.

The military aide opens the Cheget.

The Russian president chooses the most extreme nuclear strike option from Russia's Black Book. He reads the launch codes from a document inside.

As in the U.S., Russia's nuclear weapons can take just minutes to launch.

What is done cannot be undone.

45 MINUTES
Dombarovsky, Russia

Fifty-seven hundred miles from Washington, D.C., at the Dombarovsky ICBM complex in southwestern Siberia, a patch of snow sparkles in the moonlight. It is 12:48 a.m. local time, twenty miles north of Kazakhstan. Barbed-wire fencing and land mines surround the facility, with rings of automated grenade launchers and remote-controlled machine gun installations also keeping guard. As in the U.S. missile fields in Wyoming, there are doors in the earthen floor. Steel silo lids lying flush with the night sky.

To passersby, Dombarovsky is forest service country. Where milk and paper plants supply locals with jobs. To Russian nuclear forces, it is home to the most powerful, most destructive ICBM in the world. The Son of Satan ballistic missile, as it is known in the West. Russia calls these missiles the RS-28 Sarmat, in honor of a tribe of warrior-horsemen from the fifth century BCE. In much the same way, the U.S. calls its ICBMs the Minutemen, an homage to its tribe of warrior-horsemen from the American Revolutionary War. The West calling Russia's ICBMs Sons of Satan helps further the idea they are evil. That Minutemen ICBMs are good and valiant soldiers engineered to defend and protect.

No matter how the nomenclature is spun, these two arsenals of mass destruction are poised and ready to destroy the world. The madness of MAD is that the two sides are like a mirror. Like the myth of Narcissus but with a biblical twist: a madman stares in a pond, sees his image on the surface of the water, and mistakes himself for his enemy. Falling for the illusion, he attacks, slips into the water, and drowns. But not before he unleashes Armageddon first.

The U.S. has 400 ICBMs buried in silos across the land. Russia has 312 ICBMs, in silos and on road-mobile launchers. Unlike America's single-warhead Minutemen missiles, some of Russia's ICBMs can carry up to ten 500-kiloton bombs in each warhead bus. This means a single Son of Satan can transport some 5 megatons of nuclear destruction. Roughly one-half the yield of the Ivy Mike thermonuclear device, which obliterated an entire island in the Pacific, leaving behind a hole the size of fourteen Pentagons.

Russia is the largest country in the world, by far. More than 100 ICBM silos like the ones here in Dombarovsky dot its vast landscape, its eleven time zones. Russia has eleven or twelve ICBM divisions, each staffed by two to six regiments—in Barnaul, Irkutsk, Kozelsk, Novosibirsk, Nizhny Tagil, Tatishchevo, Teykovo, Uzhur, Vypolsovo, Yoshkar-Ola, and Dombarovsky.

Hans Kristensen, the director of the Federation of American Scientists' Nuclear Information Project, along with associates Matt Korda, Eliana Reynolds, and others, keep track of the arsenals of nuclear-armed nations, and release that information annually in the Bulletin of the Atomic Scientists' *Nuclear Notebook*. Arms agreements striving for parity between the two superpowers have reduced stockpiles down from the 1986 all-time high point, when there were almost 70,000 nuclear weapons between the two.

The precise numbers of warheads available for immediate launch are dizzying. In addition to changing each year, they can be counted in different ways, depending on how they are reported—and by whom. As of early 2024, the generally accepted totals (in the West) are as follows:

- Russia's 312 nuclear-armed ICBMs can carry up to 1,197 nuclear warheads, with "around 1,090" on ready-for-launch status.
- The U.S. keeps 400 nuclear weapons loaded onto its 400 ICBMs, all ready for launch.
- The U.S. keeps more of its nuclear weapons loaded onto its Ohio-class submarines, somewhere around 970.
- Russia keeps "about 640" of its nuclear warheads loaded onto its submarine-launched ballistic missiles.

"Parity" means sameness. "Nuclear parity" means the state of being relatively equal. Parity still guarantees the annihilation of everyone on either side.

"We may be likened to two scorpions in a bottle," Robert Oppenheimer once said of the arms race between the U.S. and Russia, "each capable of killing the other, but only at the risk of his own life."

Scorpions as a species will likely survive nuclear war. Arachnida with book lungs have been around for hundreds of millions of years. Scorpions came before the dinosaurs, they lived through the dinosaurs' extinction, and will likely outlive humans. After nuclear World War III, the scorpions' hard shells will protect them from the radiation that will kill off most of the humans who manage to initially survive the fireballs, the blast, and the ensuing firestorms.

Oppenheimer neglected to mention that not every scorpion battle ends in dual death. Sometimes, one wins. These armored predators can also be cannibals. The victorious scorpion sometimes eats the vanquished scorpion, like a prizefighter with a victory meal.

Here in Dombarovsky, at the nuclear launch facility hidden underground, Russian officers with the 13th Orenburg Red Banner Rocket Division prepare for launch. Parity means Russia's launch protocols are almost identical to launch protocols in the U.S.

The Russian president sends nuclear launch codes down the chain of command.

The launch codes are received in thirty-eight or thirty-nine missile regiments across Russia.

Launch officers arm their missiles.

They type in target coordinates. Turn keys.

Across Russia, ICBM silo doors blow open and their missiles launch, one after the next. Road-mobile launchers fire their missiles, one after the next.

All but a few are headed for targets in the United States—1,000 of them.

Russia keeps more than 1,000 nuclear weapons on ready-for-launch status. Here, a Sarmat ICBM—aka "Son of Satan"—test fires from a snowy field in Russia. (Ministry of Defense of the Russian Federation)

45 MINUTES, 1 SECOND
Aerospace Data Facility—Colorado

In space, 22,300 miles above the Earth, car-sized sensors in a constellation of school bus–sized U.S. early-warning satellites see hundreds of Russian ICBMs launch from their missile silos and road-mobile launchers.

In the Aerospace Data Facility in Colorado, the data start coming in across computer screens, like a fist to the throat.

First one, then ten, then a hundred, two hundred, three hundred.

It takes only seconds for the black avatars of hundreds of ICBMs to fill the screens.

There is only one thing to think in this moment.

Only one thing to say.

The Russians have launched.

From the commander, to the analysts, to the systems engineers, everyone in the classified arena here knows instantly there is nothing anyone can do to stop these intercontinental ballistic missiles from striking the United States. Hundreds of millions of Americans are about to die.

There are forty U.S. interceptor missiles remaining (of the original forty-four), thirty-six of them in Alaska, four at Vandenberg Space Force Base. Even if every one of these interceptor missiles were to defy odds and shoot down forty of the incoming warheads deployed by Russian ICBMs, another 960 warheads or so would get through.

The commander of the Aerospace Data Facility picks up the phone and sends a series of encrypted emergency messages to the Doomsday Plane, and to the U.S. Nuclear Command and Control Centers that remain standing.

- The Missile Warning Center inside Cheyenne Mountain in Colorado
- The Global Operations Center beneath Offutt Air Force Base in Nebraska
- Site R, the Alternate National Military Command Center inside Raven Rock Mountain in Pennsylvania

Three facilities that themselves are almost certainly top targets for the incoming Russian ICBMs. In the words of former vice admiral Michael J. Connor, commander of U.S. submarine forces, "anything fixed is destroyable." All personnel in each of these facilities must now prepare for two new things at once:

- To launch a massive nuclear counterattack against Russia
- To withstand a direct hit from one or more nuclear bombs

But who will stay at their posts? Who will cut and run? What matters anymore?

Part IV

THE NEXT (AND FINAL)

24 MINUTES

48 MINUTES

Cheyenne Mountain Complex, Colorado

Inside the brain stem that is Cheyenne Mountain, the commander receives the tracking data and prepares emergency messages for Site R, NORAD, NORTHCOM, and STRATCOM, in a vein similar to what happened when this all began, some forty-eight minutes ago.

On satellite comms, and from their various locations in the air and on the ground, the commanders of U.S. Nuclear Command and Control System are assembled—absent those who were at the Pentagon and are now dead.

From the bunker beneath Site R, in the Blue Ridge Mountains, the secretary of defense and the vice-chairman weigh in. With the launch of the entire Russian ICBM force, the SecDef has been sworn in as acting president.

From the airborne command center inside the Doomsday Plane—still flying in circles above the American Midwest—the STRATCOM commander awaits launch orders from the acting president. The Black Book remains open in front of him.

A review of the attack assessment is short: there are some one thousand Russian nuclear warheads headed for the United States.

There are six minutes to decide which counterattack to execute, but faster is better given the circumstances. Former CIA director General Michael Hayden explains why. Launching all-out nuclear war is "designed for speed and decisiveness," Hayden says. "It's not designed to debate the decision."

Besides, there is more hellfire to come. The dreaded SLBMs from the Russian navy are about to launch.

48 MINUTES, 10 SECONDS
Near Franz Josef Land Archipelago, Arctic Ocean

At the top of world, where the Arctic Ocean meets the Barents Sea, three Russian submarines punch their way through more than five feet of floating sea ice, each one surfacing simultaneously within a few hundred feet of the others, same as three Russian subs did flawlessly in March 2021, during a military drill.

Except, this is not a drill.

Two of the three submarines are the K-114 Tula, with the NATO reporting name Delta-IV. These nuclear-powered, ballistic missile submarines have long served as a workhorse of the Russian submarine fleet. The third is a newer Borei-class sub, faster and stealthier than its Soviet-era predecessors. Each submarine carries sixteen nuclear-tipped missiles; each missile carries four 100-kiloton warheads in each warhead bus, meaning there are 192 warheads here inside these three Russian submarines.

Three submarines. With a payload of 19.2 megatons of explosive yield.

The temperature outside is minus twenty-two degrees Fahrenheit. Winds whip across the submarines' conning towers at seventy miles per hour.

Each submarine begins launching its missiles at five-second intervals.

One missile after the next.

Each SLBM exits its missile tube and takes to the air in powered flight. It takes eighty seconds for each submarine to empty itself of its entire nuclear payload, same as Ted Postol briefed U.S. Navy officials at the Pentagon more than forty years ago, using his cartoonlike drawing as an instruction tool.

The trajectory of some of the SLBMs will send them over the North Pole and down into the continental United States. To predetermined targets that constitute U.S. Nuclear Command and Control.

Other SLBMs will travel due south, on a trajectory that will take them into Europe. To predetermined targets that constitute NATO Nuclear Command and Control, and NATO nuclear-capable bomber bases.

At roughly the same time, and thousands of miles to the southwest, another two conning towers surface, this time in the Atlantic Ocean. Each of these two Russian submarines surfaces just a few hundred miles off the East Coast of America, in locations the U.S. Navy has previously tracked them patrolling. Russian submarines have, of late, traveled so unnervingly close to America's East Coast that the Defense Department included in its Fiscal Year 2021 Budget Request to Congress a map of the alarming tracking data it has gathered on both Russian and Chinese submarines.

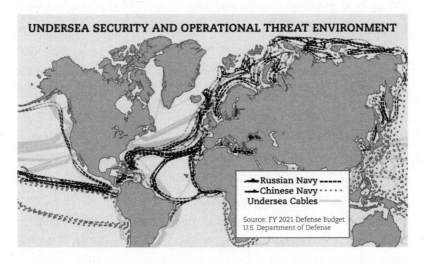

Enemy submarines patrol perilously close to America's shores.
(U.S. Department of Defense; image redrawn by Michael Rohani)

It is the astonishing speed with which ballistic missile submarines can launch nuclear weapons, and hit multiple targets nearly
simultaneously, that makes them the handmaidens of the apocalypse. Time and again, declassified nuclear war games have demonstrated that if deterrence fails, this is how it ends. With Armageddon.
With civilization being destroyed.

The submarines in the Atlantic Ocean fire their ballistic missiles, then drop back down beneath the water and vanish.

To the north, on a floating ice sheet near the Franz Josef Land
archipelago in the Arctic Ocean, three black conning towers, on
three Russian submarines, slip back beneath the whiteness and
disappear.

49 MINUTES
Raven Rock Mountain Complex, Pennsylvania

For U.S. Nuclear Command and Control, launching nuclear
weapons in this moment is not open for debate. All military
protocol and nuclear war doctrine across every decade, since the
invention of deterrence as a concept, indicate the time to launch
is now.

Except for the fact that the secretary of defense—sworn in as
acting president and still suffering from nuclear flash blindness—
has a point to argue. In this scenario, he makes his case from where
he sits in a leather office chair, inside the command bunker in the
Raven Rock Mountain Complex.

SecDef: *As acting president I am in charge of any decision to launch.*

Which is true, technically. What is also true is that the
STRATCOM commander is in possession of the universal
unlock code.

Here inside the bunker, the morale is a mix of shock, furor, and also despair.

"Not a place you want to find yourself," former secretary of defense Leon Panetta tells us. "Where you could be called to the middle of a mountain to deal with a nuclear war." Panetta also served as the director of the CIA and, before that, the White House chief of staff. "There are books, procedures, steps," Panetta explains of a time like this, "lists to tell you what to do in a crisis. But no one prepares for nuclear war."

Deterrence has failed. So have all theoretical war strategies— passively in place for decades—to further the idea that nuclear weapons make the world a safer place. Euphemistic policies like "restoring deterrence," "escalate to de-escalate," and "resolve to restrain." Policies that in this scenario are revealed to be their own ticking nuclear time bombs. Policies that seem destined to have failed. The idea that nuclear strategies like "tailored deterrence" and "flexible retaliation"—policies that promised nuclear war could be stopped after it began—are as full of folly as deterrence itself.

The despair overtaking certain minds in the Site R bunker comes from the terrible reality that has been intuitively known by many for decades. That the only way nuclear war ends is in nuclear holocaust. And now, it is only a matter of minutes until the end.

The STRATCOM commander doesn't see any need to argue. He tells the former secretary of defense, now acting as president, as commander in chief, that he has five minutes remaining to act.

And that the action he needs to take is to open the Black Book.

49 MINUTES, 30 SECONDS
Inside the Doomsday Plane, over Utah

Inside the Doomsday Plane, the STRATCOM commander reviews strike options in the Black Book. He waits for the SecDef to authorize launch, but in name only.

The STRATCOM commander has the universal unlock code in front of him. The STRATCOM commander can, and will, launch retaliatory strikes against Russia.

The STRATCOM commander controls all of the remaining nuclear weapons in the Defense Department's arsenal.

As STRATCOM commander Charles Richard told Congress, in a situation such as this, "Stratcom['s] . . . combat-ready force is prepared now to deliver a decisive response anywhere on the globe, across all domains . . ."

To be clear, "deliver a decisive response" means U.S. Strategic Command is prepared to unleash the full force of America's nuclear triad if it ever receives word of an incoming Russian attack. This means:

- Launch the ICBMs in missile silos across the U.S.
- Launch the SLBMs in Ohio-class submarines on patrol in the Atlantic and the Pacific.
- Get the U.S. bombers loaded and into the air, to drop nuclear (gravity) bombs, and air-launch cruise missiles (ALCMs).
- Get the NATO jet fighters loaded and into the air, to drop nuclear (gravity) bombs.

The long-standing "use them or lose them" strategy moves to the fore.

In roughly eight minutes, hundreds of Russian nuclear-armed SLBMs and ICBMs will begin striking the United States. U.S. Nuclear Command and Control facilities are assumed to be at the top of Russia's target list.

"Use them or lose them" means the U.S. will immediately launch everything in the nuclear triad before its fixed military targets are destroyed in the incoming nuclear attack.

As decisions are being made about which counterstrike option to hit Russia with, the former SecDef, now acting president, vocalizes a crisis-of-conscience debate.

49 MINUTES, 30 SECONDS
Raven Rock Mountain Complex, Pennsylvania

Speaking over the Advanced Extremely High Frequency satellite constellation from inside Site R, the secretary of defense presents his for-the-good-of-humanity idea. That maybe there is no point in killing hundreds of millions of people across the world in Russia. That just because hundreds of millions of innocent Americans are about to die, maybe the other half of humanity— full of so many innocents—does not have to die.

His suggestion gets dismissed without consideration.

In the words of complex systems expert Thomas Schelling, the "rationality of irrationality" has already taken hold. Rule No. 1 in nuclear war is deterrence. That each nuclear-armed nation promises never to use their nuclear weapons unless they are forced to use them. Deterrence is fundamentally predicated against harboring any kind of for-the-good-of-humanity ideas.

"Every capability in the DoD is underpinned by the fact that strategic deterrence will hold," U.S. Strategic Command insists publicly. Until the fall of 2022, this promise was pinned on

STRATCOM's public Twitter feed, then taken down. But to a private audience at Sandia National Laboratories later that same year, STRATCOM's deputy director, Lieutenant General Thomas Bussiere, admitted the danger of deterrence. "Everything unravels itself if those things are not true."

That unraveling has occurred.

In nuclear war there is no such thing as capitulation.

No such thing as surrender.

The only thing left to do is to decide which mass-attack counterstrike option to choose from in the Black Book.

It is from the former ICBM launch officer and nuclear weapons expert Bruce Blair that we know what a U.S. mass-attack counterstrike against Russia might actually look like. Blair's colleague at Princeton University, the physicist Frank von Hippel, explains.

"Until his untimely death in July 2020, Bruce Blair, more than any other outsider, enjoyed the confidence of former leaders of the United States and Russian strategic commands." This allowed Blair to report, in a 2018 monograph, "the most detailed publicly available information" about U.S. nuclear war planning, von Hippel explains. About "primary and secondary aimpoints," also known as targets, in different nuclear-armed countries the U.S. sees as potential adversaries.

Blair wrote: "There are 975 [targets] in Russia spread out across three categories: 525 for nuclear and other WMD [weapons of mass destruction facilities], 250 for [conventional] war-sustaining industry, and 200 for leadership." And that "many targets in all three categories are located in densely populated Russian [. . .] urban areas; 100 such aimpoints dot the greater Moscow landscape alone."

The clock is ticking. The secretary of defense must decide which mass-attack counterstrike option to choose from in the Black Book.

The secretary of defense chooses the most extreme option: Alpha.

Some 975 targets in Russia.

"Russia presumably has a similar set of targets in the United States," von Hippel reminds.

A full-scale nuclear exchange is about to begin. "Maximum warfighting," in the words of Bruce Blair.

The beginning and the end.

50 MINUTES
Inside the Doomsday Plane, over Utah

From inside the Doomsday Plane, the STRATCOM commander relays launch information to the nuclear triad. But he was going to do it anyway. A massive, all-out nuclear counterattack in response to the incoming Russian missiles.

On the ground across America, in ICBM missile fields in Montana, Wyoming, North Dakota, Nebraska, and Colorado, launch officers receive dozens of sets of authorization codes. In a matter of minutes, 350 silo doors will blast open and 350 Minuteman ICBMs, carrying 350 nuclear warheads, will launch. All of them headed for targets in Russia.

At Minot Air Force Base in North Dakota, and at Barksdale Air Force Base in Louisiana, the B-52 nuclear bombers prepare for takeoff. Airmen on the tarmacs race to jump-start the heavy bombers' massive engines—all of them using the cartridge start (or Cart-Start) method. This involves inserting a small, controlled explosive charge into two of each of the B-52s' eight engines, thereby allowing the aircraft to get off the ground faster than the hour or so it usually takes. Black smoke billows out. All remaining engines are started. One by one, each of the bombers joins the ominous elephant walk formation down the tarmac. One by one, they gain speed and take off.

At Whiteman Air Force Base in Missouri, the B-2 nuclear bombers prepare to roll out of their hangars, taxi down runways, and take to the air.

Which leaves the boomers. The nuclear-armed, nuclear-powered submarines. The nightmare machines. The handmaidens of the apocalypse. The vessels of death. Unlocatable by Russian missiles and therefore unstoppable. Nuclear-armed to the teeth.

The navy controls a fleet of fourteen of them, twelve of which are said to be in operation at any given time, in the Atlantic and Pacific Oceans. That two of them are always being overhauled in dry docks: one on the East Coast, at the naval base in Kings Bay, Georgia, the other on the West Coast, at the naval base in Bangor, Washington. In this moment, there are ten boomers at sea.

"Four or five of those are thought to be on 'hard alert,'" Kristensen and Korda report. That the other "four or five boats could be brought to alert status in hours or days."

Every individual, in every Nuclear Command and Control facility across America, prepares for what is about to happen.

They are not preparing for warfighting.

They are preparing to annihilate the other side. And for their own, almost certain, pending deaths.

FEMA will not send out any more messages.

America's 332 million–plus citizens will now be left completely in the dark.

51 MINUTES
NATO Airbases, Europe

At minute 51 in this scenario, at NATO airbases across Europe—in Belgium, Germany, the Netherlands, Italy, and

Turkey—the pilots who have been waiting inside hardened aircraft shelters, ready for combat, now receive orders to launch.

"The special alarm sounds," says retired F-16 air force pilot Colonel Julian Chesnutt, formerly stationed at the nuclear-capable NATO base in Aviano, Italy. "The scramble order comes down. The order that alerts pilots to nuclear mission."

Russian SLBMs are coming for them. In a matter of minutes they will strike.

NATO's nuclear bombs come out of the WS3 vaults. They are loaded onto NATO aircraft.

"NATO pilots know their bases are a primary target," aviation journalist (and former second lieutenant in the Italian Air Force) David Cenciotti tells us. "They know they have to get up into the air, fast." That what they are now facing amounts to "suicide missions."

"Nuclear mission pilots have a single target, maybe a secondary one," says Chesnutt, who was once awarded the Silver Star for gallantry in combat. And each nuclear pilot knows everything about his or her one route. "You train and train on that. You've memorized every ground feature of note. You're assuming your GPS has been jammed, and you're working entirely on inertial navigation and map memory."

Overflying Russia to drop a nuclear gravity bomb means facing down Russian radar systems (NATO aircraft are not stealth like the B-2 bomber). "Russian radars can see you," Chesnutt says, "they can track you, and will likely shoot you down. And since there's no way to defeat the Russian radar, you have to fly really low." As in just a couple of hundred feet above the ground.

NATO pilots are trained for nuclear war.

Chesnutt describes a Cold War tactic: "Just a few miles off target, you pop up and release your [nuclear] weapon. There's a parachute attached to it, that slows down the bomb as it falls." The bomb falling by parachute allows NATO pilots a little extra time to try to get out of the area. "To try and beat the nuclear blast wave." Newer model nuclear bombs glide to the target without a parachute.

"They have to get extremely close to the actual target," Cenciotti clarifies.

Most NATO pilots accept there is little hope of realistic return.

"You burn a lot of fuel at low altitude," Chesnutt tells us, "thousands of pounds of gas an hour. So, by the time you get on target, you're running out of fuel."

There will be no U.S. Air Force tanker available for midair refueling. "You have to assume your fuel tanker is shot down."

Nuclear war is final, Chesnutt says.

"And besides," he adds, "after delivering a nuclear weapon, you'd have to ask yourself, is there anything you really can come back to?"

With launch orders from the UK prime minister and now also from the acting president of the United States in place, across Europe, NATO pilots race down the tarmacs and take to the air.

52 MINUTES
Pyongyang, North Korea

Thirty-two U.S. submarine-launched nuclear warheads, transported by MIRVed Trident missiles and guided by star sighting, arrive on their targets in North Korea a little over fourteen minutes after emerging from beneath the sea, in the Pacific, somewhere north of Tinian Island. The destruction of Pyongyang, North Korea's capital city, is absolute. A majority of the city's 3 million residents are incinerated.

Each W88 nuclear warhead strikes its designated target with a precision that Sandia National Laboratories in New Mexico has boasted publicly about, for decades. "[The warhead] always works

when we want it to and never when we don't," program manager
Dolores Sanchez says of the W88. "The arming, fuzing [*sic*], and
firing assembly [are] the brains of the warhead," and a Sandia
warhead is very smart.

The W88 warheads have a yield of 455 kilotons each. The bomb
that destroyed Hiroshima was 15 kilotons; Nagasaki was 21 kilotons. The amount of explosive power that strikes North Korea in
this scenario is almost too much for the mind to comprehend. As
President Kennedy once remarked after a briefing on likely nuclear
death tolls: "And we call ourselves the human race."

MIRV stands for multiple independently targetable reentry
vehicle, which means very little to most people—and certainly
nothing to the millions of people the MIRVs will kill—and yet it
has meant quite a lot to nuclear war planners and defense analysts
over decades past.

A MIRV, like its acronym states, is a weapon system that carries
multiple nuclear warheads in its warhead bus—each one capable
of striking an independent target, including ones hundreds of miles
apart. If MIRV minutia seems like too much detail to consider
when the world is about to end, it is important because it helps
explain how fast global nuclear war unfolds. How tragic and ironic
it is that human beings developed slow and steady over hundreds
of thousands of years, culminating in the creation of vast and complex civilizations, only to get zeroed out in a war that takes less
than a few hours from beginning to end.

Since the 1960s, when MIRVs first came to be, an estimated
hundreds of billions of dollars have been spent designing, developing, expanding, and perfecting MIRV technology. On indus-
trializing and mass-producing MIRVs. And then, after the arms
reduction talks of the 1980s, the world's nuclear experts decided
MIRVs were "destabilizing" to world peace. And so, tens of billions
more U.S. taxpayer dollars were spent de-MIRVing the MIRVs.

"This step," proclaimed the U.S. Defense Department in one of its Nuclear Posture Reviews, "will enhance the stability of the nuclear balance by reducing the incentives for either side to strike first."

After thousands of U.S. MIRVed ICBMs were designed, built, siloed, and pointed at the other side, it was decided a MIRVed missile in an underground silo was too "lucrative" a target. The logic went like this. If one ICBM in, say, Wyoming contained ten warheads in its nose cone, that silo was (or could be) seen as too tempting of a target for an enemy to destroy with a preemptive nuclear strike.

Lots of arguments later, the MIRVs were disarmed, dismantled, deconstructed, disposed of; some of them were destroyed. But only the MIRVs on land. In the submarines, the nuclear missiles were deemed okay to remain MIRVed, for a strange logic that went like this. A nuclear submarine is not really a target because it can't be located, it being stealthy and under the sea. And so, missiles on Ohio-class submarines have remained MIRVed.

And now it is a legion of these MIRVed Tridents that strikes North Korea in the first U.S. nuclear counterstrike against the nation that recklessly and foolishly—and why, we simply don't know—started nuclear World War III in this scenario.

In the words of John Rubel, a mass extinction event is underway.

The first nuclear bombs to hit North Korea strike the supreme leader's known residences in and around Pyongyang. These palaces and villas double as military headquarters, and are therefore considered by U.S. war planners to be central components of North Korea's Nuclear Command and Control.

Residence No. 55, the Central Luxury Mansion in the Ryongsong District, is hit. The leader's private train station, the man-made lakes, and the anti-artillery sites guarding the palace here, they all get vaporized in the nuclear bomb blast. The same goes for the horses waiting in the stables and the children swimming in the pool.

Everything in a three-mile-diameter ring is mowed down, all the people incinerated, all things ablaze. This horror will happen eighty-one more times in the next few minutes.

Residence No. 15, in Jungsung-dong, is struck. Its fireball destroys the adjoining Central Committee of the Party Complex, its cavern of underground tunnels and bunkers below. Residence No. 85, in East Pyongyang, is hit. Its fields of domesticated deer and fishing ponds are there one instant, gone the next. Residence No. 16, in the central district, is obliterated, as is the Party Research Facility and everyone working there, next door. The Ryokpo and Samsok Residences in the western suburbs disappear in fire and blast, as does the lakeside residence at Kangdong, a summer retreat nineteen miles north of Kim Il Sung Square.

Mushroom clouds stretch out over the city and merge into a dense mass of particulates. Of organic and inorganic matter. Particles of humans and buildings and bridges and cars, all cremated on the spot. Between the fireballs, the blast, and the several-hundred-mile-per-hour winds, the city is flattened end to end. By nightfall, all 772 square miles of Pyongyang, known locally as the Capital of the Revolution, will be engulfed in a mega-cyclone of fire that burns and burns until there is nothing left to burn.

Gone is the city's Russian-style architecture, its high-rise apartment buildings, its orderly grid. Gone are Pyongyang's people on bicycles, on foot, in cars. People standing, sleeping, pausing, brushing their teeth are all killed in nuclear flash, fire, and blast. Nuclear weapons destroy everyone, and everything, in Kim Il Sung Square, in the Mansudae Assembly Hall, in the First of May Stadium, the Juche Tower, the Arch of Triumph, the Ryugyong Hotel (also known as Building 105), the 105-story-tall unfinished, pyramid-shaped skyscraper designed as a middle finger to the West. Come nightfall, everything from the Sunan International Airport to the Korea Bay will be reduced to barren, smoldering soil.

As in Washington, D.C., millions of people have been incinerated on the go, melted into streets and surfaces, sucked into hurricanes of fire. People have been impaled by flying shards and crushed under buildings. Everywhere, human beings are screaming and burning and hemorrhaging to death. The destruction, pain, and suffering here is identical to the destruction, pain, and suffering halfway across the world in the United States. And one must accept—and understand—that this is all but a speck of the mass carnage to follow, worldwide.

Across North Korea, twenty more nuclear bombs strike the nation's nuclear facilities. The Yongbyon Nuclear Scientific Research Center, in the central northwest, explodes in a nuclear fireball. This place houses a radiochemical lab, a uranium enrichment plant, and two nuclear reactors. And so, precisely what happened in Diablo Canyon roughly thirty minutes ago now happens here: nuclear core materials melt down. The Devil's Scenario.

To strike a nuclear reactor with any explosive weapon violates Rule 42 of the International Committee of the Red Cross. But nuclear war has no rules.

If you win, you need not have to explain.

With core meltdowns underway, and with the facility's spent fuel rods spewing out a radioactive witches' brew, the land here has also now become uninhabitable for an interminable amount of time.

Along the country's northwestern coast, the Sohae Satellite Launching Station and its ICBM engine test facility are struck with nuclear bombs. Sohae, located seventy miles northwest of Pyongyang, is just thirty miles from Dandong, China, population 2 million. If China intended on staying out of this conflict, the sudden killing or wounding of hundreds of thousands of Chinese citizens will now drag China and its arsenal of 410 nuclear weapons into this rapidly unfolding, all-out nuclear war.

In North Korea's northern region, a nuclear bomb strikes the

Punggye-ri nuclear test site, where underground tests conducted between 2006 and 2017 allowed North Korea to transform purchased or stolen nuclear plans into the sprawling nuclear weapons program that started this war. Punggye-ri is 110 miles from the Russian border, with Russia's port city of Vladivostok just another 85 miles north. Kangson, a clandestine uranium enrichment site along the Pyongyang-Nampo Expressway, is hit. As is Sino-ri, an undeclared missile base in the mountains. Sangnam-ni and Musudan-ri missile launching sites, also within range of the Russian border, are struck in rapid succession. In a few more minutes an additional fifty ICBMs will strike North Korea, the fifty ICBMs that Russia mistook as 100 or more coming for them.

In a matter of minutes, eighty-two nuclear warheads kill millions of North Korean citizens, none of whom did anything to bring any of this upon themselves; same as the Americans killed minutes ago in Washington, D.C., and around Diablo Canyon, did nothing personally to harm those now dead and dying halfway across the world.

U.S. submarine–launched Trident missiles are a beast of a weapon system. The namesake, the trident, is a three-pronged pole arm created by humans for spearfishing, or for combat against other humans—we have no way of knowing which came first. How old the trident actually is in conception, no one knows that, either. Prehistoric, for sure. Humans' ability to do science has helped humans refine killing. Helped us evolve from a hand-to-hand warfighter to one who can push a button, or turn a key, and kill millions of people on the other side of the world.

What will become of humanity after nuclear war? The dinosaurs had a 165-million-year run. They came, they dominated, they evolved. Then an asteroid hit Earth and the dinosaurs went extinct (not counting their descendants, birds). No trace of the killer reptiles was found by anyone, that we know of, for 66 million

years. Until just a few hundred years ago, in 1677, when the director of Oxford's Ashmolean Museum, Robert Plot, found a dinosaur
femur in the village of Cornwall and drew it for a science journal,
misidentifying the bone as belonging to a giant.

After nuclear war, who, if anyone, will know we were once here?

52 MINUTES
Mt. Paektu, North Korea

N orth Korea's leader is nowhere near Pyongyang. He is in a
bunker 1,900 feet below Mt. Paektu in Samjiyon County,
North Korea. A bunker that is understood to be as close to being
nuclear bomb–proof as any of the nuclear bunkers in Russia or the
United States.

Mt. Paektu is an active stratovolcano that last erupted more
than 1,000 years ago. Its emerald water caldera, called Heaven
Lake, has long been entwined with state propaganda. In stories
that require North Koreans to pretend its rulers are semidivine. In
this scenario, it is in this bunker beneath Heaven Lake mountain
where North Korea's supreme leader intends to ride out nuclear
war. He may die in the process, but such is the life of a mad king.
Après moi, le déluge.

For decades, North Korea's leaders have constructed vast underground facilities (UGFs in military parlance) for themselves to hide
out in before, during, and after a nuclear exchange. "North Korea's
UGF program is the largest and most fortified in the world," the
Defense Intelligence Agency reported in 2021, "estimated to con-
sist of thousands of UGFs and bunkers designed to withstand U.S.
bunker-buster bombs." This network of subterranean buildings is
said to be connected internally by railways and roads, some with
remote-controlled bridges and movable gates. "The entire nation

must be made into a fortress," Supreme Leader Kim Il Sung publicly proclaimed in 1963. "We must dig into the ground to protect ourselves."

Defectors recount stories of polished marble walkways, escape hatches, and tunnel shafts interconnecting these underground warrens. North Korea's leadership has enough food, water, and medical supplies, they say, to hide out underground for years, or even decades. That these bunkers have backup generators and air circulation systems to allow the regime to remain alive, cut off from a postnuclear-war world for as long as necessary. That the Supreme Leader keeps with him a tunnel-boring machine, so that he can choose when, where, and how he will eventually dig himself out of the nuclear rubble.

During the Cold War, when Russia was the country's main benefactor, Soviet scientists shared with their fellow communists the engineering techniques that made all this tunneling possible. That enabled North Korea to build some of the best underground fortresses in the world. In the 1960s, Soviet scientists used as a metric the fact that a U.S. bomber, carrying a B-53 bomb with a 9-megaton yield, could destroy a facility built down to 1,889 feet, "in wet soil or wet soft rock." Which may explain why the bunker beneath Mt. Paektu has been built 1,900 feet underground.

It is 4:55 a.m. local time here at Mt. Paektu. The Supreme Leader is briefed by his advisors about what is going on in the United States. How Washington, D.C., has been destroyed, how the Devil's Scenario is underway on the California coast, how many people are dead. Like the president of Russia, North Korea's leader is said to obsessively watch news of the Western world on satellite TV. By now—just fifty-two minutes into this scenario—many channels have ceased broadcasting in the U.S., which means the leader's access to information is extremely limited. The North Korean military has no early-warning system of its own, not in the air or on the ground. "Communication in and out of Mt. Paektu relies entirely on an embedded telephonic system," Michael Madden tells us, "like the old-school landlines. The Supreme Leader only knows what is happening in his own country based on what his advisors, the Personal Secretariat, tell him is going on."

Still, the Supreme Leader in this scenario all but expected Pyongyang to be leveled in a massive nuclear counterstrike. And he is not yet done wreaking havoc. He holds a wild card that he intends to use. Nuclear bombs cause other kinds of mass destruction when creatively applied. Now North Korea's leader intends on settling a score.

It has been nearly a decade since the West released that satellite image of the Korean peninsula at night. The one with the northern half (North Korea) looking dark and foreboding with barely any electric lights but with the southern half (South Korea) looking shiny and bright. To a mad king, this comparing image was like a poke in the eye. For weeks after the picture was released, in international news stories, the West ridiculed North Korea as being an "electricity-poor" country that was "energy bankrupt." What happens next is revenge for that insult.

North Korea's Supreme Leader is in possession of a nuclear weapon engineered to strip the United States of its energy. To show the world what "electricity-poor" can really mean.

For decades, the U.S. EMP Commission—formally known as the Commission to Assess the Threat to the United States from Electromagnetic Pulse (EMP) Attack—has been warning Congress about the catastrophic dangers of a nuclear weapon exploded directly over the homeland, in the upper atmosphere or in space. The EMP Commission has, for decades, asserted that a high-altitude EMP attack will damage or destroy America's entire block power grid.

The degree of danger this weapon poses to the U.S. has been the subject of vitriolic debate. "This is the favorite nightmare scenario of a small group of very dedicated people," one pundit told NPR in 2017. At a congressional hearing that same year, "Empty Threat or Serious Danger? Assessing North Korea's Risk to the Homeland," the EMP Commission doubled down on its warning, submitting written testimony entitled "North Korea Nuclear EMP Attack: An Existential Threat."

Former CIA officer and the EMP Commission's long-serving chief of staff Dr. Peter Pry said in an interview for this book shortly before his death in 2022, "If North Korea detonates a high-altitude EMP over America, it's Electric Armageddon."

If.

52 MINUTES, 30 SECONDS
Redstone Arsenal, Huntsville, Alabama

Inside the Army Space and Missile Defense Command headquarters at Redstone Arsenal near Huntsville, Alabama—birthplace of America's ICBM—the commander watches on a radar screen as a North Korean satellite moves into position. The satellite in this scenario is similar to one launched by North Korea on February 6, 2016, and known as KMS-4 (Kwangmyongsong-4), or Bright Star-4. In the West, the KMS-4 identifier was NORAD 41332, which allowed interested parties to track its orbit around Earth, which people did until June 30, 2023, when it fell out of orbit and decayed.

NORAD ID: 41332
Int'l Code: 2016-009A
Perigee: 421.1 km
Apogee: 441.4 km
Inclination: 97.2°

Period: 93.1 minutes
Semi major axis: 6802 km
RCS: Unknown
Launch date: February 7, 2016
Source: North Korea (NKOR)
Launch site: Yunsong, DPRK (YUN)

As the commander here at Redstone watches the radar screen, he and everyone else in this room fear they are about to watch this satellite explode. Or, more precisely, watch the satellite detonate. That they are just moments away from witnessing what the EMP Commission has been warning various Senate and House committees about since its first report in 2004. That this kind of satellite might not be a reconnaissance or communications satellite, as North Korea has claimed, but a small nuclear weapon orbiting the Earth, ready to detonate on command over the United States—in the ionosphere, and destroy the entire U.S. power grid.

It was in 2012 that high-altitude EMP fears widened beyond the commission and into the mainstream. That is when a NASA rocket scientist turned NBC News space consultant named Jim Oberg visited North Korea to investigate the idea that North Korea was developing an EMP weapon. Oberg was initially skeptical about what he'd heard. "There [had] been fears expressed that North Korea might use a satellite to carry a small nuclear warhead into orbit and then detonate it over the United States for an EMP strike," Oberg wrote in the *Space Review.*

Trained as a nuclear weapons engineer, Oberg says he initially thought "these concerns seem[ed] extreme and [would] require an astronomical scale of irrationality on the part of the regime." But after traveling to North Korea to examine the country's satellite control facilities and hardware, Oberg reported back that he'd changed his mind. He became convinced that what he saw, in fact, presented an existential threat to the United States.

Oberg called it the Doomsday Scenario.

"The most frightening aspect," Oberg wrote of what he witnessed, "is that exactly such a scale of insanity is now evident in the rest of [North Korea's] 'space program.' That Doomsday Scenario . . . has become plausible enough to compel the United States to take active measures" to stop such a thing, Oberg warned. To make sure that a North Korean satellite, capable of carrying a small nuclear warhead, never "be allowed to reach orbit and ever overfly the United States."

But no actions were taken and in February 2016 North Korea successfully launched this kind of satellite into space—a satellite with a payload big enough to carry a small nuclear warhead. North Korean officials insisted it was carrying a 470-megahertz UHF radio payload into orbit, designed only to broadcast patriotic songs to its citizens. And maybe it was. But the satellite's orbit was an unusual south-to-north orbit, one that allowed it to fly directly over the United States, including over Washington, D.C., and New York City. The following year, North Korea published a technical paper called "The EMP Might of Nuclear Weapons," zeroing out the idea they were being assigned a military intention they did not possess.

Oberg's Doomsday Scenario was lining up as possible.

Behind closed doors, EMP Commission officials again briefed Congress. "Russia, China, and North Korea now have the capability to conduct a nuclear EMP attack against the U.S. All have practiced or described contingency plans to do so," the commissioners warned. This technology was now being referred to in open-source literature as "'Super' EMP weapons."

Writing in the Cipher Brief (a media outlet staffed by former directors of the CIA, DIA, NSA, and others), Pry got more specific.

North Korea's satellites, he wrote, "resemble a Russian secret weapon developed during the Cold War called the Fractional Orbital Bombardment System (FOBS)," a weapon system "that would have used a nuclear-armed satellite to make a surprise EMP attack on the United States." As EMP Commission chairman, Pry was privy to information gleaned at a classified briefing in which two "very senior Russian generals" warned this "Super EMP knowledge had been transferred to North Korea," Congress heard.

Ambassador Henry Cooper, former director of the U.S. Missile Defense Agency, went on record with his worst-case-scenario fears regarding a high-altitude electromagnetic pulse detonated over the United States: "The result could be to shut down the U.S. electric power grid for an indefinite period, leading to the death within a year of up to 90 percent of all Americans."

In 2021, U.S. Strategic Command conducted more than 360 nuclear command and control exercises and war games. How many involved nuclear war with North Korea remains classified. How many involved high-altitude EMP weapons is also classified, as are all Intelligence Community reports on Super-EMP threats. But we know from Richard Garwin—architect of the first thermonuclear weapon, and one of the longest-serving advisors to the Defense Department—that mad king logic concerns U.S. Nuclear Command and Control.

In mad king logic, in this scenario, it follows that North Korea's supreme leader wants to cripple the United States in an act of revenge. Wants to set America back to a time before there was electricity, before modern weapon systems existed. Before America had weapons of mass destruction and could fight push-button, or turn-key, wars.

The mad king in this scenario intends to set America back to pre-electric times. When it left other countries alone. When kings across the world had vast armies and fought their neighbors directly to reclaim conquered lands. All without the threat of America getting involved.

North Korea's stated goal since the 1950s has been reunification with the South, by force. And now, from deep inside a bunker beneath Mt. Paektu, the mad king prepares to detonate a high-altitude EMP weapon already flying in an orbit over the United States. He must wait for several more minutes for the space satellite to get into the exact right position.

In the meantime, the mad king in this scenario attacks Seoul.

53 MINUTES
Osan Air Base, Republic of Korea (South Korea)

Inside an underground command bunker at Osan Air Base in South Korea, the U.S. commander stares at satellite images and video streams from surveillance drones keeping watch on the border with the North, less than fifty miles away.

Outside, on Osan's tarmac, most of the F-16 Fighting Falcons and A-10 Thunderbolts await combat. Some are already in the air, flying sorties over the Yellow Sea. Others remain lined up on the tarmac, waiting for launch clearance. Waiting until after the attacking Trident nuclear missiles and incoming ICBMs finish their job against the North.

The commander watches the screen. That North Korea hides its jet fighters in underground bases inside its mountainous terrain is well known to the U.S. military, and it hides road-mobile launch vehicles in a similar fashion. North Korean ground forces "operate thousands of long-range artillery and rocket systems along the entire length of the DMZ," wrote Defense Intelligence Agency analysts in a 2021 monograph. And that this is an ever present, existential threat. "Collectively this capability holds South Korean citizens and a large number of U.S. and South Korean military installations at risk," the Pentagon's intelligence agency warned. "The North could use this capability to inflict severe damage and heavy casualties on the South with little warning."

And in this scenario, it is about to.

In a well-rehearsed salvo, out from its camouflaged bases stream dozens, then hundreds, of North Korean launch vehicles. They move into position, stop, and begin firing off hundreds, and then thousands, of small- and medium-sized rockets.

In forested areas nearby, railcars stop on their tracks.

Their tops slide open.

Scores of Hwasong-9 (Scud-ER/Scud-D) short-range missiles launch from out of these rail-mobile launchers, on a trajectory into the South. All at once. All headed for three targets: Osan Air Base, Camp Humphreys, and the center of Seoul.

More than 10,000 artillery shells and 240-millimeter rockets fly toward South Korea in a colossal, coordinated, mass-casualty attack.

The weapons of mass destruction loaded into these small rockets are not nuclear weapons, they are chemical weapons. "North Korea has a chemical warfare (CW) program that could comprise up to several thousand metric tons of chemical warfare agents, and the capability to produce nerve, blister, blood, and choking agents," Defense Intelligence Agency analysts warned in their 2021 report.

The U.S. commander at Osan watches what is happening in real time. Outside, in a ring around the Osan Air Base, America's billion-dollar Terminal High Altitude Area Defense system detects this barrage of incoming missiles. Its systems alert and react. THAAD's anti-missile missiles fire, but in vain.

More than 10,000 projectiles coming in from the north are far too many for THAAD to engage. THAAD systems see a few of the Scuds and manage to shoot several of them down. But the smaller rockets firing out of the North Korean 240-millimeter launchers are just nine and a half inches wide, the diameter of a standard dinner plate. Too thin for the THAAD system to accurately identify, let alone engage, en masse.

THAAD fails. Again, and again.

"THAAD can handle one or a few missiles at a time," military historian Reid Kirby tells us. But Osan, Camp Humphreys, and Seoul are being targeted by thousands of projectiles filled with Sarin nerve agent. In an article for the *Bulletin of the Atomic Scientists*, Kirby did the math on what would happen in what he terms a "Sea of Sarin" attack, basing casualty rates "on a generalized application of how chemical weapons operate." Using a "likely overall rate of . . . 10,800 rounds every 15 minutes," Kirby calculates, coupled with the fact that "the Sarin payload of each 240 mm rocket is known to be 8 kilograms per rocket," and while also taking into consideration "misfires and duds . . ." Kirby maintains that a 240-ton Sarin attack on South Korea would inflict a 25 percent casualty rate on Seoul. The casualty numbers are horrific: between 650,000 and 2.5 million civilians dead, with another 1 to 4 million more injured.

For survivors of a nerve agent attack, the outcome is gruesome. "A fair number might enter a persistent vegetative state due to anoxia," or lack of oxygen, Kirby says.

54 MINUTES
Boyds, Maryland

In America, in the rural, unincorporated community of Boyds, Maryland, the president lies on the forest floor, bleeding out. He is helpless and forlorn. The creeks in the area flood this time of year, and he can hear the nearby rush and flow of water.

The earth around him is cold and damp. He has wet himself from trauma and shock.

Will anyone find him here?

The president hears, or thinks he hears, the rotor blades on a quick reaction force helicopter circling overhead, looking for him. But the trees around him include evergreens, and the canopy is dense. They cannot, and will not, see him.

In books about Vietnam, soldiers and airmen stuck in a similar position as he is now—stuck among the trees in the jungles of Vietnam and Laos, that is—were often rescued by daring helicopter pilots and crews. It was not just luck that saved these men, although luck can sometimes play a powerful part. Men in combat in Vietnam were taught to carry on their person a small piece of mirror—a means to signal for help should they get separated or lost. The president is not equipped with anything like that. Not since George H. W. Bush has a U.S. president seen combat. America's twenty-first-century presidents have grown accustomed to being taken care of by teams of people who satisfy their every need.

The president shouts in the forest, but no one can hear him scream.

55 MINUTES
Redstone Arsenal, Huntsville, Alabama

I n Huntsville, Alabama, the commander is on his feet, watching what is happening on the radar screen in front of him. He is there at the moment when a satellite—similar to the KMS-4 satellite Bright Star-4—all of a sudden explodes.

There is only one thing to think in this moment. Only one thing to say.

North Korea just detonated a Super-EMP.

The electricity surges, then ceases to flow. This is a military facility, which means backup generators kick in without interruption.

But everyone here knows that generators run on fuel and that the electric pumping of fuel has just come to a permanent and fatal end.

▪

55 MINUTES, 10 SECONDS
The Doomsday Scenario

Inside the bunker beneath Mt. Paektu, North Korea's Supreme Leader is told that the Super-EMP weapon has detonated as planned. Like a nuclear sword of Damocles hanging overhead, it was hidden in a reconnaissance satellite overflying the U.S. on a south-to-north orbit all this time.

The weapon exploded at an altitude of 300 miles above the United States. Over Omaha, Nebraska.

The Doomsday Scenario has come to pass.

An electromagnetic pulse weapon detonated in the ionosphere does not harm people, animals, or plants on the ground. It is silent. In space there is no atmosphere to carry sound. An EMP weapon causes no structural damage. For the millions of Americans sheltered inside the basements of their homes, had nuclear bombs not just destroyed Washington, D.C., and Diablo Canyon in California, the situation might seem like just another power outage at first. But this is not that.

Steven Wax, chief scientist for the Defense Threat Reduction Agency (an organization that began as part of the Manhattan Project), warned in 2016, "A nuclear detonation at an altitude of five hundred kilometers [300 miles] over Omaha, Nebraska, will generate an EMP that covers the contiguous landmass of the United States."

The Super-EMP delivers a three-phased (E1, E2, and E3) electromagnetic shockwave so powerful that industrial-strength surge suppressors and lightning arresters designed to block high-voltage spikes are rendered useless, all at once. "The pulse passes through all but the most hardened, military-grade safety devices as if they weren't even there," says Jeffrey Yago, an electrical engineer, military consultant, and advisor to EMP Commission chief Dr. Peter Pry.

"An air-burst EMP would be a devastating blow," America's former cyber chief, retired Brigadier General Gregory J. Touhill tells us. And that few people can really comprehend the devastating reality of EMP because they do not have access to the government's classified information. "Twenty-six years ago I wrote a monograph about an EMP event," Touhill says. "It's still classified."

The high-altitude EMP weapon that just exploded over Nebraska in this scenario damages or destroys major portions of all three of America's electrical grids—the West Coast grid, the East Coast grid, and the Texas grid—all at once. And as a result, one after the next, the nation's system of interconnected, extra-high-voltage transformers begins to fail. "[When] the pulse hits, it sends the equipment out of control. Out of sync," says Touhill. "It's the EMP collateral effects [that] are the problem."

Across the United States, these collateral effects are apocalyptic. Electric Armageddon unfurls.

Twenty-first-century America is a complex system of systems powered by electricity and engineered with microprocessing chips. The nation's approximately 11,000 utility-scale electric power plants, 22,000 generators, and 55,000 substations experience a massive, calamitous, cascade-type failure. Huge swaths of America's 642,000 miles of high-voltage transmission lines and its 6.3 million miles of distribution lines begin to shut down.

The nation's transportation system is crippled near simultaneously. Of America's 280 million registered vehicles, "10 percent of the vehicles on the road [are] suddenly not running anymore," EMP commissioner Dr. William Graham warned the Senate

Armed Services Committee in 2008—long before America's cars and trucks were engineered with so many electronic microprocessing components.

Without power steering or electric brakes, vehicles coast to a stop or crash into other vehicles, into buildings, into walls. Stalled and crashed vehicles block lanes of traffic on roads and bridges everywhere, no longer just in places where people have been fleeing nuclear bombs but in tunnels and on overpasses, on big and small roads, in driveways and in parking lots across the nation. There is pandemonium everywhere. America is already under nuclear attack. There is no way to flee. No way to escape. Being stuck in a country-wide traffic jam without any electric power affects is a nightmare for millions of travelers. But a far more devastating sequence of events is underway and cannot be stopped: America's control system architecture begins to fail.

"The real problem . . . with EMP," physicist and architect of the Ivy Mike thermonuclear device Richard Garwin tells us, are "SCADA systems going down." (Garwin's seminal 1954 paper on EMP is still classified).

SCADA stands for Supervisory Control and Data Acquisition, a computer-based, human-interfaced control system architecture that gathers and analyzes industrial equipment information across America's critical infrastructure sectors, then delivers that information to the people working within the system, allowing them to do their jobs. "SCADA going down becomes an instant out-of-control nightmare," says Yago. "SCADA systems supervise the logic controllers that interface with machinery at every major and minor industrial plant across the United States." SCADA systems control railroad routers, lift-gates on dams, gas and oil refinery transmissions, assembly lines, air traffic control, port facilities, fiber optics, GPS systems, hazardous materials, the defense industry's industrial base in entirety.

Without SCADA systems working, all hell breaks loose, all at once. SCADA systems regulate everything from boiler pressure at manufacturing plants to the mixing of chemicals at water treatment facilities across America. SCADA systems control ventilation and filtering systems, open and close valves, control large motors and pumps, switch electronic circuits on and off. With the failure of SCADA systems, thousands of subway trains, passenger trains, and freight trains traveling in every direction, many on the same tracks, collide with one another, crash into walls and barriers, or derail. Elevators stop between floors, or speed to the ground and crash. Satellites (including the international space station) shift out of position and begin falling to Earth. America's fifty-three remaining nuclear power plants, all now operating on backup systems, have just begun to collectively run out of time.

In the air, the effects are unconditionally nightmarish. It is peak operating time for commercial aircraft across the United States. Thousands of commercial airplanes using fly-by-wire technology systems lose wing and tail controls, lose cabin pressure and landing gear, lose instrument landing systems as they head violently toward the ground. One class of passenger aircraft is mercifully spared, namely the older model 747s, used by the Defense Department for its Doomsday Planes. "747 pilots still use a foot pedal and a yoke, mechanically linked to the control surfaces," Yago tells us. "There's no fly-by-wire technology there."

The critical infrastructure systems on the ground fail in succession. Without SCADA systems controlling the more than 2.6 million miles of pipeline through which America's oil and gas products flow, millions of valves rupture and explode. Combustion sensors on coal-fired boiler systems suffer the wrong mix of air and fuel, causing them to ignite and blow. With the motorized valves on America's water-delivery systems no longer under anyone's control, billions of gallons of water passing through America's aqueducts surge uncontrollably. Dams burst. Mass flooding begins sweeping infrastructure and people away.

There will be no more fresh water. No more toilets to flush. No sanitation. No streetlights, no tunnel lights, no lights at all, only candles, until there are none left to burn. No gas pumps, no fuel. No ATMs. No cash withdrawals. No access to money. No cell phones. No landlines. No calling 911. No calls at all. No emergency communication systems except some high-frequency (HF) radios. No ambulance services. No hospital equipment that works. Sewage spills out everywhere. It takes less than fifteen minutes for disease-carrying insects to swarm. To feed on piles of human waste, on garbage, on the dead.

America's complex system of systems comes to a sudden, apocalyptic halt. In the ensuing fear and mayhem, people revert to their most basic, mammalian instincts. To using their five senses, their hands, and their feet. People everywhere sense imminent danger all around. They sense that whatever just happened is the beginning of the savagery, not the end.

People abandon their vehicles and begin to flee on foot. They exit buildings, run down stairs, and outdoors. People in subway trains and on buses, in halted elevator cars, work to pry open emergency exits and doors. They crawl, walk, and run for their lives.

The most basic human instinct is to survive. Evolution got us this far. From hunter-gatherers to men on the moon. From spear fishermen to people who sing "Happy Birthday" to one another, across continents, on Zoom.

Humans are wired to advance. Humans do whatever it takes.

And yet, nuclear war zeros it all out.

Nuclear weapons reduce human brilliance and ingenuity, love and desire, empathy and intellect, to ash.

In this moment, the most horrifying part of the shock and the despair is revelation, about what life will be like from this second forward. Followed by the stark realization that no one did anything substantial to prevent nuclear World War III. That this didn't have to happen.

And now it is too late.

Apes on a Treadmill

One day in 1975 *Foreign Policy* magazine published an essay written by a defense official turned nuclear disarmament advocate named Paul C. Warnke. This essay, called "Apes on a Treadmill," remains prescient to this day. In it, Warnke criticized not only how insanely dangerous nuclear weapons are, but how wasteful the entire nuclear arms race is, and always has been. He called it a "'monkey see, monkey do' phenomenon," with all participants copying one another's aggressive moves, and getting absolutely nowhere, like unintelligent beasts.

Even worse, Warnke pointed out, was that the runners in the race didn't seem to realize there was no way for any one person, or any one group, to actually win. That we are all apes on a treadmill, slaving away. The visual seared in people's minds and the article faded from view.

Then in 2007, writing in the *Proceedings of the National Academy of Sciences*, a group of young scientists inadvertently provided a fascinating new twist to the apes on a treadmill idea. The scientists were exploring bipedalism, the theory that our ancient ancestors learned to walk upright because it took less energy than quadrupedal knuckle-walking. To advance this hypothesis, they equipped five chimpanzees and four people with oxygen masks, and then put them on treadmills. The scientists collected data about oxygen usage in the apes and in the humans to see what they might learn. They wanted to know if energy expenditure could account for why some apes evolved to develop the intellect of today's humans, while others stayed behind in the jungle, as unenlightened beasts.

In gathering the data, an unexpected anecdote came to the fore, one that shines a light on Warnke's essay. As it turns out, some of the chimps didn't want to participate in the treadmill experiment. Anthropologist David Raichlen, one of the scientists involved, told Reuters journalist Will Dunham what he observed of the apes.

"These guys [the apes] are smart enough that they would hit the stop button on the treadmill when they were done," Raichlen said. In other words, if an ape didn't want to continue on the race to nowhere, "they'd just hit the stop button or they'd jump off."

A question remains: If the apes know how to get off the treadmill, why don't we?

57 MINUTES
The Handmaidens of the Apocalypse Arrive

U.S. Strategic Command headquarters gets hit first. By an onslaught of nuclear warheads launched from Russian subs that surfaced off the East Coast minutes ago. The warheads strike Offutt Air Force Base in Nebraska with the goal of destroying STRATCOM's underground Global Operations Center. This Nuclear Command and Control bunker was designed to withstand a direct hit from a single 1-megaton nuclear weapon, not necessarily a catastrophic bombardment by multiple 100-kiloton warheads—near simultaneously. Decades ago, defense scientists calculated that one bomb with a yield of 1 megaton destroys 80 to 100 square miles (not counting the mass fire), while ten smaller bombs, each with a yield of 100 kilotons, destroys an area more than twice that size.

The light around each of the exploding weapons superheats the air to millions of degrees, creating massive nuclear fireballs that expand in diameter at millions of miles per hour, the heat so intense all concrete surfaces explode, metal melts, humans transform into combusting carbon.

Some people belowground will burn to death slowly, others will carbonize instantly depending on where they are when the bombs detonate. Offutt Air Force Base as well as all of greater Omaha, Nebraska—birthplace of the pink hair curler and Butter Brickle ice cream—and a great majority of the nearly half-million people living here are incinerated.

At nearly the same time, another torrent of 100-kiloton warheads strikes Raven Rock Mountain Complex in Pennsylvania. The payload yields don't mean much of anything anymore—100, 400, or 500 kilotons, 1 or 2 megatons, MIRVed or not MIRVed.

Everything in America's Nuclear Command and Control System is in the process of being systematically destroyed. The original Raven Rock building plans were drawn by the same engineer who designed Hitler's bunker beneath Berlin. In the end of that war, it wasn't the barrage of allied firepower that killed Hitler. He shot himself in the head.

The Raven Rock Mountain Complex is supposed to function as a centerpiece of America's Continuity of Operations Plans. To keep the federal government performing "essential functions," even after a nuclear war. But like STRATCOM, Site R was designed to withstand a direct hit from a 1-megaton weapon, not a barrage of warheads decimating everything around as far as the eye can see. The president of the United States—lying on the forest floor some forty-five miles to the southeast—becomes a casualty of this nuclear deluge. His body catches on fire, and he carbonizes.

The next targets hit by a volley of Russian submarine-launched ballistic missiles are in Colorado. At the Missile Warning Center inside Cheyenne Mountain, at NORAD headquarters at Peterson Space Force Base in Colorado Springs, and at Buckley Space Force Base in Aurora. These nuclear warfighting facilities, and all their supporting facilities, absorb multiple MIRVed Russian warheads all at once. For the more than 1 million people living here at the eastern foot of the Rocky Mountains, it is as if the whole world has been set on fire.

Another stream of 100-kiloton warheads strikes multiple military targets across numerous states. The intention is to destroy all redundant components of U.S. Nuclear Command and Control in a matter of minutes. In Louisiana, Barksdale Air Force Base gets hit. The once mighty headquarters of Global Strike Command, home to the nation's nuclear-armed B-52 long-range bombers, is no more.

In Montana, Malmstrom Air Force Base is annihilated by nuclear warheads. Malmstrom is the base that operates, maintains, and oversees 150 Minuteman III ICBMs. All of the Minuteman III ICBMs have launched from their silos and are now on a ballistic trajectory to strike Russia. Payback for Russia's decision to launch. In North Dakota, Minot Air Force Base—home to another arsenal of Minuteman III ICBMs—is similarly destroyed. Same goes for the F. E. Warren Air Force Base in Wyoming.

On the East Coast, in the coastal town of Cutler, Maine (population 500), the VLF transmitter facility, providing one-way communications to the navy's ballistic missile submarines, is hit and destroyed. Same goes for the Jim Creek Naval Radio Station, outside Arlington in Washington State, and for a third facility in Lualualei, Hawaii, a large coastal valley in O'ahu, whose name translates as "beloved one spared."

As this final blitzkrieg of SLBM warheads strikes and destroys their targets, all that remains of America's Nuclear Command and Control are its Doomsday Planes in the air and its Trident submarines at sea.

As the 1960 Single Integrated Operational Plan for General Nuclear War foretold, the war is now just about numbers.

About a mass extermination plan that leaves billions of human beings dead.

58 MINUTES
Aviano Air Base, Italy

Targets across Europe get hit at the same time.

A slew of the Russian SLBMs launched from the Arctic Ocean hit NATO bases across Europe. In a ruinous barrage of nuclear explosions, air bases in Belgium, Germany, the Netherlands,

Italy, and Turkey become consumed in fire and obliterated by blast.

Nuclear warheads inside Russian MIRVed ICBMs fly on depressed trajectories and strike London, Paris, Berlin, Brussels, Amsterdam, Rome, Ankara, Athens, Zagreb, Tallinn, Tirana, Helsinki, Stockholm, Oslo, Kyiv, and other targets in a wave of mass extermination. All enemies of Russia, from the Russian military's point of view.

Obliterated in this mayhem are not just the millions of people living, working, and visiting these places, but also scores of civilization's engineering masterpieces: Rome's Colosseum, Notre Dame de Paris, Hagia Sophia, Stonehenge, the Parthenon. Iconic representations of human ingenuity and imagination disappear in a succession of nuclear fireballs: the Rijksmuseum in Amsterdam, the Banya Bashi Mosque in Bulgaria, the National Library of Finland, Estonia's Toompea Castle, the Temple of Augustus in Ankara, Big Ben. Like everything in Washington, D.C., it was all there one moment, and then, just seconds later—gone.

59 MINUTES
The Atlantic Ocean

America is not done launching its own nuclear missiles. The Trident submarines receive final launch orders from Doomsday Planes flying over the ocean, as designed during the Cold War. These final launch messages allow U.S. aircraft to communicate with subsurface ballistic missile systems even after the U.S. electric grid has gone down. After U.S. Nuclear Command and Control has unraveled and failed.

These last U.S. launch orders are performed using the very low frequency system, which transmits at 15 to 60 kilohertz, also known as the AN/FRC-117 survivable low-frequency communications system.

Flying in circles over the Atlantic Ocean, the last of the E-6B Doomsday Fleet airplanes deploys its five-mile-long antennae. This long, thin wire trails out an opening in the back of the airplane until it becomes stabilized by a small parachute, called a drogue.

The E-6B airplane goes into a steep bank turn, like a spiral, sending out its final nuclear launch messages one digit at a time. VLF bandwidth has a very low data transfer rate, just thirty-five alphanumeric characters per second. This is slower than the first-generation dial-up modems, but fast enough to transmit final Emergency Action Messages to Trident submarines thousands of miles away.

Messages that, in turn, allow the Tridents to deliver one final nuclear blow as a follow-on punch to the entire U.S. nuclear triad of weapons that is presently on its way to targets across Russia.

The commands are received.

It will take another fifteen minutes or so for the last of the Trident missiles to begin launch.

No one in America, including the submarine crews, will end up knowing if, or what, these missiles hit.

The epic, existential tragedy is that these last and final nuclear battle maneuvers cease to matter on anyone's scoreboard.

Everyone loses.

Everyone.

72 MINUTES

United States of America

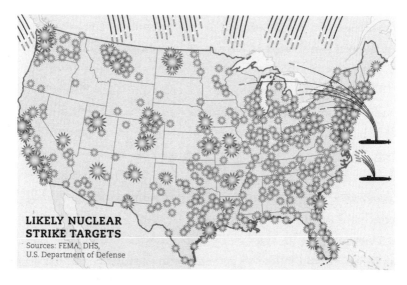

**LIKELY NUCLEAR
STRIKE TARGETS**
Sources: FEMA, DHS,
U.S. Department of Defense

*Likely nuclear strike targets in the continental United States.
(FEMA, DHS, U.S. Department of Defense; image by Michael Rohani)*

At minute 72 of a conflict that began at 3:03 p.m. EST, 1,000 Russian nuclear warheads begin striking America in a twenty-minute-long barrage of nuclear hellfire. One thousand nuclear warheads strike a nation already decimated by 192 Russian SLBM warheads and two North Korean thermonuclear bombs. North Korea's third and final ICBM—launched from the Hoejung-ni underground facility in Hwapyong County, North Korea—failed upon reentry.

The barrage of 1,000 nuclear weapons strikes a nation already stripped of electricity and littered with the dead bodies of nuclear bomb blast victims, victims of radiation poisoning, of airplane, train, subway, and automobile crashes, of chemical explosions, of floods from burst dams.

There are 1,000 flashes of light, superheating the air in each ground zero to 180 million degrees Fahrenheit.

1,000 fireballs, each one more than a mile in diameter.

1,000 steeply fronted blast waves.

1,000 walls of compressed air, accompanied by several-hundred-mile-per-hour winds pushing forward from the 1,000 fireballs, mowing down everything, and everyone, in the path.

1,000 American cities and towns, where all engineered structures in a five-, six-, or seven-mile radius change physical shapes, collapse, and burn.

1,000 cities and towns with molten asphalt streets.

1,000 cities and towns with survivors impaled to death by flying debris.

1,000 cities and towns filled with tens of millions of dead. With tens of millions of unfortunate survivors suffering fatal third-degree burns.

People naked, tattered, bleeding, and suffocating.

People who don't look—or act—like people anymore.

1,000 ground zeros transforming into 1,000 mega-fires, each soon to be burning over an area of 100 or more square miles.

Across America and Europe, hundreds of millions of people are dead and dying, while hundreds of military aircraft fly circles in the air until they run out of fuel; while the last of the Trident submarines move stealthily out at sea, patrolling in circles until the crews run out of food; while survivors hide out in bunkers until they dare go outside, or run out of air.

Survivors who eventually, inevitably emerge from these bunkers to face what Nikita Khrushchev foresaw when he said, "The survivors will envy the dead."

The world's first nuclear explosion occurred on July 16, 1945, at a site on the plains of the Alamogordo Bombing Range, known locally as the Jornada del Muerto.

How the story of nuclear weapons began is how it will end.

Jornada del Muerto. The Journey of the Dead Man.

Part V

THE NEXT 24 MONTHS AND BEYOND
(OR, WHERE WE ARE HEADED
AFTER A NUCLEAR EXCHANGE)

DAY ZERO:
AFTER THE BOMBS STOP
United States of America

Nuclear winter is cold and dark.
(Image by Achilleas Ambatzidis)

I t is very cold and it is very dark. The nuclear bombs sent aloft from all sides eventually stop striking targets. The high-yield ground and air bursts eventually cease.

Across America, everything continues to burn. Cities, suburbs, towns, forests. The smoke produced from burning skyscrapers and other tall buildings generates a noxious smog of pyrotoxins. Burning building materials, including fiberglass and insulation, spew cyanides, vinyl chloride, dioxins, and furans into the atmosphere. This haze of lethal smoke and gases kills survivors and further poisons the scorched earth.

Large scale, 100-to-200-mile-radius rings of fire push out from each of the 1,000 ground zeros across America. At first, there seems to be no end in sight to the destruction from these mass fires. With no pumped water to put anything out, these fires ignite new fires, trapping and killing people who managed to survive the initial mass extermination that came with the full-scale nuclear exchange.

Across less-densely populous areas of America, notably in the Western states, forest fires rage. Coniferous trees in particular cannot handle radioactive fallout. They die and topple over, creating gigantic piles of kindling wood for ensuing fires. The intense firestorms create further apocalyptic conditions with cascading consequences. Oil and natural gas supplies, coal seams, and peat bogs burn for months on end. As a by-product of all these cities and forests burning across America—and also across Europe, Russia, and parts of Asia—so intensely, for so long, some 150 Tg (about 330.6 billion pounds) of soot gets lofted into the upper troposphere and stratosphere. This black, powdery soot blocks out the sun. Its warming rays disappear.

"The density of soot would reduce global temperatures by roughly 27 degrees Fahrenheit," climatologist Alan Robock explains. "In America, it would be more like a drop of 40 degrees Fahrenheit, slightly less near the oceans."

The Earth plunges into a new horror called nuclear winter.

The concept of nuclear winter first caught the world's attention in October 1983 when *Parade* magazine (then read by more than 10 million Americans) featured on its cover a spooky image of a darkened Earth and news of a "special report" inside, authored by one of the world's most famous scientists, Carl Sagan. "Would nuclear war be the end of the world?" Sagan asked, and answered: "In a nuclear 'exchange,' more than a billion people would instantly be killed. But the long-term consequences could be much worse." Consequences that Sagan, his former students James B. Pollack and O. Brian Toon, and meteorologists Thomas P. Ackerman and Richard P. Turco laid out in terrifying detail in a paper published two months later, in the journal *Science.*

The paper was attacked by other scientists and by the Defense Department. "They said nuclear winter is irrelevant," recalls Professor Brian Toon, one of the original authors. "They called it Soviet disinformation." But behind closed doors and in writings that have only recently seen the light of day, those at the very heart of the nuclear weapons complex knew the threat of nuclear winter was real. The result of a large-scale nuclear exchange, wrote scientists with the Defense Nuclear Agency, would be "atmospheric trauma"—and with "serious potential for severe consequences" for Earth's "weather and climate."

"Of course there are uncertainties with nuclear winter scenarios," physicist Frank von Hippel tells us today. "But there's no uncertainty if you inject that much soot into the atmosphere after a [full-scale] nuclear war." In the original nuclear winter paper, the authors acknowledged their modeling had limitations. It was 1983. Computers were still in their infancy. And now, decades later, state-of-the-art modeling systems show atmospheric trauma from nuclear winter will, in fact, be even more severe. "Our first models [in 1983] said nuclear winter would last about one year," Toon explains. "New data suggests the Earth's recovery time would be more like ten years." That the sun's warming rays will reduce by roughly 70 percent.

All life depends upon the sun. Sun equals life. Plants require sunlight to grow. Animals need plants for food. This includes *Homo sapiens* on the ground, birds in the air, worms in the soil, fish in the sea. The Sun's energy drives Earth's ecosystem, the complex bio-logical system of interacting organisms in which we all live. With billions of tons of sooty particles lofted into the atmosphere after a nuclear war, the structure of the Earth's troposphere changes.

The troposphere is the first (and lowest) layer of the Earth's

After a full-scale nuclear exchange, the Earth's atmosphere will change.
(National Oceanic and Atmospheric Administration)

atmosphere, extending up to, on average, 7.5 miles in height. Most of the Earth's weather happens here. The troposphere holds all the air that plants need for photosynthesis and that animals need to breathe. It contains 99 percent of Earth's water vapor. After nuclear war, because of the alteration of the troposphere, the weather changes overnight.

This is how the world becomes so cold and so dark.

Temperatures plunge. Severe and prolonged low temperatures grip the Earth. The region worst affected is the midlatitudes, the part of the Northern Hemisphere between 30 and 60 degrees lat-itude. This includes the United States and Canada, Europe, East Asia, and Central Asia. With these extreme temperature drops, summer weather becomes like winter. Toon says, "New data shows that in places like Iowa and Ukraine, the temperature will not go above freezing for six years."

When nuclear World War III began in this scenario, it was March 30, early spring. In Los Angeles, the temperature plunges to below freezing. The killing frosts decimate tropical plant life and destroy crops across the region. In places like North Dakota, Michigan, and Vermont, where average temperatures hovered in the teens (Fahrenheit), the temperature plunge means subzero weather for prolonged periods of time. Bodies of fresh water become entombed in thick sheets of ice. In the extreme north, Arctic Sea ice expands by 4 million square miles, more than 50 percent greater than present-day ice sheets. Normally ice-free coastal regions freeze over, leading to what modern geophysicists call a "Nuclear Little Ice Age."

The elements are not the only death sentence that looms. As the postwar weeks and months pass, survivors fighting the bitter cold become sick with radiation poisoning. Strontium-90, iodine-131, tritium, cesium-137, plutonium-239, and other radioactive products swept up into the mushroom clouds and dispersed around the earth as fallout continue to contaminate the environment. Death by radiation is an excruciating way to die. As acute vomiting and diarrhea run their course, bone marrow and intestinal destruction sets in. The lining on victims' organs ruptures and hemorrhages. The insides of people's bodies liquify as blood vessel lining sloughs away. These are grueling maladies to endure in a hospital, near impossible to overcome in the cold and the dark, on the run from firestorms and toxic smoke.

Those who continue to live suffer chromosomal damage and blindness. Many will become sterile, or semi-sterile, with reproductivity further reduced over time. There isn't enough uncontaminated food and water to go around. Humans fight for these resources. Only the ruthless survive.

For 10,000 or 12,000 years, modern humans have depended on agriculture to survive. Agriculture is dependent on the Earth's ecosystem to produce food and supply fresh water to nourish people, animals, and plants. Months of cold and almost no sunlight after nuclear World War III triggers another series of fatal assaults on the Earth's ecosystem. Rainfall is reduced by 50 percent. This means the death of agriculture. The death of farming. The death of crops. After 10,000 years of planting and harvesting, humans return to a hunter-gatherer state.

Before the war, meat and produce were grown on farms, shipped through the supply chain to distribution centers, supermarkets, stores, and farmers' markets. Legumes and cereals were among the staples stored locally in cities and towns. When transportation stopped, when there was no fuel to pump, and no vehicles to drive, the distribution of food ceased. What was stored locally burned, radiated, froze, or has rotted. The people who survived the blast, wind, and fire effects of the initial nuclear war—who survived radiation poisoning and bitter cold—now begin starving to death.

Across the Northern Hemisphere killing frosts and subfreezing temperatures destroy crops. Farm animals freeze to death or die of thirst or starvation. Humans are unable to start farming communities in rural areas far from ground zeros because there is very little left to grow. Monthslong firestorms have heated soil to where the soil has become barren. Dormant seeds are damaged or dead. Severely malnourished survivors scavenge for roots and insects to eat, not unlike the starving citizens of North Korea before the war.

The search for uncontaminated water rivals the quest for food. The radical temperature drop means that bodies of fresh water in the north temperate zone freeze over, in some places under a foot of ice. Getting surface water becomes a near-impossible task for most humans. For many animals, it also means death.

Lakes not frozen under deep sheets of ice have become contaminated with chemical waste products. When they finally unfreeze, they will be further poisoned by millions of thawing corpses. Water systems everywhere are in ruin. Between the nuclear explosions and the ensuing mega-fires, America's oil and gas storage facilities ruptured and blew apart; hundreds of millions of gallons of toxic chemicals have spilled into rivers and streams, poisoning the water and killing aquatic life. Toxins leach into the earth and drain down into the water table. Coastal areas, saturated in extreme fallout, are littered with dead marine life.

Hurricane-level storms rage along the ocean, the result of extreme temperature changes between land and maritime air masses. Survivors who make it to the water's edge in search of food have no means of getting out on the sea to fish. Filter-feeding shell-fish in shallow waters—mussels, snails, and clams—have mostly been killed off by radiation poisoning. Those still living are deadly to consume.

In streams, lakes, rivers, and ponds, a mass extinction is under-way. Reduced light devastates microscopic aquatic plant life. As phytoplankton die off, oxygen depletes, and the marine food chain disrupts, further destroying the ecosystem. After nuclear war and nuclear winter, photosynthesis can no longer keep up with plant metabolism. The plants begin to die.

This happened 66 million years ago, after an asteroid struck Earth and shut out the sun. "Seventy percent of the species on the planet (that we know of) died, including all the dinosaurs," says Toon. "They either starved or froze to death," and that "a nuclear war would have many of the same phenomena that the dinosaurs experienced." Plants require sunlight for energy to grow shoots and fruits. Herbivores eat the plants. Carnivores eat the herbivores and each other. Everything on Earth lives and dies, breaks down and decomposes, all of it creating new soil in which new living things grow. This is the food chain. Not anymore.

After nuclear winter, the food chain breaks down.

Nothing new grows in the cold and the dark.

In this scenario, in all but a small region of the Southern Hemisphere (including Australia, New Zealand, Argentina, and parts of Paraguay), widespread famine grips the Earth.

The conclusion drawn in 2022—by ten scientists working on four continents, in a paper for *Nature Food*—is succinct: "More than 5 billion could die from a [nuclear] war between the United States and Russia."

After many months, the cold and the dark become less severe. The intense effects of radioactive fog and haze diminish. The toxic smog dissipates. Light from the sun shines down on the earth once again. And with the sunlight comes yet another set of lethal consequences of nuclear war.

The sun's warming rays are now killer ultraviolet rays.

For millions of years, the ozone layer protected all living things from the sun's harmful ultraviolet rays, acting like a gentle shield. Not after nuclear war. Nuclear explosions and the ensuing firestorms inject mass amounts of nitrous oxides into the stratosphere. As a result, more than half the ozone layer is in ruin. A 2021 study on "Extreme Ozone Loss Following Nuclear War," conducted with computational support by the National Science Foundation, found that after a fifteen-year period the ozone would lose as much as 75 percent of its shielding power worldwide. Survivors must move underground. Into the damp and the dark. Into spaces infested with spiders and insects, like sucking louse.

Aboveground, as the sunlight dawns, things are as vile as they are below. In this new spring sun, a great thawing begins. This includes the thawing out of millions of frozen corpses now rotting in the unfiltered sun. First there was cold and famine, now there is harsh sunlight, pathogens, and plague.

Insects swarm. The warm weather after nuclear winter becomes a breeding ground for disease. A study by the United Nations Scientific Committee on the Effects of Atomic Radiation found that insects are far less sensitive to radiation than vertebrates, owing to their physiology and short life cycles. Hordes of winged and multi-legged bugs are everywhere, and are multiplying. Many of these insects' natural predators, like birds, have mostly been killed off by the cold and the dark. The return of the sun's warming rays brings with it massive outbreaks and epidemics of insect-borne diseases like encephalitis, rabies, and typhus.

A grand evolutionary shift is underway.

Like after the dinosaurs.

In this post-nuclear world, the tiny-bodied, fast-reproducing species thrive, while the large-bodied animals—including humans—struggle at the edge of extinction.

The question remains: Will nuclear weapons bring on the end of the species that made these nuclear weapons in the first place?

Only time will tell if we humans will survive.

24,000 Years Later
United States of America

Years pass. Hundreds of years. Thousands of years.

The life-sustaining capacity of the terrestrial environment, greatly reduced at first, becomes revitalized and rejuvenated. Temperatures return to prewar conditions. New species develop and thrive.

So much has been damaged, but planet Earth has a way of always recovering and repairing herself, at least so far. The soil rebounds, as does the quality of the water supply. The ultraviolet rays that sent human survivors underground have softened and become nurturing again.

If human beings do survive, how will they begin anew? And will these new humans of the future become archaeologists? Will they ever know we were all once here?

Ten thousand . . . twenty thousand . . .

Twenty-four thousand years pass.

Roughly twice as long as the approximate amount of time it took for humans to evolve from hunter-gatherers to today. The radiation poisoning from nuclear World War III has naturally decayed.

Will future humans find any traces of us? Of our societies that we once built, advanced, and made thrive?

If so, perhaps that discovery will be like the discovery story of a German archaeologist named Klaus Schmidt and a young graduate student named Michael Morsch.

One day in October 1994, Schmidt made a discovery in remote Turkey that rewrote civilization's timeline, pushing it back thousands of years. This discovery remains shrouded in puzzles and mysteries. But the place exists as a metaphor for all of us as civilized people. For all that we know, and at the same time for all that we don't know, about our collective future and past.

Göbekli Tepe, a neolithic site in Turkey, was rediscovered by archeologists after being buried for nearly 12,000 years. (Photograph by Dr. Oliver Dietrich)

Klaus Schmidt was familiar with this area owing to an archaeological dig he'd been working on at the time, and he was made curious by a story he'd heard in the villages around the nearby city of Sanliurfa. It was said there was a hill in a valley not far away, a place where an abundance of flint stone could be found poking out of the earth.

Flint stone, a sedimentary rock, was used by early humans to make stone tools and start fires back in the Stone Age.

Schmidt asked around the villages to see if anyone was familiar with this place, which, decades earlier, had apparently been misidentified by an American archaeologist named Peter Benedict as being some kind of medieval cemetery. Misidentified, then forgotten about.

Until, that is, an elderly man in Örencik Koy, Şavak Yildiz, told Schmidt, yes, he knew about this place. Locals called it Göbekli Tepe Ziyaret, or the Potbellied Hill Pilgrimage Site. The way to find the site, said Yildiz, was to look for a lonely tree on top of a hill. And because this tree was the only thing growing in an otherwise vast expanse of desolate terrain, it was said to have magical powers.

People called it the wishing tree and would journey there, Yildiz told Schmidt, "to present important desires to the branches and thus the wind." In his book *Göbekli Tepe: A Stone Age Sanctuary in South-Eastern Anatolia*, Schmidt recalled how Yildiz helped arrange for a taxi driver to take him to this mysterious site, and for a local teenage boy to act as a guide. Accompanying Schmidt on the journey that day was the archaeology graduate student Michael Morsch.

Morsch tells us how the area outside the bustling city of Sanliurfa was a vast and barren wasteland. "Hundreds of square miles of red-brown earth littered with stones and patches of dry grass," Morsch recalls. Very little could flourish there, or so it seemed. It was as if no one had ever lived there at all.

They drove for eight miles, until the road came to an end. The group exited the taxi and began walking along a goat path toward what was rumored to maybe be the site in question.

"We moved through a bizarre landscape of black-gray stone blocks which again and again made [little] barriers," Schmidt wrote, "forcing us to change our course to the left and to the right," zigzagging, as if walking through an ankle-high labyrinth of natural stone. Finally, the group reached the end of this strange terrain, which opened up to a wide expanse where one could see for miles—all the way to the horizon.

Looking out over the land, Schmidt felt disappointment. "Nowhere [was] the slightest archeological trace, only those of flocks of sheep and goats which were taken here every day to their barren meadows," he lamented.

Then he saw the tree.

"It was almost a picture postcard image," Schmidt wrote. The wishing tree, alone, "on the highest peak of the mound, obviously marking a Ziyaret."

The wishing tree at Göbekli Tepe, in 2007. Today it is a UNESCO World Heritage Site. (Photograph by Dr. Oliver Dietrich)

Of course, thought Morsch. *A pilgrimage site.*

"We had found Göbekli Tepe," Morsch recollects of that moment in time.

But what was here? With his scientist's eye, Schmidt wondered. "Which of nature's powers could be supposed to have created this pile of earth on the highest part of this limestone ridge?"

In other words, what—or who—made this hill?

A geologist might say that the hill was created by movement from the Earth's plates. A religious man might invoke God. Schmidt, an archaeologist, recognized right away that what he was looking at was a man-made tel.

A tel is an artificial topographical feature consisting of material left behind by generations of humans who once lived there. Excitement rose within him. As it turned out, he had discovered a lost civilization. Lost for nearly 12,000 years. But not only that, Klaus Schmidt had found something that would change modern man's very definition of civilization itself. Of how the very human concept of science and technology systems first came to be.

Schmidt and a team of archaeologists began excavating the hill. They discovered pot shards and stone walls. They discovered huge pieces of quarried stone carved with wild animals like fox, vultures, and cranes. They discovered giant T-shaped pillars standing upright nearly twenty feet tall. But most important of all, they discovered a vast system of rooms, halls, and open-air auditoriums. Spaces with benches and altars carefully carved of this same stone, brought here mysteriously from a stone quarry located many miles away.

Before this find, scientists' general view of civilization was that science and technology had been born out of agriculture. Out of farming. That only after humans had learned to domesticate plants and animals did they transition from the nomadic hunter-gathers they once were to become civilized. To build communities and societies. To design and create complex systems of things.

Göbekli Tepe disrupted this long-held, foundational idea.

The site was constructed by prehistoric architects, builders, and engineers. Architects who existed before agriculture and farming came to be. Hunter-gatherer humans who dreamed up this science-based project known to us today as Göbekli Tepe. They organized work parties to carry out what they had to have carefully and systematically mapped out, or imagined, in their minds. These were hunter-gatherer humans with a complex system of systems in play. With an elegant understanding of a systems architecture. Of hierarchical command and control.

As of early 2024, no living quarters have yet been found at Göbekli Tepe. No cemeteries, no bones. In other words, people didn't live here, it seems, but they gathered here—for centuries, perhaps even thousands of years.

Why? We don't know. To do what? We don't know.

And then, even more mysteriously, the archaeological record suggests that over a relatively short period of time, thousands of years ago at Göbekli Tepe, some unknown catastrophe struck. Not a natural one, like an earthquake, or a meteor strike, or a flood. Instead, rather suddenly, the entire place was over. Done. Disused. Backfilled in with earth and stone.

If this was by intention, or disaster, scientists have yet to discern. Excavations continue, and the mystery remains. From that enigmatic moment forward, Göbekli Tepe became a buried time capsule. It lay hidden beneath the earth for thousands of years.

What happened at Göbekli Tepe? What caused these humans to suddenly meet their end? Michael Morsch has no answer to this riddle.

"We can tell you what they ate," Morsch says, referring to modern man's astonishing ability to gather plant DNA from fireplaces and pits used 12,000 years ago. "We can tell you what animals they hunted, but we can't tell you what they were thinking. Or what happened to them."

For us, millennia after a full-scale nuclear exchange, it could be the same. Humans of the future could find remnants of our present-day civilization and wonder—*How did it fall into disuse? What happened to them?*

In the dawn of the nuclear age, Albert Einstein was asked what he thought about nuclear war, to which he is said to have responded,

"I know not with what weapons World War III will be fought, but World War IV will be fought with sticks and stones."

Stones, attached to sticks (or spears), are how Stone Age people fought wars. The Stone Age—that vast prehistoric period that lasted for several million years, during which humans used stones to make tools—ended some 12,000 years ago, right around the time that hunter-gatherers are understood to have built Göbekli Tepe.

Albert Einstein feared nuclear weapons could, and might, put an end to the advanced civilization that mankind had spent the last 12,000 years creating. Einstein feared that humans could become hunter-gatherers again, all because of a terrible weapon civilized humans had created to use in wars against their fellow so-called civilized humans.

The story you have just read imagines exactly this. A story where 12,000 years of civilization in the making gets reduced to rubble in mere minutes and hours. This is the reality of nuclear war. For as long as nuclear war exists as a possibility, it threatens mankind with Apocalypse. The survival of the human species hangs in the balance.

In the aftermath of a full-scale nuclear exchange, survivors of nuclear war and nuclear winter would find themselves in a savage world entirely unrecognizable to anyone alive today, Carl Sagan forewarned. That, save a few tribes in the Amazon or military-trained preppers, almost no one living today has actual hunter-gatherer survival skills. That after a nuclear war, even the heartiest of survivors would have great difficulty navigating a world poisoned by radiation, malnourished and disease-ridden, while living mostly underground, riding out the cold and the dark. "The population size of *Homo sapiens* conceivably could be reduced to prehistoric levels or below," Sagan wrote.

Small groups of people would interbreed to survive, producing offspring genetically compromised, some blind. Everything collectively learned by all of us, and all that has been passed down to us by our ancestors, would become myth.

With time, after a nuclear war, all present-day knowledge will be gone. Including the knowledge that the enemy was not North Korea, Russia, America, China, Iran, or anyone else vilified as a nation or a group.

It was the nuclear weapons that were the enemy of us all. All along.

ACKNOWLEDGMENTS

Nuclear war is insane. Every person I interviewed for this book knows this. Every person. The whole premise of using nuclear weapons is madness. It is irrational. And yet here we are. Russian president Vladimir Putin recently said that he is "not bluffing" about the possibility of using weapons of mass destruction. North Korea recently accused the U.S. of having "a sinister intention to provoke a nuclear war." We all sit on the razor's edge. What if deterrence fails? "Humanity is just one misunderstanding, one miscalculation away from nuclear annihilation," United Nations Secretary-General António Guterres warned the world in the fall of 2022. "This is madness," he says. "We must reverse course." How true. The fundamental idea behind this book is to demonstrate, in appalling detail, just how horrifying nuclear war would be.

Fittingly, I must first thank the dead. Alfred O'Donnell (1922–2015) taught me about nuclear bombs. In our interviews, over four and a half years, he shared with me information that was not only extraordinary, but unparalleled. As a member of EG&G's four-man arming party (responsible for final connection checks before all nuclear tests), O'Donnell wired, armed, and/or fired some 186 of America's atmospheric, underwater, and space-based nuclear weapons, including the ones at Operation Crossroads. Colleagues called O'Donnell "The Triggerman."

Ralph "Jim" Freedman (1927–2018), also with EG&G, photographed thousands of these nuclear bomb tests, at the Nevada Test Site and in the Marshall Islands. I chronicle his eyewitness account of watching the 15-megaton Castle Bravo bomb detonate in *The Pentagon's Brain*.

Dr. Albert D. "Bud" Wheelon (1929–2013) shared with me tales from his legendary career of "firsts." He helped develop America's first intercontinental ballistic missile (the Atlas), America's first spy satellite (code-named Corona), and he served as the CIA's first director of its Directorate of Science and Technology (DS&T). He was also the "mayor of Area 51" (his words). His life's work was dedicated to preventing World War III, Wheelon told me.

Colonel Hervey S. Stockman (1922–2011) lived an extraordinary life. He fought Nazis in World War II, flying sixty-eight missions in a P-51 Mustang. He was the first man to fly over the Soviet Union in a U-2 spy plane. He flew radiation sampling runs through megaton-sized thermonuclear bomb clouds in the Marshall Islands. He flew missions in the Vietnam War until he was shot at, crashed, was captured, tortured, and made a prisoner of war for almost six years. After his March 1973 release, Hervey insisted on wearing his POW uniform to medal ceremonies, much to the Pentagon's chagrin. "The invitations stopped coming," he told me. "They wanted war heroes, not former prisoners."

Charles H. Townes (1915–2015), who won the Nobel Prize in 1964, left a profound impact on my thinking (which I write about in *Phenomena*). The concept of dual use technology—science that can be used to help or to harm—is a paradox. Townes's invention, the laser, has done so much to benefit mankind, from laser surgery to laser printers, but the Pentagon's classified laser weapons program is fostering a new kind of arms race.

Dr. Walter Munk (1917–2019), geophysicist and ocean scientist, worked on anti-submarine warfare and marine acoustics for the Navy. He generously shared with me stories of ocean science experiments he conducted during nuclear bomb tests in the Pacific. He advised presidents, held the title of Secretary of the Navy Research Chair in Oceanography, and revolutionized man's understanding of the sea. Colleagues called him the "Einstein of the Oceans."

Edward Lovick Jr. (1919–2017), the grandfather of stealth technology and longtime employee of Lockheed Skunk Works, taught me many things over ten years of interviews. His take on scientific revelation is priceless. Lovick unlocked the long-held quest for stealth technology serendipitously, he explained—while changing his child's diaper. His "Eureka!" moment came when he realized the secret to stealth was absorption.

Paul S. Kozemchak (1948–2017), DARPA's longest-serving employee, shared a shocking story with me, in a 2014 interview, that planted a seed for this book. "Guess how many nuclear missiles were detonated during the Cuban Missile Crisis?" he asked, then continued: "I can tell you that the answer is not 'none.' The answer is 'several,' as in four." Two by the U.S. (on October 20 and October 26, 1962), and two by the Soviet Union (on October 22 and October 28, 1962), each of which was exploded in space. Firing off nuclear weapons tests in a DEFCON 2 environment was testing fate.

Marvin L. "Murph" Goldberger (1922–2014), founder of the Jason advisory panel, designed many weapons systems for the Pentagon. He shared with me his vast knowledge about sensor technology and its role in command and control. He also shared a regret. Goldberger told me he wished he'd spent more time doing science for science's sake and not doing science for war. "At the end of your life you think about these things," he said.

Dr. Jay W. Forrester (1918–2016), a pioneer in computer engineering and the father of System Dynamics, schooled me on a fundamental concept underpinning nuclear command and control: it is a system of systems. A giant machine made of many moving parts. Knowing this, and knowing all machines eventually break, is a terrifying thought.

Researching, reporting, writing, and publishing a book requires an enormous amount of help. Of ingenuity and generosity from lots of people, and also good old-fashioned hard work. A few individuals I would like to thank here are: John Parsley, Steve Younger, Sloan Harris, Matthew Snyder, Tiffany Ward, Alan Rautbort, Frank Morse, Jake Smith-Bosanquet, Sarah Thegeby, Stephanie Cooper, Nicole Jarvis, Ella Kurki, and Jason Booher. Thank you Claire Sullivan, production editor, and Rob Sternitzky, copyeditor, for staying eagle-eyed all the way to the end.

Many sources assisted me on background, or on deep-background, as we say in the biz, some going back ten and twelve years. I thank you. And a huge nod of gratitude for everyone bold and brave who went on the record and allowed me to quote them in this scenario. In particular I'd like to thank Glen McDuff and Ted Postol, who read early (messy) drafts of the manuscript and pointed out where I needed to dig in and report certain things more deeply. Thank you Jon Wolfsthal and Lt. Gen. Charles Moore (ret), for reading closer-to-final page proofs with a rare precision that comes with having spent decades in the nation's service. Thank you Hans Kristensen for reading and proofing nuclear warhead and weapon system numbers with an expertise (and level of patience) that seems unrivaled. Ben Kalin provided excellent fact-checking. Thanks to John Tyler Moore at the Los Alamos National Laboratory Archives, Max Howell, manuscript archivist at the Niels Bohr Library and Archives, and everyone at the National Archives and Records Administration over the years, but particularly Richard Peuser, David Fort, and Tom Mills. Thank you to Cynthia Lazaroff for her insight on the subject of nuclear dangers. And to Paulina Sokolovsky, Julia Grinberg, and Nathan Sokolovsky for helping me with Russian translations. I want to thank Shane Salerno of The Story Factory for bringing me the idea for this book and for working with me on the manuscript. Thank you to archaeologists Dr. Oliver Dietrich and Dr. Jens Notroff, who have worked at Göbekli Tepe over the years and shared with me their insights about that remarkable and mysterious place.

It takes a village to accomplish everything that is worthwhile. My village includes: Tom Soininen (the person from whom I inherited the talking stick), Alice Soininen (miss you, Mom), Julie Soininen Elkins, John Soininen, Kathleen and Geoffrey Silver, Rio and Frank Morse, Kirston Mann, Ellen Collett, Nancie Claire, Judith Edelman. And of course, nothing I do happens without the brilliance and the endlessly inspiring ideas I get from Kevin, Finley, and Jett; you guys are my best friends.

NOTES

ABBREVIATIONS USED IN NOTES

CRS	Congressional Research Service, digital collection
CSIS	Center for Strategic and International Studies, digital collection
DIA	Defense Intelligence Agency, digital collection
DoD	U.S. Department of Defense, digital collection
DSOH	U.S. Department of State, Office of the Historian, digital collection
DNI	Director of National Intelligence, digital collection
GAO	Government Accountability Office, digital collection
FAS	Federation of American Scientists, digital collection
FEMA	Federal Emergency Management Agency, digital collection
ICAN	International Campaign to Abolish Nuclear Weapons, digital collection
IDA	Institute for Defense Analyses, digital collection
LANL	Los Alamos National Laboratory, digital collection
LANL-L	Los Alamos National Laboratory, research library
LM	Lockheed Martin, digital collection
MDA	Missile Defense Agency, digital collection
NARA	National Archives and Records Administration, College Park, MD
NASA	National Aeronautics and Space Administration, digital collection
NA-R	National Archives, Ronald Reagan Library, digital collection
NA-T	National Archives, Harry S. Truman Library, digital collection
NAVY	U.S. Navy, digital collection
NOAA	National Oceanic and Atmospheric Administration
NRC	Nuclear Regulatory Commission, digital collection
NRO	National Reconnaissance Office, digital collection
NSA-GWU	National Security Archive, George Washington University, digital collection
OSD	Office of the Secretary of Defense, digital collection
OSTI	Department of Energy, Office of Scientific and Technical

Information, digital collection

RTX	Raytheon, digital collection
SIPRI	Stockholm International Peace Research Institute, digital collection
SNL	Sandia National Laboratories, digital collection
STRATCOM	U.S. Strategic Command, digital collection
USSF	U.S. Space Force, digital collection
WH	White House, digital collection

AUTHOR'S NOTE

xi **Declassified documents:** "Atomic Weapons Requirements Study for 1959 (SM 129-56)," Strategic Air Command, June 15, 1956 (Top Secret Restricted Data, Declassified August 26, 2014), NARA; "SIOP Briefing for Nixon Administration," XPDRB-4236-69, National Security Council, Joint Chiefs of Staff, January 27, 1969, LANL-L. Further examples are noted throughout.

xi **"fears most":** Interview with Andrew Weber. See also, Dr. Peter Vincent Pry, "Surprise Attack: ICBMs and the Real Nuclear Threat," Task Force on National and Homeland Security, October 31, 2020. "Surprise attack is the most likely nuclear scenario because of U.S. vulnerabilities, adversary strategic posture and paranoid strategic culture, and U.S. strategic culture that regards nuclear war, and especially nuclear surprise attack, as 'unthinkable.'"

xi **how U.S. Nuclear Command:** "Admiral Charles A. Richard, Commander, U.S. Strategic Command, Holds a Press Briefing," transcript, DoD, April 22, 2021. "We made bolt out of the blue unlikely. Ballistic missile submarines, the responsiveness of the intercontinental leg, our postures, our policies, the way we execute. The reason bolt out of the blue is unlikely is because it's probably not going to work; right." This book's scenario begins where STRATCOM postures and policies fail, and the Bolt out of the Blue attack happens.

xii **"world could end":** Interview with Robert Kehler.

PROLOGUE: HELL ON EARTH

xvii **human mind to comprehend:** Nuclear weapons effects in this scenario stem from Samuel Glasstone and Philip J. Dolan, eds., *The Effects of Nuclear Weapons*, 3rd ed. (Washington, DC: Department of Defense and Department of Energy [formerly the Atomic Energy Commission]), 1977. The 653-page book is also referred to as "Department of the Army Pamphlet No. 50-3." My author copy, acquired during a research trip to the Los Alamos National Laboratory in 2021, came with a "Nuclear Bomb Effects Computer," developed by the Lovelace Biomedical and Environmental Research Institute Inc., tucked in a sleeve at the back. This circular slide rule allows for personal calculations regarding nuclear bomb effects—things like at what distance from a nuclear explosion a third-degree burn is likely to occur on a human, and therefore: "skin graft required." The horrific effects that nuclear bombs have on people and on cities are based on data from the atomic bombs dropped by the U.S. military on Hiroshima and Nagasaki, in August 1945. The data was originally compiled by the DoD and the AEC into *The Effects of Atomic Weapons*, issued in 1950 when the explosive energies of nuclear bombs were in the thousands of tons of TNT, i.e., kiloton range; these weapons were designed to destroy entire cities. With the development of the thermonuclear (hydrogen) bomb in the 1950s, explosive energies of nuclear weapons advanced into the millions of tons, i.e., megaton range; these weapons were designed to destroy entire nations. In later editions of *Effects*, new data from atmospheric tests conducted in the Pacific and in the United States were included. Nuclear weapons in general, and their effects in particular, have been reported in a wide variety of ways. "There are inherent difficulties in making exact measurements of weapons effects," Glasstone writes. "The results are often dependent upon circumstances which are difficult, and sometimes impossible, to control even in tests and would certainly be unpredictable in the event of an attack." Thus, the scenario you are about to read pulls its information from data in *Effects* and also probable effects that scientists and academics have spent decades compiling, and whose work is noted throughout—many of whom I have interviewed. "[T]wo weapons of different design may have the same explosive energy yield yet differ markedly in their actual effects," Glasstone makes clear. A present-day example of how imprecise numbers related to nuclear weapons have been, and remain, comes from Richard L. Garwin, the American physicist who drew the physical plans for the world's first thermonuclear device (i.e., the Super), and whom I interviewed numerous times for this book. That weapon, called Ivy Mike, is reported as having had an explosive yield of 10.4 megatons. And yet Garwin refers to the bomb's yield as being 11 megatons; he said this to me (repeatedly, in recorded Zoom interviews) and also to David Zierler in a 2020 oral history for the Center for History of Physics of the American Institute of Physics (AIP), the transcript of which is available online. I use 10.4 megatons in my narrative, not because Garwin can, or needs to be, "proven" right or wrong, but because reporting it in this book as 11 megatons will almost certainly generate corrective responses. This is not to discount the efforts of the curious Google searcher, but to underscore the fraught nature of certitude regarding nuclear weapons and their effects. "Numbers should be seen as evocative, not definitive," says nuclear weapons historian Alex Wellerstein. To envision the probable effects of a nuclear weapon exploded on your city or town, I encourage readers to visit NUKEMAP (alexwellerstein.com), an interactive map designed and programmed by Wellerstein based on declassified data from *Effects* and Mapbox API. "[It's] a rare case of a twenty-first-century tool about a controversial technology that has allowed people of differing opinions to at least agree on the basic technical dimensions of the problem," he says. For further reading on nuclear effects, see: Harold L. Brode, "Fireball Phenomenology," RAND Corporation, 1964; Office of Technology Assessment, *The Effects of Nuclear War*, May 1979; Theodore Postol, "Striving for Armageddon: The U.S. Nuclear Forces Modernization Program, Rising Tensions with Russia, and the Increasing Danger of a World Nuclear Catastrophe Symposium: The Dynamics of Possible

Nuclear Extinction," New York Academy of Medicine, February 28–March 1, 2015, author copy; Lynn Eden, *Whole World on Fire: Organizations, Knowledge, and Nuclear Weapons Devastation* (Ithaca, NY: Cornell University Press, 2004), ch. 1: "Complete Ruin"; Steven Starr, Lynn Eden, Theodore A. Postol, "What Would Happen If an 800-Kiloton Nuclear Warhead Detonated above Midtown Manhattan?" Bulletin of the Atomic Scientists, February 25, 2015.

xvii **five times hotter:** Theodore A. Postol, "Possible Fatalities from Superfires Following Nuclear Attacks in or Near Urban Areas," in *The Medical Implications of Nuclear War*, eds. F. Solomon and R. Q. Marston (Washington, D.C.: National Academies Press, 1986), 15.

xvii **X-ray light:** Glasstone and Dolan, *The Effects of Nuclear Weapons*, 276.

xvii **5,700 feet across:** Glasstone and Dolan, *The Effects of Nuclear Weapons*, 38; Theodore Postol, "Striving for Armageddon: The U.S. Nuclear Forces Modernization Program, Rising Tensions with Russia, and the Increasing Danger of a World Nuclear Catastrophe Symposium: The Dynamics of Possible Nuclear Extinction," New York Academy of Medicine, February 28–March 1, 2015, slide 12, author copy; interview with Ted Postol.

xviii **Ground zero is zeroed:** Glasstone and Dolan, *The Effects of Nuclear Weapons*, "Characteristics of the Blast Wave in Air," 80–91.

xviii **everything flammable:** "Nuclear Weapons Blast Effects: Thermal Effects: Ignition Thresholds," LANL, July 9, 2020; Glasstone and Dolan, *The Effects of Nuclear Weapons*, 277.

xviii **great firestorm:** Eden, *Whole World on Fire*, 25–36.

xviii **1 to 2 million more:** NUKEMAPS, 1 MT airburst/target Pentagon calculates ~500,000 estimated dead, with ~1 million more injuries. Noting there are ~2.6 million people in the ~25-mile diameter (1 psi) blast range in this scenario, half of which will have third-degree burns that require amputation, the probable dead and dying in this scenario are 1 to 2 million.

xviii **Lincoln and Jefferson memorials:** Eden, *Whole World on Fire*, 17.

xix **35,000 people:** Toni Sandys, "Photos from the Washington Nationals' 2023 Opening Day," *Washington Post*, March 31, 2023.

xix **third-degree burns:** Office of Technology Assessment, *The Effects of Nuclear War*, 21. "A 1-Mt explosion can cause third-degree burns (which destroy skin tissue) at distances of up to 5 miles [8 km]. Third-degree burns over 24 percent of the body, or second-degree burns over 30 percent of the body, will result in serious shock, and will probably prove fatal unless prompt, specialized medical care is available." Note how assessments vary: "Nuclear Weapon Blast Effects," (see: *Thermal Effects: Ignition Thresholds*) LANL, July 9, 2020, 12–14. Third-degree burns, 1 megaton, 12 kilometers (7.45 miles).

xix **2,000 specialized burn unit beds:** R. D. Kearns et al., "Actionable, Revised (v.3), and Amplified American Burn Association Triage Tables for Mass Casualties: A Civilian Defense Guideline," *Journal of Burn Care & Research* 41, no. 4 (July 3, 2020): 770–79.

xix **decades doing this math:** For defense scientists, see: Office of Technology Assessment, *The Effects of Nuclear War*, table 2: "Summary of Effects, Immediate Deaths." For civilian scientists, see: William Daugherty, Barbara Levi, and

Frank von Hippel, "Casualties Due to the Blast, Heat, and Radioactive Fallout from Various Hypothetical Nuclear Attacks on the United States," National Academy of Sciences, 1986.

xix **gruesome calculations:** "Mortuary Services in Civil Defense," Technical Manual: TM-11-12, United States Civil Defense, 1956.

 xx **heavily guarded federal facilities:** Author tour of Joint Base Anacostia-Bolling.

xxi **two pulses:** Glasstone and Dolan, *The Effects of Nuclear Weapons*, 277. Pulse length is dependent upon bomb size.

xxi **appalling statistics:** The archivist is Chris Griffith of the Atomic Archive, digital collection.

xxi **pushing out like a bulldozer:** Interview with Ted Postol. See also Steven Starr, Lynn Eden, Theodore A. Postol, "What Would Happen If an 800-Kiloton Nuclear Warhead Detonated above Midtown Manhattan?" Bulletin of the Atomic Scientists, February 25, 2015.

xxi **three miles farther ahead:** Glasstone and Dolan, *The Effects of Nuclear Weapons*, 38.

xxi **80 miles per hour:** "Sandy Storm Surge & Wind Summary," National Climate Report, NOAA, October 2012. The 253 mph wind was measured on Barrow Island, Australia, April 10, 1996.

xxii **250 to 350 feet per second:** Glasstone and Dolan, *The Effects of Nuclear Weapons*, 27.

xxii **reverse suction effect:** Interview with Ted Postol; Glasstone and Dolan, *The Effects of Nuclear Weapons*, 29, 82, 85.

xxii **five then ten miles:** Glasstone and Dolan, *The Effects of Nuclear Weapons*, 28–33, table 2.12.

xxii **Sagan warned:** Ehrlich et al., *The Cold and the Dark*, 9.

xxiii **act like torch lighters:** Eden, *Whole World on Fire*, 25.

xxiii **becomes blinded:** Office of Technology Assessment, *The Effects of Nuclear War*, 21.

xxiii **raining birds:** Interview with Al O'Donnell, who witnessed this during nuclear tests.

xxiii **"self-survive":** Interview with Craig Fugate.

PART 1: THE BUILDUP

3 **a secret plan:** "History of the Joint Strategic Target Planning Staff: Background and Preparation of SIOP-62," History & Research Division, Headquarters Strategic Air Command. (Top Secret Restricted Data, Declassified Feb 13, 2007), 1.

3 **600 million people:** Ellsberg, *The Doomsday Machine*, 3.

3 **A multitude:** Rubel, *Doomsday Delayed*, 23–24.

4 **firsthand witness:** Ibid., 24–30.

4 **His words:** Ibid., 27.

5 **"Each man climbed":** Ibid., 24.

5 **"red ribbons":** Ibid., 25.

5 **"the plan":** Ibid.

6 **what went on:** To learn more about how the public came to know about SIOP-62, see William Burr, ed., "The Creation of SIOP-62: More Evidence on the Origins of Overkill," Electronic Briefing Book No. 130, NSA-GWU, July 13, 2004; Kaplan, *The Wizards of Armageddon*, 262–72; Ellsberg, *The Doomsday Machine*, 2–3.

7 **single strike:** George V. LeRoy, "The Medical Sequelae of the Atomic Bomb Explosion," *Journal of the American Medical Association* 134, no. 14 (August 1947): 1143–48. McDuff cites different numbers: "Killed at Hiroshima, 64,500 by mid-November. Killed at Nagasaki 39,214 by end of November." A. W. Oughterson et al., "Medical Effects of Atomic Bombs: The Report of the Joint Commission for the Investigation of Effects of the Atomic Bomb in Japan," vol. 1, Army Institute of Pathology, April 19, 1951, 12.

7 **chaos and confusion:** Sekimori, *Hibakusha: Survivors of Hiroshima and Nagasaki*, 20–39.

8 **1.1 miles from ground zero:** Setsuko Thurlow, "Vienna Conference on the Humanitarian Impact of Nuclear Weapons," Federal Ministry, Republic of Austria, December 8, 2014; Testimony of Setsuko Thurlow, "Disarmament and Non-Proliferation: Historical Perspectives and Future Objectives," Royal Irish Academy, Dublin, March 28, 2014.

8 **1,900 feet:** John Malik, "The Yields of the Hiroshima and Nagasaki Explosions," LA-8819, UC-34, LANL, September 1985.

8 **to kill the most people:** As a member of the target selection committee, von Neumann decided which Japanese cities were chosen as atomic targets. The president's Medal for Merit given to him cited "devotion to duty," and "sustained enthusiasm."

8 **"Then I started hearing":** Setsuko Thurlow, "Setsuko Thurlow Remembers the Hiroshima Bombing," Arms Control Association, July/August 2020 (here and after).

9 **15 kilotons of TNT:** John Malik, "The Yields of the Hiroshima and Nagasaki Nuclear Explosions," LA-8819, UC-34, LANL, September 1985, 1. Nagasaki is listed as 21 kilotons.

9 **"Parts of the bodies were missing . . . eyeballs":** Setsuko Thurlow, "Setsuko Thurlow Remembers the Hiroshima Bombing," Arms Control Association, July/August 2020.

10 **"Embedded in my neck":** Hachiya, *Hiroshima Diary*, 2.

10 **"running, stumbling, falling . . . head.":** Ibid.

13 **in the making:** William Burr, ed., "The Creation of SIOP-62: More Evidence on the Origins of Overkill," Electronic Briefing Book No. 130, NSA-GWU, July 13, 2004.

13 **third bomb:** William Burr, ed., "The Atomic Bomb and the End of World War II," Document 87, Telephone transcript of General Hull and General Seaman—1325—13 Aug 45, Electronic Briefing Book No. 716, NSA-GWU, August 7, 2017.

13 **"like school science projects":** Interview with Glen McDuff (here and after).

14 **grand, celebratory affair:** Interview with Al O'Donnell, who helped wire the bombs as an EG&G engineer.

15 **classified until 1975:** "Enclosure 'A.' The Evaluation of the Atomic Bomb as a Military Weapon: The Final Report of the Joint Chiefs of Staff Evaluation Board for Operation Crossroads," Joint Chiefs of Staff, NA-T, June 30, 1947, 10–14.

15 **"a threat to mankind":** Ibid., 10.

15 **"used in numbers":** Ibid., 13. "The United States has no alternative but to continue the manufacture and stockpiling of weapons [and] in such quantities, and at such a rate of production, as will give it the ability to overwhelm swiftly any potential enemy."

16 **By 1947:** Glen McDuff and Alan Carr, "The Cold War, the Daily News, the Nuclear Stockpile and Bert the Turtle," LAUR-15-28771, LANL.

16 **By 1950:** Ibid., slide 100.

16 **"depopulate vast areas":** "Enclosure 'A': The Evaluation of the Atomic Bomb as a Military Weapon: The Final Report of the Joint Chiefs of Staff Evaluation Board for Operation Crossroads," Joint Chiefs of Staff, NA-T, June 30, 1947, 10.

17 **"most destructive, inhumane":** "What Happens If Nuclear Weapons Are Used?" ICAN.

17 **"I am the architect":** Interview with Richard Garwin (here and after, unless noted).

18 **"an evil thing":** Enrico Fermi and I. I. Rabi, "The General Advisory Committee Report of October 30, 1949, Minority Annex: An Opinion on the Development of the 'Super,'" DSOH, October 30, 1949.

18 **"it's still evil":** When I asked Garwin if he wishes he'd never designed the Super, he replied: "I wish it couldn't have been built. I knew it was dangerous. I didn't really worry about how these things would be used."

18 **unprecedented yield:** "Operation Ivy: 1952," United States Atmospheric Nuclear Weapons Tests, Nuclear Test Personnel Review, Defense Nuclear Agency, DoD, OSTI, December 1, 1982, 1.

18 **"14 buildings the size of the Pentagon":** Ibid.,188.

19 **mad rush:** Interview with Glen McDuff; Glen McDuff and Alan Carr, "The Cold War, the Daily News, the Nuclear Stockpile and Bert the Turtle," LAUR-15-28771, LANL, slides 19, 31, 60.

21 **31,255:** "Size of the U.S. Nuclear Stockpile and Annual Dismantlements (U)," Classification Bulletin WNP-128, U.S. Department of Energy, May 6, 2010.

24 **280,000 employees:** U.S. Strategic Command, History, Fact Sheet, STRATCOM.

24 **Joint Strategic Targeting Planning Staff:** "History of the Joint Strategic Targeting Planning Staff: Background and Preparation of SIOP-62," History & Research Division, Headquarters Strategic Air Command. (Top Secret Restricted Data, Declassified Feb 13, 2007), Document 1, 28.

24 **plan for General Nuclear War:** Rubel, *Doomsday Delayed*, 24–27, 62; Ellsberg, *The Doomsday Machine*, 2–3, 6–8.

24 **neighboring countries:** "Atomic Weapons Requirements Study for 1959 (SM 129-56)," Strategic Air Command, June 15, 1956 (Top Secret Restricted Data, Declassified 2014), LANL-L.

25 **climate effects:** Interview with Ted Postol.

25 **"It showed that deaths":** Rubel, *Doomsday Delayed*, 26.

25 **one man did:** Ibid., 27. Rubel writes "someone" in a back row interrupted to ask: "What if this isn't China's war? What if this is just a war with the Soviets? Can you change the plan?" The general answered, "We can, but I hope nobody thinks of it, because it would really screw up the plan." Fred Kaplan assigns this question to Shoup. Kaplan, *The Wizards of Armageddon*, 270.

26 **Nobody seconded Shoup's dissent:** Interview with Fred Kaplan.

26 **ninety-minute meeting:** "Coordinating the Destruction of an Entire People: The Wannsee Conference," National WWII Museum, January 19, 2021, author copy.

27 **"deep heart of darkness":** Rubel, *Doomsday Delayed*, 27.

27 **some 600 million:** Ellsberg, *The Doomsday Machine*, 3.

27 **"a family of plans':** Hans M. Kristensen and Matt Korda, "Nuclear Notebook: United States Nuclear Weapons, 2023," *Bulletin of the Atomic Scientists* 79, no. 1 (January 2023): 33. From the original document: with partial classification downgrade executed by Daniel L. Karbler, Major General, U.S. Army, Chief of Staff, U.S. Strategic Command, "USSTRATCOM OPLAN 8010-12 Strategic Deterrence and Force Employment (U)," July 30, 2012.

27 **U.S. stockpile . . . more than 5,000 warheads:** Ibid., 28–52. In addition to the 1,770 deployed, the U.S. has 1,938 warheads in reserve and another 1,536 warheads retired and waiting to be dismantled.

28 **total inventory . . . roughly the same:** Hans M. Kristensen, Matt Korda, and Eliana Reynolds, "Nuclear Notebook: Russian Nuclear Weapons, 2023," *Bulletin of the Atomic Scientists* 79, no. 3 (May 2023): 174–99. In addition to its 1,674 deployed, Russia has 2,815 strategic and nonstrategic warheads in storage and another 1,400 retired (largely intact) and waiting to be dismantled. In an interview with Hans Kristensen, he clarified that not only are the numbers fluid, but there is no way of knowing with certainty what the Russians have on alert.

28 **"Armageddon":** Katie Rogers and David E. Sanger, "Biden Calls the 'Prospect of Armageddon' the Highest Since the Cuban Missile Crisis," *New York Times*, October 6, 2022.

PART II: THE FIRST 24 MINUTES

33 **The Hwasong-17:** Josh Smith, "Factbox: North Korea's New Hwasong-17 'Monster Missile,'" Reuters, November 19, 2022.

33 **SBIRS ("sibbers"):** James Hodgman, "SLD 45 to Support SBIRS GEO-6 Launch, Last Satellite for Infrared Constellation," Space Force, August 3, 2022.

34 **mission ground station:** "National Reconnaissance Office, Mission Ground Station Declassification, 'Questions and Answers,'" NRO, October 15, 2008, 1.

34 **jealously guarded**: No former USAF and/or Space Command officers would discuss this facility with me. Much OSINT comes from former CIA scientist Allen Thomson, "Aerospace Data Facility-Colorado/Denver Security Operations Center Buckley AFB, Colorado," version of 2011-11-28, FAS, a 230-page compilation of declassified documents and public domain information.

34 **responsible for:** "National Reconnaissance Office, Mission Ground Station Declassification, 'Questions and Answers,'" NRO, October 15, 2008, 2.

35 **"There are others":** Interview with Doug Beason.

36 **lighted match:** Interview with Richard Garwin.

36 **onboard signal processing:** "FactSheet: Defense Support Program Satellites," USSF.

36 **more than 9,000:** "United States Space Command, Presentation to the Senate Armed Services Committee, U.S. Senate," Statement of General James H. Dickinson, Commander, United States Space Command, March 9, 2023. "As of this year there are 8,225 satellites in low Earth orbit and nearly 1,000 satellites in geosynchronous Earth orbit (GEO)." Different numbers abound. In April 2022 the Outer Space Objects Index, United Nations Office for Outer Space Affairs, put the number at 8,261—of which 4,852 satellites are active—as being an increase of 11.84 percent from the year before.

37 **1,968 missile launches:** Sandra Erwin, "Space Force tries to Turn Over a New Leaf in Satellite Procurement," *Space News*, October 20, 2022.

37 **continues to notify:** "Russia to Keep Notifying U.S. of Ballistic Missile Launches," Reuters, March 30, 2023.

37 **more than 100:** Mari Yamaguchi and Hyung-Jin Kim, "North Korea Notifies Neighboring Japan It Plans to Launch Satellite in Coming Days," Associated Press, May 29, 2023.

37 **None of them were announced:** Interview with Joseph Bermudez Jr. "North Korea does not preannounce military launch tests."

39 **beneath the Pentagon:** The bunker is almost never photographed and rarely discussed. One exception involves former president Trump. After a 2019 visit, the sitting president broke protocol and talked about his visit, likening the Pentagon's nuclear command center to a movie set and describing the generals who worked there as being "better looking than Tom Cruise, and stronger." Trump said he told the generals, "This is the greatest room I've ever seen."

39 **hundreds of people:** Michael Behar, "The Secret World of NORAD," *Air & Space*, September 2018.

40 **three primary missions:** "National Military Command Center (NMCC)," Federal Emergency Management Agency, Emergency Management Institute, FEMA.

40 **dot moving ominously:** General Hyten: "Pictures that we see on the screen will tell me exactly where the missile is, how high it is, how fast it is going, where the predicted impact point is. All those kind of issues happen in a matter of, in a small number of minutes." Said in conversation with Barbara Starr (reported with Jamie Crawford), "Exclusive: Inside the Base That Would Oversee a US Nuclear Strike," CNN, March 27, 2018.

40 **"It's hard to capture":** Rachel Martinez, "Daedalians Receive First-Hand Account of National Military Command Center on 9/11," Joint Base McGuire-Dix-Lakehurst, *News*, April 9, 2007.

42 **Space Delta 4:** "Fact Sheet: Defense Support Program Satellites," MDA.

42 **three commands:** NORAD is a U.S. and Canada binational organization charged with aerospace warning, aerospace control, and protection for North

America; NORTHCOM is tasked with protecting the territory and national interests of the U.S. (including Puerto Rico, Canada, Mexico, the Bahamas) as well as air, land, and sea approaches. In wartime, NORTHCOM would be designated the primary defender against an invasion of the United States; STRATCOM is responsible for Strategic Deterrence, Nuclear Operations, Nuclear Command, Control, and Communications (NC3) Enterprise Operations, Joint Electromagnetic Spectrum Operations, Global Strike, Analysis and Targeting, and Missile Threat Assessment.

43 **Its job:** "Fact Sheet: Long Range Discrimination Radar (LRDR), Clear Space Force Station (CSFS), Alaska," MDA, August 23, 2022.

44 **"keen eyes":** Zachariah Hughes, "Cutting-Edge Space Force Radar Installed at Clear Base," *Anchorage Daily News*, December 6, 2021. There are other radars focused on early warning (like TACMOR) being deployed.

45 **enough track data:** Interview with Ted Postol.

45 **Cheyenne Mountain Complex:** Michael Behar, "The Secret World of NORAD," *Air & Space*, September 2018; "Fact Sheet: Cheyenne Mountain Complex," DoD.

45 **"surprise attack":** Interview with William Perry (here and elsewhere, except when noted).

46 **"brain stem":** Randy Roughton, "Beyond the Blast Doors," *Airman*, April 22, 2016.

47 **1-megaton:** To note, reported numbers vary; 1 megaton is common. In Behar's 2018 official tour-based article on the complex, it's described as "a bunker capable of withstanding a 30-kiloton nuclear blast."

47 **More than 3,500:** "US Strategic Command's New $1.3B Facility Opening Soon at Offutt Air Force Base," Associated Press, January 28, 2019.

47 **"ten different ways":** Jamie Crawford and Barbara Starr, "Exclusive: Inside the Base That Would Oversee a US Nuclear Strike," CNN, March 27, 2018.

48 **nuclear operations:** Statement of Charles A. Richard, Commander, United States Strategic Command, before the House Armed Services Committee, March 1, 2022. See also "Nuclear Matters Handbook 2020," OSD.

48 **duty of the STRATCOM commander:** Senate Armed Services Committee, Advance Policy Questions for General Anthony J. Cotton, U.S. Air Force Nominee for Appointment to the Position of Commander, U.S. Strategic Command, September 15, 2022, 3. "Section 162(b) of title 10, United States Code, provides that the chain of command runs from the president to the secretary of defense and from the secretary of defense to the combatant commands. Section 163(a) of title 10 further provides that the president may direct communications to combatant commanders through the chairman of the Joint Chiefs of Staff." As I note here, this becomes tenuous when the CJCS is almost certainly about to die.

48 **summed up his responsibility** "Reflections and Musings by General Lee Butler," *General Lee Speaking* blog, August 17, 2023.

49 **"If somebody launches":** General Hyten with Barbara Starr, "Exclusive: Inside the Base That Would Oversee a US Nuclear Strike," CNN, March 27, 2018, 3:30. (Quotes sourced from Hyten's audio, not from CNN transcript.)

49 **Battle Deck:** "U.S. Strategic Command's New $1.3B Facility Opening Soon at Offutt Air Force Base," Associated Press, January 28, 2019.

50 **ever-growing staff:** Michael Behar, "The Secret World of NORAD," *Air & Space*, September 2018.

50 **satellite communications:** "Nuclear Matters Handbook 2020," OSD, 21. The AEHF satellite constellation, which recently replaced the twenty-five-plus-year-old MILSTAR system, "is designed to operate through EMP and nuclear scintillation. It is jam resistant." Further systems include: Advanced Beyond Line-of-Sight Terminals (FAB-T), Global Aircrew Strategic Network Terminal (Global ASNT), Minuteman Minimum Essential Emergency Communications Network Program Upgrade (MMPU), and Presidential and National Voice Conferencing (PNVC).

51 **E-ring's high-shined:** Author visit to the Pentagon.

52 **the War Room:** "The Evolution of U.S. Strategic Command and Control and Warning, 1945–1972: Executive Summary (Report)," Vol. Study S-467, IDA, June 1, 1975, 117–19.

53 **the Jason scientists:** Interview with Marvin "Murph" Goldberger, Jason cofounder.

53 **York's personal papers:** ODR&E Report, "Assessment of Ballistic Missile Defense Program," PPD 61–33, 1961, York Papers, Geisel Library.

54 **"threatens us with annihilation":** Ibid.

54 **Boost Phase . . . detonates on its target:** Interview with Ted Postol. "Terminal Phase begins when the warhead's motion begins to be altered by Earth's thin upper atmosphere, at altitudes of roughly fifty to sixty miles. . . . The Terminal Phase ends when the warhead detonates on target."

54 **not a lot has been verified:** Interview with Joseph Bermudez.

55 **nine countries:** For statistics on nuclear-armed nations and their arsenals, see: "Nuclear Weapons Worldwide: Nuclear Weapons Are Still Here—and They're Still an Existential Risk," Union of Concerned Scientists, n.d.

56 **ten aircraft:** Zachary Cohen and Barbara Starr, "Air Force 'Doomsday' Planes Damaged in Tornado," CNN, June 23, 2017; Jamie Kwong, "How Climate Change Challenges the U.S. Nuclear Deterrent," Carnegie Endowment for International Peace, July 10, 2023.

56 **"ultimately unsuccessful":** Stephen Losey, "After Massive Flood, Offutt Looks to Build a Better Base," *Air Force Times*, August 7, 2020.

57 **"Our military is":** Rachel S. Cohen, "Does America Need Its 'Doomsday' Plane'?" *Air Force Times*, May 10, 2022.

57 **then execute those orders:** "Nuclear Matters Handbook 2020 [original not "Revised"]," OSD, 22–24; "Nuclear Command, Control, and Communications: Update on Air Force Oversight Effort and Selected Acquisition Programs," GAO, August 15, 2017. To note: the Handbook was initially released as a 374-page document, then as a "revised" 282-page document.

57 **another two to three minutes:** Interview with Ted Postol.

58 **decades-old policy:** William Burr, ed., "The 'Launch on Warning' Nuclear Strategy and Its Insider Critics," Electronic Briefing Book No. 674, NSA-GWU, June 11, 2019. "White House science advisers and Pentagon planners were

reluctant to accept a strategy based on launching a retaliatory blow after absorbing a Soviet first strike," says William Burr.

58 **"This is policy":** Interview with William Perry.

59 **"a key aspect":** William Burr, ed., "The 'Launch on Warning' Nuclear Strategy and Its Insider Critics," Electronic Briefing Book No. 674, NSA-GWU, June 11, 2019.

59 **"Inexcusably dangerous":** Ibid.

59 **"Keeping so many weapons":** "Leaders Urge Taking Weapons Off Hair-Trigger Alert," Union of Concerned Scientists, January 15, 2015.

60 **Frank von Hippel urged:** Interview with Frank von Hippel.

60 **"President Biden . . .":** Frank N. von Hippel, "Biden Should End the Launch-on-Warning Option," Bulletin of the Atomic Scientists, June 22, 2021.

63 **civilian positions:** The secretary of defense position is unique within the U.S. government as one of two civilian positions within the military chain of command (Section 113, U.S. Code).

63 **does not—and cannot:** "Authority to Order the Use of Nuclear Weapons," Hearing before the Committee on Foreign Relations, United States Senate, November 14, 2017, 45.

64 **"except, most likely":** Interview with William Perry. Perry served Presidents Carter and Clinton directly.

64 **six minutes:** William Burr, ed., "The 'Launch on Warning' Nuclear Strategy and Its Insider Critics," Electronic Briefing Book No. 43, Document 03, June 22, 1960, NSA-GWU, June 11, 2019. One top secret memorandum (declassified) argued the NATO missile force needed to be "ready to react two to five minutes after warning."

64 **"Six minutes":** Reagan, *An American Life*, 257.

65 **"Civilization as we know it":** Interview with William Perry.

65 **president's detail:** Interview with Lew Merletti. Merletti served as director of the U.S. Secret Service as well as the former special agent in charge of the presidential protective detail for President Clinton. He began his career during the Carter administration and was a founding member (No. 007) of the Secret Service Counter Assault Team, its paramilitary unit.

66 **"No one":** Interview with Jon Wolfsthal; Jon Wolfsthal, "We Never Learned the Key Lesson from the Cuban Missile Crisis," *New Republic*, October 11, 2022.

66 **"Many presidents":** Interview with William Perry.

66 **"are recallable":** "On the Record; Reagan on Missiles," *New York Times*, October 17, 1984. The news conference was on May 13, 1982.

66 **"many people clung":** Interview with William Perry.

66 **"twilight underworld":** Rubel, *Doomsday Delayed*, 27. For another take: Ellsberg, *The Doomsday Machine*, 102–3.

67 **50 percent of North Korea's ICBMs:** Interview with Peter Pry. See also Vann H. Van Diepen, "March 16 HS-17 ICBM Launch Highlights Deployment and Political Messages," 38 North, March 20, 2023. The number takes into consideration launches in "crisis mode," as opposed to a scripted military test.

68 **reach the continental United States:** Hyonhee Shin, "North Korea's Kim Oversees ICBM Test, Vows More Nuclear Weapons," Reuters, November 2022.

68 **examine satellite imagery:** "SBIRS satellites would identify the missile from the intensity, and change in intensity, of its rocket plume," Postol explains, that "the acceleration and rollover over the missile would also be used to identity type," a capability that as of 2023 is considered routine.

68 **the RD-250:** Theodore A. Postol, "The North Korean Ballistic Missile Program and U.S. Missile Defense," MIT Science, Technology, and Global Security Working Group, Forum on Physics and Society, Annual Meeting of the American Physical Society, April 14, 2018, 100-page slide presentation, author copy.

69 **"sold to North Korea":** Interview with Ted Postol; interview with Richard Garwin.

69 **having drawn the plans:** Interview with Richard Garwin; Joel N. Shurkin, *True Genius*, 57. Only recently has it been established that credit for Ivy Mike's design goes to Richard Garwin, not Teller. Garwin figured out how to make Teller's theoretical idea physically work. Shurkin writes, "Richard Rhodes, who wrote about the definite history of the bomb, missed it because no one told him including Garwin." This anecdote is indicative of how secrecy works.

70 **Postol clarifies:** Interview with Ted Postol. See also Richard L. Garwin and Theodore A. Postol, "Airborne Patrol to Destroy DPRK ICBMs in Powered Flight," Science, Technology, and National Security Working Group, MIT, Washington, D.C., November 27–29, 2017, 26-page slide presentation, author copy.

70 **time frame is imperative:** Ibid., 23.

71 **"We proposed":** Interview with Richard Garwin.

73 **"akin to shooting":** Tim McLaughlin, "Defense Agency Stopped Delivery on Raytheon Warheads," *Boston Business Journal*, March 25, 2011.

73 **ten-step process:** "GMD Intercept Sequence," Missile Threat, Missile Defense Project, CSIS, author copy. The GMD intercept sequence goes like this: 1) The enemy launches an attacking missile; 2) Infrared satellites detect the launch; 3) Forward-based U.S. early-warning radars track the attacking missile; 4) The attacking missile releases its warhead and its decoys (the threat cloud) to confuse the radars; 5) U.S. ground-based radar tracks the warhead and its decoys; 6) Interceptors are launched from Vandenberg or Fort Greely; 7) The exoatmospheric kill vehicle separates from the interceptor; 8) SBX tracks the warhead and its decoys and attempts to determine warhead; 9) Exoatmospheric kill vehicle views warhead and its decoys; 10) Intercept [hopefully].

74 **sensor system:** "Raytheon Fact Sheet: Exoatmospheric Kill Vehicle," RTX. The EKV seeks out its target using multicolor sensors, an onboard computer system, and a rocket motor that helps it steer in space.

75 **Now it houses:** "A Brief History of the Sea-Based X-Band Radar-1 (SBX-1)," MDA, May 1, 2008.

75 **sold to Congress:** "$10 Billion Flushed by Pentagon in Missile Defense," *Columbus Dispatch*, April 8, 2015.

75 **baseball-sized object:** In 2007, MDA director Henry Obering made this statement to Congress. See: "Shielded from Oversight: The Disastrous US Approach to Strategic Missile Defense, Appendix 2: The Sea Based X-band Radar," Union of Concerned Scientists, July 2016, 4.

75 **hovering 870 miles:** David Willman, "The Pentagon's 10-Billion-Dollar Radar Gone Bad," *Los Angeles Times*, April 5, 2015.

76 **Critics call the SBX:** Ibid.; Ronald O'Rourke, "Sea-Based Ballistic Missile Defense—Background and Issues for Congress," CRS, December 22, 2009.

76 **$176 billion:** "Costs of Implementing Recommendations of the 2019 Missile Defense Review," Congressional Budget Office, January 2021, fig. 1.

76 **clamshell-shaped:** Carla Babb, "VOA Exclusive: Inside U.S. Military's Missile Defense Base in Alaska," *Voice of America*, June 24, 2022, video at 4:14; Ronald Bailey, "Quality of Life Key Priority for SMDC's Missile Defenders and MPs in Remote Alaska," U.S. Army Space and Missile Defense Command, February 8, 2023.

76 **Russia has:** Hans M. Kristensen et al., "Status of World Nuclear Forces," FAS, March 31, 2023. In late 2023, DoD raised its estimate of China's stockpile.

77 **mostly for show:** "Fact Sheet: U.S. Ballistic Missile Defense," Center for Arms Control and Proliferation, updated May 10, 2023. Q: "Do these systems work?" A: "Despite the assurances of MDA officials, presently, these defense systems have an uneven testing record. The Government Accountability Office found that the MDA failed to meet its planned testing goals in fiscal year (FY) 2019."

78 **Karako anthropomorphizes:** Aaron Mehta, "US Successfully Tests New Homeland Missile Defense Capability," Breaking Defense, September 13, 2021.

78 **"most strategic place":** Julie Avey, "Long-Range Discrimination Radar Initially Fielded in Alaska," U.S. Space Command, 168th Wing Public Affairs, December 9, 2021.

78 *This is Clear:* Carla Babb, "VOA Exclusive: Inside U.S. Military's Missile Defense Base in Alaska," *Voice of America*, June 24, 2022, video at 4:14.

79 **simulation test tape:** "Strategic Warning System False Alerts," Committee on Armed Services, House of Representatives, U.S. Congress, June 24, 1980.

79 **Perry tells us:** Interview with William Perry.

80 **"I'll never forget":** "Ex-Defense Chief William Perry on False Missile Warnings," NPR, January 16, 2018.

80 **Hundreds of miles above:** Interview with Richard Garwin. See also Richard L. Garwin, "Technical Aspects of Ballistic Missile Defense," presented at Arms Control and National Security Session, APS, Atlanta, March 1999.

81 **riddled with failure:** "National Missile Defense: Defense Theology with Unproven Technology," Center for Arms Control and Proliferation, April 4, 2023. "When the Missile Defense Agency (MDA) tests GMD, it assumes prime weather and lighting conditions—and, being a test, it knows the timing and other information that no enemy would provide."

81 **"strategic pause":** Jen Judson, "Pentagon Terminates Program for Redesigned Kill Vehicle, Preps for New Competition," *Defense News*, August 21, 2019.

81 **is attempted:** Interview with Ted Postol. "When the interceptor 'opens its eyes' at about 600 km range, it sees dozens of bright points of light, [but] only one of them is the actual warhead. Since the interceptor has no way to tell which point of light is real and which is a decoy, and it must choose within fifteen seconds, it simply chooses one of the dozens of potential targets."

82 **Philip Coyle:** Philip Coyle, *Nukes of Hazard* podcast, May 31, 2017.

82 **able to override:** James Mann, "The World Dick Cheney Built," *Atlantic*, January 2, 2020.

82 **"highly, highly, highly":** Interview with Robert Kehler.

84 **"The authority is inherent":** "Defense Primer: Command and Control of Nuclear Forces," CRS, November 19, 2021. See also "Statement of General C. Robert Kehler," U.S. Air Force (Ret.), before the Senate Foreign Relations Committee, November 14, 2017, 3.

84 **"six-minute deadline":** Bruce Blair, "Strengthening Checks on Presidential Nuclear Launch Authority," Arms Control Association, January/February 2018; David E. Hoffman, "Four Minutes to Armageddon: Richard Nixon, Barack Obama, and the Nuclear Alert," *Foreign Policy*, April 2, 2010.

85 **Merletti tells us:** Interview with Lew Merletti.

85 **"They are designed":** "Presential Emergency Action Documents," Brennan Center for Justice, May 6, 2020.

86 **"I observed four F84F aircraft":** Harold Agnew and Glen McDuff, "How the President Got His 'Football,'" LAUR-23-29737, LANL, n.d., author copy.

87 **"[a] 3-digit code":** Ibid.

87 **the general's documented concerns:** "Letter to Major General A. D. Starbird, Director, Divisions of Military Application, U.S. Atomic Energy Commission, 'Subject: NATO Weapons' from Harold M. Agnew," January 5, 1961, LAUR-23-29737, LANL.

87 **"why not all nuclear weapons":** As above, and also: "Attachment 1: The NATO Custody Control problem," 5–7, LAUR-23-29737, LANL.

87 **"This is how":** Interview with Glenn McDuff.

88 **"SIOP Briefing":** Memorandum for the Chief of Staff, U.S. Air Force, Subject: Joint Staff Briefing of the Single Integrated Operational Plan (SIOP), NSC/Joint Chiefs of Staff, LANL-L, January 27, 1969, 7.

88 **These details include:** Interview with Glen McDuff; "Authority to Order the Use of Nuclear Weapons," Hearing before the Committee on Foreign Relations, United States Senate, November 14, 2017; Michael Dobbs, "The Real Story of the 'Football' That Follows the President Everywhere," *Smithsonian*, October 2014.

88 **Hair-Trigger Alert:** Bruce G. Blair, Harold A. Feiveson, and Frank N. von Hippel, "Taking Nuclear Weapons off Hair-Trigger Alert," *Scientific American*, November 1997.

88 **order the launch:** Hans M. Kristensen and Matt Korda, "Nuclear Notebook: United States Nuclear Weapons, 2023," *Bulletin of the Atomic Scientists* 79, no. 1 (January 2023): 28–52.

89 **nuclear triad includes:** "America's Nuclear Triad," Defense Department Fact Sheet, DoD. To note: 100 warheads at NATO bases is "estimated." See Hans M. Kristensen and Matt Korda, "Increasing Evidence That the US Air Force's Nuclear Mission May Be Returning to UK Soil," FAS, August 23, 2023.

90 **"Denny's breakfast menu":** Nancy Benac, "Nuclear 'Halfbacks' Carry the Ball for the President," Associated Press, May 7, 2005.

90 **"so much death":** Interview with Glen McDuff.

91 **DEFCON 2:** Interview with Paul Kozemchak. See also "The Cuban Missile Crisis, October 1962," DSOH.

92 **"jamming the president":** Bruce Blair, "Strengthening Checks on Presidential Nuclear Launch Authority," *Arms Control Today,* January/February 2018.

93 **bunker beneath Offutt:** "U.S. Strategic Command's New $1.3B Facility Opening Soon at Offutt Air Force Base," Associated Press, January 28, 2019.

93 **identical copy:** Jamie Crawford and Barbara Starr, "Exclusive: Inside the Base That Would Oversee a US Nuclear Strike," CNN, March 27, 2018.

93 **Colonel Carolyn Bird:** Ibid.

93 **nuclear strike advisor:** David Martin, "The New Cold War," *60 Minutes,* September 18, 2016.

94 **weather officer:** Ibid.

94 **"half the population of China":** Rubel, *Doomsday Delayed,* 26.

94 **Alpha, Beta, and/or Charlie options:** Memorandum for the Chief of Staff, U.S. Air Force, Subject: Joint Staff Briefing of the Single Integrated Operational Plan (SIOP), NSC/Joint Chiefs of Staff, LANL-L, January 27, 1969, 3.

94 **"deliver a decisive response":** U.S. Strategic Command 2023 Posture Statement, Priorities, STRATCOM.

94 **missile launch officer:** Bruce Blair, "Strengthening Checks on Presidential Nuclear Launch Authority," Arms Control Association, January/February 2018. "Submarines and bombers would be the primary attackers in a scenario involving North Korea. With two boats typically on launch-ready patrol in the Pacific Ocean, the sub force would be capable of quickly firing about 200 warheads roughly 15 minutes after the president gave the order. If the order came without a prior raising of alert readiness, however, the boats would surface to confirm its validity." For more on Blair: Andrew Cockburn, "How to Start a Nuclear War," *Harper's,* August 2018, 18–27.

95 **numerous military targets:** "A Satellite View of North Korea's Nuclear Sites," *Nikkei Asia,* n.d.

95 **warships stationed there:** "Development of Russian Armed Forces in the Vicinity of Japan," Japan Ministry of Defense, July 2022.

96 **"My staff":** "Transcript: Secretary of Defense Lloyd J. Austin III and Army General Mark A. Milley, Chairman, Joint Chiefs of Staff, Hold a Press Briefing Following Ukrainian Defense Contact Group Meeting," DoD, November 16, 2022.

96 **frantically dialing:** Nancy A. Youssef, "U.S., Russia Establish Hotline to Avoid Accidental Conflict," *Wall Street Journal,* March 4, 2022; Phil Stewart and Idrees Ali, "Exclusive: U.S., Russia Have Used Their Military Hotline Once So Far during Ukraine War," Reuters, November 29, 2020.

98 **B-2 . . . in Iceland:** Interview with David Cenciotti.

99 **before detonating:** Interview with Hans Kristensen.

99 **Kristensen tells us:** Kris Osborn, "The Air Force Has Plans for the B61-12 Nuclear Bomb," *National Interest,* October 7, 2021.

100 **"the Program":** Interview with Craig Fugate.

100 **"German autobahn":** Lee Lacy, "Dwight D. Eisenhower and the Birth of the Interstate Highway System," U.S. Army, February 20, 2018. To note: DOT has published guest essays saying this is "myth"; according to the U.S. Army it is fact.

100 **Continuity of Operations Plan:** Frances Townsend, "National Continuity Policy Implementation Plan," Homeland Security Council, August 2007. This 102-page document includes the unclassified strategy for mass evacuation and relocation of federal government agencies, including the White House.

100 **Fugate clarifies:** Interview with Craig Fugate.

101 **"Can you keep":** Interview with Craig Fugate.

102 **Fugate predicts:** Interview with Craig Fugate. "There are a few classified programs that have *very* minimal capacity, and are designed to survive this. But that's primarily dedicated to defense."

105 **seriously concerned:** Interview with William Perry.

105 **"survivors will envy the dead":** "Letter from Jacqueline Kennedy to Chairman Khrushchev," DSOH, December 1, 1963. She wrote, "He used to quote your words in some of his speeches—'In the next war the survivors will envy the dead.'"

105 **Site R:** Interview with William Perry. In our discussions, Perry would refer to the facility as the Alternate Military Command Center, which is unclassified, and during the Cold War was "officially" located at Fort Ritchie, Maryland, southwest of Site R. For more history on the Deep Underground Command Center, see "Memorandum from the Joint Chiefs of Staff to Secretary of Defense McNamara," DSOH, September 17, 1964.

105 **closest proximity:** Interview with William Perry.

106 **breached the surface:** Josh Smith and Hyunsu Yi, "North Korea Launches Missiles from Submarine as U.S.–South Korean Drills Begin," Reuters, March 13, 2023.

108 **vault doors:** Clarke, *Against All Enemies*, 18.

108 **read briefings:** Charles Mohr, "Preserving U.S. Command after a Nuclear Attack," *New York Times*, June 29, 1982.

109 **"likely be decapitated":** Interview with William Perry. See also "Bill Perry's D.C. Nuclear Nightmare," an animated video created for *At the Brink: A William J. Perry Project*. The video depicts a scenario involving a 15-kiloton explosion in D.C.; 80,000 people die instantly, including the president, vice president, speaker of the House, and 320 members of Congress.

110 **"The smart thing":** Interview with William Perry.

110 **"My position, as secretary of defense":** Interview with William Perry.

111 **national command authority:** "Air Force Doctrine Publication 3-72, Nuclear Operations," U.S. Air Force, DoD, December 18, 2020, 14, 16–18. Officially: the Nuclear Command and Control System (NCCS) and/or the Nuclear Command, Control, and Communications (NC3) system.

111 **overrides protocol:** "Who's in Charge? The 25th Amendment and the Attempted Assassination of President Reagan," NAR-R.

111 **"easier to find a grapefruit-sized object in space":** Interview with Michael J. Connor.

113 **eighty nuclear warheads:** Hans M. Kristensen and Matt Korda, "Nuclear Notebook: United States Nuclear Weapons, 2023," *Bulletin of the Atomic Scientists* 79, no. 1 (January 2023): 28–52; "United States Submarine Capabilities," Nuclear Threat Initiative, March 6, 2023; Sebastien Roblin, "Armed to the

Teeth, America's Ohio-Class Submarines Can Kill Anything," *National Interest*, August 31, 2021.

113 **launching twenty:** "Ballistic Missile Submarines (SSBNs)," SUBPAC Commands: Commander, Submarine Force Atlantic, NAVY, 2023. There used to be 24 SLBMs onboard each submarine (each missile with multiple, independently targeted warheads), however, under provisions of the New Strategic Arms Reduction Treaty, four missile tubes have been permanently deactivated on each submarine.

113 **armed with multiple nuclear warheads:** "Ballistic Missile Submarines (SSBNs)," SUBPAC Commands: Commander, Submarine Force Atlantic, NAVY, 2023.

114 **near simultaneously:** Interview with Ted Postol.

114 **individual targets:** "Multiple Independently-targetable Reentry Vehicle (MIRV)," Fact Sheet, Center for Arms Control and Non-Proliferation, n.d.

114 **"If Washington was attacked":** Interview with Ted Postol.

114 **highly regarded:** Interview with Richard Garwin.

115 **"all its missiles in about eighty seconds":** Ted Postol, "CNO Brief Showing Closely Spaced Basing was Incapable of Launch," 22-page slide presentation, 1982. Drawing is slide no. 8. For impact of Postol presentation, see Richard Halloran, "3 of 5 Joint Chiefs Asked Delay on MX," *New York Times*, December 9, 1982.

116 **"should deter":** Sebastien Roblin, "Ohio-Class: How the U.S. Navy Could Start a Nuclear War," *19FortyFive*, December 3, 2021.

116 **Richard Garwin warns:** Interview with Richard Garwin.

116 **speck of dust:** Rosa Park, ed., "Kim Family Regime Portraits," HRNK Insider, Committee for Human Rights in North Korea, 2018.

116 **defector Yeonmi Park:** "The Joe Rogan Experience #1691, Yeonmi Park," *The Joe Rogan Experience* podcast, August 2021.

116 **Malnutrition is commonplace:** Ifang Bremer, "3 Years into Pandemic, Fears Mount That North Korea Is Teetering toward Famine," *NKNews*, February 15, 2023.

117 **parasitic worms:** Andreas Illmer, "North Korean Defector Found to Have 'Enormous Parasites,'" BBC News, November 17, 2017.

117 **"North Korea is almost completely dark":** "Korean Peninsula Seen from Space Station," NASA, February 24, 2014. To note: the International Space Station is the biggest satellite in orbit.

117 **"anywhere in the world":** CNN Editorial Research, "North Korea Nuclear Timeline Fast Facts," CNN, March 22, 2023.

118 **eighty submarines:** "North Korea Submarine Capabilities," Fact Sheet, Nuclear Threat Initiative, October 14, 2022.

118 **underwater platform:** "North Korea Fires Suspected Submarine-Launched Missile into Waters off Japan," BBC News, October 2021.

118 **Romeo class:** Interview with H. I. Sutton; H.I. Sutton, "New North Korean Submarine: ROMEO-Mod," Covert Shores Defense Analysis, July 23, 2019; "North Korea–Navy," Janes, March 21, 2018.

119 **"North Korean submariner":** For a more staid account of North Korea's nuclear weapons: "DPRK Strategic Capabilities and Security on the Korean

Peninsula: Looking Ahead," International Institute for Strategic Studies and Center for Energy and Security Studies, July 1, 2019; Pablo Robles and Choe Sang-Hun, "Why North Korea's Latest Nuclear Claims Are Raising Alarms," *New York Times*, June 2, 2023; Ankit Panda, "North Korea's New Silo-Based Missile Raises Risk of Prompt Preemptive Strikes," *NK News*, March 21, 2023.

120 **"in shallow water":** Interview with Ted Postol.

122 **successfully fire:** Masao Dahlgren, "North Korea Tests Submarine-Launched Ballistic Missile," Missile Threat, CSIS, October 22, 2021.

122 **intended purpose:** "KN-23 at a Glance," Missile Threat, CSIS Missile Defense Project, CSIS, July 1, 2019; Jeff Jeong, "North Korea's New Weapons Take Aim at the South's F-35 Stealth Fighters," *Defense News*, August 1, 2019.

122 **KN-23 is roughly:** "KN-23 at a Glance," Missile Threat, CSIS Missile Defense Project, CSIS, July 1, 2019.

124 **missile has fins:** "President of State Affairs Kim Jong Un Watches Test-Firing of New-Type Tactical Guided Weapon," *Voice of Korea*, March 17, 2022; "Assessing Threats to U.S. Vital Interests, North Korea," Heritage Foundation, October 18, 2022.

125 **gate guard here:** "2018 Nuclear Decommissioning Cost Triennial Proceeding, Prepared Testimony," Pacific Gas and Electric Company, table IV.2.1: "Security Posts and Staffing Forecast," 30.

125 **developed its Aegis program:** "Aegis the Shield (and the Spear) of the Fleet: The World's Most Advanced Combat System," LM; "U.S. and Allied Ballistic Missile Defenses in the Asia-Pacific Region, Fact Sheets & Briefs," Arms Control Association, n.d.

125 **thousands of miles away from:** "Navy Aegis Ballistic Missile Defense (BMD) Program: Background and Issues for Congress," CRS, August 28, 2023.

126 **deployed overseas:** Testimony of Vice Admiral Jon A. Hill, USN Director, Missile Defense Agency before the Senate Armed Services Committee Strategic Forces Subcommittee, May 18, 2022, 5.

126 **Congress discussed:** Mike Stone, "Pentagon Evaluating U.S. West Coast Missile Defense Sites: Officials," Reuters, December 2, 2017; "Navy Aegis Ballistic Missile Defense (BMD) Program: Background and Issues for Congress," CRS, April 20, 2023.

126 **enters Terminal Phase:** D. Moser, "Physics/Global Studies 280: Session 14, Module 5: Nuclear Weapons Delivery Systems, Trajectories and Phases of Flight of Missiles with Various Ranges," 110-page slide presentation, slide 47, author copy.

126 **Rule 42:** "Rule 42. Work and Installations Containing Dangerous Forces," International Committee of the Red Cross, International Humanitarian Law Databases; George M. Moore, "How International Law Applies to Attacks on Nuclear and Associated Facilities in Ukraine," Bulletin of the Atomic Scientists, March 6, 2022.

127 **thousands-of-years-long nuclear catastrophe**: Interview with Glen McDuff.

127 **secret discussions:** "Cabinet Kept Alarming Nuke Report Secret," *Japan Times*, January 22, 2012.

127 **"the Devil's Scenario":** "Lessons Learned from the Fukushima Nuclear Accident for Improving Safety and Security of U.S. Nuclear Plants," National

Research Council, National Academies Press, 2014, 40; "Cabinet Kept Alarming Nuke Report Secret," *Japan Times,* January 22, 2012.

127 **"Japan dodged a bullet,":** Declan Butler, "Prevailing Winds Protected Most Residents from Fukushima Fallout," *Nature,* February 28, 2013.

127 **"cautionary tale":** "Reflections on Fukushima NRC Senior Leadership Visit to Japan, 2014," NRC, December 2014, 18.

128 **remain highly radioactive:** "Spent Nuclear Fuel, Options Exist to Further Enhance Security," Report to the Chairman, Subcommittee on Energy and Air Quality, Committee on Energy and Commerce, U.S. House of Representatives, GAO, July 2003, 319. The GAO called spent nuclear fuel "one of the most hazardous materials made by man. The fuel's intense radioactivity can kill a person exposed directly to it within minutes."

128 **pumps to fail:** Amanda Matos, "Thousands of Half-Lives to Go: Weighing the Risks of Spent Nuclear Fuel Storage," *Journal of Law and Policy* 23, no. 1 (2014): 316.

128 **Every three years:** "Backgrounder on Force-on-Force Security Inspections," NRC, March 2019.

128 **Fifty-eight miles up . . . 4,000 miles per hour:** Calculations performed by Ted Postol.

128 **displace 3 to 4 million people:** Richard Stone, "Spent Fuel Fire on U.S. Soil Could Dwarf Impact of Fukushima: New Study Warns of Millions Relocated and Trillion-Dollar Consequences," *Science,* May 24, 2016.

128 **"trillion-dollar consequences":** Peter Gwynne, "Scientists Warn of 'Trillion-Dollar' Spent-Fuel Risk," *Physics World* 29, no. 7 (July 2016); Richard Stone, "Spent Fuel Fire on U.S. Soil Could Dwarf Impact of Fukushima: New Study Warns of Millions Relocated and Trillion-Dollar Consequences," *Science,* May 24, 2016.

129 **core collapse:** Ralph E. Lapp, "Thoughts on Nuclear Plumbing," *New York Times,* December 12, 1971.

129 **Lapp explained:** "Report of Advisory Task Force on Power Reactor Emergency Cooling," U.S. Atomic Energy Commission, 1968 ("Ergen Report").

129 **Devil's Scenario:** Interview with Ted Postol. Comparisons aid in understanding: "The Chernobyl meltdown released about 100 million Curies of radiation. The meltdown and evaporation of the nuclear reactor's core from the detonation [in this scenario] would release about fifty to sixty times more radiation than that released at Chernobyl, and the radiation initially released from the 300-kiloton detonation itself would be even larger—about 300 to 400 times greater than the radioactivity released at Chernobyl."

131 **permanent government:** Interview with William Perry.

132 **components include:** "Nuclear Command, Control, and Communications: Update on Air Force Oversight Effort and Selected Acquisition Programs," GAO-17-641R, GAO, August 15, 2017; "Nuclear Matters Handbook 2020," OSD, 18–21.

132 **did not make public:** "Nuclear Triad: DOD and DOE Face Challenges Mitigating Risks to U.S. Deterrence Efforts," GAO, Report to Congressional Committees, May 2021, 1.

132 **mil aide opens:** Interview with Lew Merletti; "Nuclear Briefcases," Nuclear Issues Today, Atomic Heritage Foundation, June 12, 2018.

133 **Eighty-two targets:** Note: this scenario models (similarly) after Bruce Blair's estimation of 80 targets (aimpoints) in North Korea. Bruce G. Blair with Jessica Sleight and Emma Claire Foley, "The End of Nuclear Warfighting: Moving to a Deterrence-Only Posture. An Alternative U.S. Nuclear Posture Review," Program on Science and Global Security, Princeton University Global Zero, Washington, D.C., September 2018, 38–39.

133 **nearly noiseless:** "Donald Trump's Flying Beast: 7 Things about the World's Most Powerful Helicopter," *Economic Times*, February 21, 2020.

134 **authenticates as fact:** Dave Merrill, Nafeesa Syeed, and Brittany Harris, "To Launch a Nuclear Strike, President Trump Would Take These Steps," Bloomberg, January 20, 2017.

134 **110-ton concrete:** Aaron M. U. Church, "Nuke Field Vigilance," *Air & Space Forces*, August 1, 2012.

135 **Echo-01:** The launch facility in this scenario is modeled after that described in ibid.

135 **300-kiloton thermonuclear weapon:** Hans M. Kristensen and Matt Korda, "Nuclear Notebook: United States Nuclear Weapons, 2023," *Bulletin of the Atomic Scientists* 79, no. 1 (January 2023): 28–52. See also SIPRI estimates to clarify which missiles might have 330-kiloton warheads.

136 **"use them or lose them":** Interview with Joseph Bermudez.

136 **"weren't called Minutemen for nothing":** Bruce Blair, "Minuteman Missile National Historic Site," interview transcript, U.S. National Park Service.

136 **400 ICBM silos:** Hans M. Kristensen and Matt Korda, "Nuclear Notebook: United States Nuclear Weapons, 2023," *Bulletin of the Atomic Scientists* 79, no. 1 (January 2023): 35. The current ICBM force consists of 400 Minuteman III missiles located at the 90th Missile Wing at F.E. Warren AFB, Wyoming; the 341st Missile Wing at Malmstrom AFB, Montana; and the 91st Missile Wing at Minot AFB, North Dakota; underground silos stretch out across Montana, North Dakota, Wyoming, Nebraska and Colorado. Each of the 400 ICBMs carries one warhead, but could theoretically hold two or three warheads each. "Fifty silos are kept 'warm' to load stored missiles, if necessary."

136 **"If Wyoming":** "Missiles and the F. E. Warren Air Force Base," Wyoming Historical Society, 2023.

136 **directly to the STRATCOM commander:** Aaron M. U. Church, "Nuke Field Vigilance," *Air & Space Forces*, August 1, 2012.

137 **encrypted orders:** Dave Merrill, Nafeesa Syeed, and Brittany Harris, "To Launch a Nuclear Strike, President Trump Would Take These Steps," Bloomberg, January 20, 2017.

137 **recently updated:** Daniella Cheslow, "U.S. Has Made 'Dramatic Change' in Technology Used for Nuclear Code System," *Wall Street Journal*, October 14, 2022.

137 **Emergency Action Team:** Mary B. DeRosa and Ashley Nicolas, "The President and Nuclear Weapons: Authority, Limits, and Process," Nuclear Threat Initiative, 2019, 2.

137 **3.4 seconds:** Eli Saslow, "The Nuclear Missile Next Door," *Washington Post*, April 17, 2022.

138 **cruising height of 500 to 700 miles:** Interview with Ted Postol.

138 **spies everywhere:** Interview with Albert "Bud" Wheelon (February 2010), first director of the Directorate of Science and Technology (DS&T) at the CIA.

PART III: THE NEXT 24 MINUTES

142 **"Large, hilly land masses":** Glasstone and Dolan, *The Effects of Nuclear Weapons*, 92. "It is important to emphasize, in particular, that shielding from blast effects behind the brow of a large hill is not dependent upon line-of-sight considerations . . . blast waves can easily bend (or diffract) around apparent obstructions"; interview with Glen McDuff.

143 **Bert the Turtle:** "Duck and Cover, Bert the Turtle," Archer Productions, Federal Civil Defense Administration, 1951.

143 **electromagnetic pulse destroyed:** Interview with Peter Pry.

144 **X . . . shuts down:** Interview with Gregory Touhill.

145 **technology in the 1950s:** SLBMs are called the "First Leg of the Future Triad," with the Regulus SSM-N-8, in service from 1954–1963. Glen McDuff, "Navy Nukes," LAUR-16-25435, LANL, Navy Systems 101, August 9, 2016, author copy.

145 **hitting a nuclear reactor with a missile:** C. V. Chester & R. O. Chester, "Civil Defense Implications of a Pressurized Water Reactor in a Thermonuclear Target Area," *Nuclear Applications and Technology* 9, no. 6 (1970): 786–95.

145 **wall suffered:** "History of SNL Containment Integrity Research," SNL, June 18, 2019, 24.

145 **300 trillion calories:** Eden, *Whole World on Fire*, 16.

146 **around five pounds:** "JCAT Counterterrorism Guide for Public Safety Personnel," Bomb Threat Standoff Distances, DNI, n.d., 1, author copy.

146 **"early fireball":** Eden, *Whole World on Fire*, 17.

146 **Carl Sagan warned:** Carl Sagan, "Nuclear War and Climatic Catastrophe: Some Policy Implications," *Foreign Affairs*, Winter 1983/84.

146 **unprecedented amount:** Interview with Ted Postol.

146 **"size of a marble":** Glasstone and Dolan, *The Effects of Nuclear Weapons*, 37.

146 **2,000 metric tons:** "PG&E Letter DIL-18-019," director, Division of Spent Fuel Management, NRC, December 17, 2018; interview with Glen McDuff.

147 **"will spontaneously combust":** Diablo Canyon Decommissioning Engagement Panel Spent Fuel Workshop." Embassy Suites Hotel, San Luis Obispo, February 23, 2019, 116-page slide presentation, slide 3.

147 **radioactive brew:** Frank N. von Hippel and Michael Schoeppner, "Reducing the Danger from Fires in Spent Fuel Pools," *Science & Global Security* 24, no. 3 (2016): 152.

147 **dry cask field:** "Diablo Canyon Decommissioning Engagement Panel Spent Fuel Workshop," Embassy Suites Hotel, San Luis Obispo, February 23, 2019, 116-page slide presentation.

147 **10 percent of all Californians:** "Nuclear Power Provided about 10% of California's Total Electricity Supply in 2021," U.S. Energy Information

Administration, September 19, 2022 (eia.gov). The number of Californians is from California Department of Finance, Press Release, May 1, 2023.

148 **can't fly overhead:** Interview with Ted Postol.

148 **"The fire [can]not be extinguished":** Glen Martin, "Diablo Canyon Power Plant a Prime Terror Target/Attack on Spent Fuel Rods Could Lead to Huge Radiation Release," *San Francisco Chronicle*, March 17, 2003.

148 **"Two New Jerseys":** Interview with Frank von Hippel. The rephrasing came after considering a scenario where a nuclear missile strikes a nuclear power plant, as opposed to a major fire alone. Von Hippel's original statement was to the *Chronicle*. See also Robert Alvarez et al., "Reducing the Hazards from Stored Spent Power-Reactor Fuel in the United States," *Science and Global Security* 1, no. 1 (January 2003): 1–51.

148 **"shatter into a zillion pieces":** Interview with Glen McDuff.

150 **senior commanders of the General Staff:** Alexis A. Blanc et al., "The Russian General Staff: Understanding the Military's Decision Making Role in a 'Besieged Fortress,'" RAND Corporation, 2023; Andrei Kartapolov, "The Higher the Combat Capabilities of Russian Troops, the Stronger the CSTO," Parliamentary Assembly of the Collective Security Treaty Organization (RU), December 22, 2022.

150 **"I honestly don't think":** Interview with Leon Panetta.

151 **supercomputer:** "A New Supercomputer Has Been Developed in Russia," Fact Sheet, Ministry of Science and Education of the Republic of Azerbaijan, June 14, 2017.

151 **"colossal" power:** "Potential of Russian Defense Ministry's supercomputer colossal—Shoigu," TASS Russian News Agency, December 30, 2016. For more on this, see: "Focus on the Center," Rossiya 24 TV channel, 2016.

152 **known as Tundra:** Bart Hendrickx, "EKS: Russia's Space-Based Missile Early Warning System," *The Space Review*, February 8, 2021; "Tundra, Kupol, or EKS (Edinaya Kosmicheskaya Sistema)," Gunter's Space Page (space.skyrocket.de).

153 **deeply flawed:** Anthony M. Barrett, "False Alarms, True Dangers: Current and Future Risks of Inadvertent U.S.-Russian Nuclear War," RAND Corporation, 2016.

153 **"Tundra is not great":** Interview with Pavel Podvig. "But Russia has an early-warning system that works differently than in the United States."

153 **"don't work accurately":** Interview with Ted Postol.

153 **"Moscow could think":** Interview with Ted Postol. See also Theodore A. Postol, "Why Advances in Nuclear Weapons Technologies are Increasing the Danger of an Accidental Nuclear War between Russia and the United States," Hart Senate Office Building, Washington, D.C., March 26, 2015.

154 **"fragile early-warning system":** Theodore A. Postol, "Why Advances in Nuclear Weapons Technologies are Increasing the Danger of an Accidental Nuclear War between Russia and the United States," Hart Senate Office Building, Washington, D.C., March 26, 2015.

154 **"gigantic, spasmodic":** Interview with Ted Postol. See also David K. Shipper, "Russia's Antiquated Nuclear Warning System Jeopardizes Us All," *Washington Monthly*, April 29, 2022.

154 **"Russia is the only country":** Interview with Robert Kehler.

154 **Sikorsky VH-92A:** Dan Parsons, "VH-92 Closer to Being 'Marine One' but Comms System Could Still Cause Delays," The War Zone, May 2, 2022.

154 **likely will destroy:** Interview with Jeffrey Yago.

155 **"Russia live-tested an EMP":** Interview with Peter Pry. Pry died in 2022. Dr. Peter Vincent Pry, "Russia: EMP Threat: The Russian Federation's Military Doctrine, Plans, and Capabilities for Electromagnetic Pulse (EMP) Attack," EMP Task Force on National and Homeland Security, January 2021, 5. Pry cites Jerry Emanuelson's work on Soviet Test 184, on October 22, 1962.

155 **Paperclip scientist Georg Rickhey:** Georg Rickhey, "Condensed Statement of My Education and Activities," NARA, Record Group 330, March 4, 1948; Bundesarchiv Ludwigsburg, Georg Rickhey file, B162/25299, author copy. For more on Rickhey, see Jacobsen, *Operation Paperclip*, 79–80, 251–260.

156 **the words of former:** Bruce G. Blair, Sebastien Philippe, Sharon K. Weiner, "Right of Launch: Command and Control Vulnerabilities after a Limited Nuclear Strike," War on the Rocks, November 20, 2020.

157 **also accompanied 24/7/365:** Fred Kaplan, "How Close Did the Capitol Rioters Get to the Nuclear 'Football'?" *Slate*, February 11, 2021. This fact came to light in 2021, during Trump's impeachment trial.

158 **"things can go wrong":** Interview with Glen McDuff.

159 **assessment changed:** Elizabeth Shim, "CIA Thinks North Korean Missiles Could Reach U.S. Targets, Analyst Says," United Press International, November 18, 2020; Bruce Klingner, "Analyzing Threats to U.S. Vital Interests, North Korea," Heritage Foundation, October 18, 2022.

159 **critical special missions support:** "Defense Information Systems Agency Operations and Maintenance, Defense-Wide Fiscal Year (FY) 2021 Budget Estimates," DoD, 3, author copy.

159 **only combat support agency . . . over 4 million users:** Ibid.

160 **rotating its nacelles:** "CV-22 Osprey," U.S. Air Force Fact Sheet, 2020; "Bell Boeing V-22 Osprey Fleet Surpasses 500,000 Flight Hours," press release, Boeing Media, October 7, 2019.

160 **"does not have enough range":** Interview with Hans Kristensen.

160 **"The hole. It's very dangerous":** Interview with Leon Panetta.

161 **"ready to fight tonight":** Secretary of Defense Lloyd J. Austin III and Secretary of State Antony Blinken press conference, transcript, DoD, March 18, 2021.

161 **protection gear:** Interview with Julian Chesnutt.

162 **fifty nuclear bombs:** Jon Herskovitz, "These Are the Nuclear Weapons North Korea Has as Fears Mount of Atomic Test," Bloomberg, November 14, 2022. "Experts estimate that North Korea has assembled 40 to 50 nuclear warheads, the fewest among the nine nations with nuclear weapons. However, one estimate, from a 2021 study by the RAND Corp. and Asan Institute, put the number as high as 116." See also Bruce G. Blair with Jessica Sleight and Emma Claire Foley. "The End of Nuclear Warfighting: Moving to a Deterrence-Only Posture. An Alternative U.S. Nuclear Posture Review," Program on Science and Global Security, Princeton University Global Zero, Washington, D.C., September 2018, 38.

162 **largest megacity:** "Greater Seoul Population Exceeds 50% of S. Korea for First Time," *Hankyoreh*, January 7, 2020.

162 **the base relies on:** David Choi, "South Korean Presidential Candidates Spar over Need for More THAAD Missile Defense," *Stars and Stripes*, February 4, 2022.

163 **THAAD's weakness:** Interview with Reid Kirby; Reid Kirby, "Sea of Sarin: North Korea's Chemical Deterrent," Bulletin of the Atomic Scientists, June 21, 2017.

164 **incinerating:** Office of Technology Assessment, *The Effects of Nuclear War*, 15–21.

165 **sun at noon:** Glasstone and Dolan, *The Effects of Nuclear Weapons*, "The Fireball," 2.03–2.14, 27.

165 **blinded by it:** Office of Technology Assessment, *The Effects of Nuclear War*, 21.

165 **5,700 feet in diameter:** Glasstone and Dolan, *The Effects of Nuclear Weapons*, "The Fireball," 2.03–2.14, 27–29.

165 **blast wave:** Glasstone and Dolan, *The Effects of Nuclear Weapons*, "The Blast Wave," 2.32–2.37, 38–40.

165 **Ring 1:** Also see Wellerstein.com, NUKEMAPS. For a 1 MT airburst with the Pentagon as the target, the fireball radius is 0.6 miles radius, ~1.2 miles diameter ("anything inside the fireball is effectively vaporized"). Ring 1 ("most residential buildings collapse, injuries are universal") is 4.5 miles radius, ~9 miles diameter. Ring 2 ("thermal radiation radius, 3000 degree burns") is ~7.5 miles radius, ~15 miles diameter. Ring 3 ("glass windows can be expected to break") ~12.5 miles radius, ~25 miles diameter.

165 **rare survivors:** "Planning Guidance for Response to a Nuclear Detonation, Second Edition," Federal Interagency Committee, Executive Office of the President, Washington, D.C. Interagency Policy Coordinating Subcommittee for Preparedness & Response to Radiological and Nuclear Threats, June 2010, 14–29. To note: consequences are based on a 10-kiloton nuclear explosion; in this scenario a 1-megaton weapon is exploded (see Office of Technology Assessment, *The Effects of Nuclear War*, with 1-megaton comp).

166 **cloud cap:** Glasstone and Dolan, *The Effects of Nuclear Weapons*, table 2.12, "Rate of Rise of Radioactive Cloud from a 1-Megaton Air Burst," 31–32.

166 **"no survivors":** Office of Technology Assessment, *The Effects of Nuclear War*, 27.

166 **haunting words:** Interview with Robert Kehler.

167 **"Attention":** In 2021, the Russian Ministry of Defense released video of a launch crew at Serpukhov-15, simulating a response to a nuclear missile launch. (YouTube: Минобороны России). Dmitry Stefanovich, of the Center for the Russian Academy of Sciences, describes the sequence as being based on a single ICBM launched from a missile field associated with F. E. Warren Air Force Base in Wyoming. See also Thomas Newdick, "Take a Rare Look Inside Russia's Doomsday Ballistic Missile Warning System," The War Zone, February 16, 2021.

167 **"subordinated directly":** Interview with Pavel Podvig. For more on the General Staff, see Alexis A. Blanc et al., "The Russian General Staff: Understanding the Military's Decision Making Role in a 'Besieged Fortress,'" RAND Corporation, 2023.

168 **became suspicious:** Peter Anthony, dir., *The Man Who Saved the World*, Statement Films, 2013.

168 **Petrov:** David Hoffman, "'I Had a Funny Feeling in My Gut,'" *Washington Post* Foreign Service, February 10, 1999; "Person: Stanislav Petrov," Minuteman Missile National Historic Site, National Park Service, 2007.

168 **"look like one hundred:"** Interview with Ted Postol. I also discussed this with Pavel Podvig. In 1983, Tundra did not yet exist. The old system, known as Oko (Eye), was known to fault.

171 **THIS IS NOT A DRILL:** On January 13, 2018, the Emergency Alert System erroneously texted cell phones across Hawaii with the message: "Emergency Alert: BALLISTIC MISSILE THREAT INBOUND TO HAWAII. SEEK IMMEDIATE SHELTER. THIS IS NOT A DRILL," which turned out to be a false alarm, author copy (screenshot of Lucas Mobley's cell phone, who was there).

171 **emergency sirens:** "Early Warning System Sirens, Fact Sheet," San Louis Obispo County Prepare, n.d.

171 **trying to evacuate:** Jack McCurdy, "Diablo Nuclear Plant: Disaster Waiting to Happen?" Cal Coast News, April 7, 2011. Diablo has on site some 2,642 assemblies (bundles) of spent fuel and 1,136 metric tons of uranium.

173 **35,804 in Russia:** Robert S. Norris and Hans M. Kristensen, "Nuclear Weapon States, 1945–2006," *Bulletin of the Atomic Scientists* 62, no. 4 (July/August 2006): 66; 23,305 in U.S. comes from: "Size of the U.S. Nuclear Stockpile and Annual Dismantlements (U)," Classification Bulletin WNP-128, U.S. Department of Energy, May 6, 2010. The number is for the two superpowers only. It increased further; by 1986 Russia had produced an additional 10,000 warheads bringing the total to ~70,000 warheads.

173 **Proud Prophet:** "Proud Prophet-83, After Action Report," Joint Exercise Division, J-3 Directorate, Organization of the Joint Chiefs of Staff, OSD, January 13, 1984.

173 **examples of complex systems:** Interview with Jay W. Forrester, father of the field of System Dynamics, creator of the first computer animation, and one of the inventors of magnetic core memory.

173 **models to discern and predict:** "War and Peace in the Nuclear Age, Interview with Thomas Schelling," *At the Brink*, WGBH Radio, March 4, 1986.

173 **"The power to hurt":** Schelling, *Arms and Influence*, 2.

173 **"a catastrophe":** Bracken, *The Second Nuclear Age*, 88.

176 **"His people asked me":** Paul Bracken, "Exploring Alternative Futures," *Yale Insights*, September 15, 2021. Bracken interview conducted and edited by Ted O'Callahan.

177 **ready 24/7/365 to orchestrate:** Alex McLoon, "Inside Look at Offutt Air Force Base's Airborne 'Survivable' Command Center," transcript, KETV, ABC-7, April 27, 2022.

177 **well-rehearsed:** Rachel S. Cohen, "Does America Need Its 'Doomsday Plane'?" *Air Force Times*, May 10, 2022.

177 **"certain amount of minutes":** Jamie Crawford and Barbara Starr, "Exclusive: On Board the 'Doomsday' Plane That Can Wage Nuclear War," CNN, March 31, 2018.

178 **fly in circles:** Interview with Ed Lovick.

178 **If its satellite comms go:** To note: details of comms and data processing capabilities are, generally, classified. Further, many legacy comms systems are being upgraded to Survivable Super High Frequency (SSHF).

179 **flying through nuclear mushroom:** Interview with Hervey Stockman.

179 **ARGUS infrared system could:** Interview with Patrick Biltgen.

180 **"depopulate vast areas":** "Enclosure 'A': The Evaluation of the Atomic Bomb as a Military Weapon: The Final Report of the Joint Chiefs of Staff Evaluation Board for Operation Crossroads," Joint Chiefs of Staff, NA-T, June 30, 1947, 10–14.

180 **Levin told listeners:** "Salt Life: Go on Patrol with an Ohio-Class Submarine That's Ready to Launch Nuclear Warheads at a Moment's Notice," *National Security Science* podcast, LA-UR-20-24937, DoD, August 14, 2020.

180 **uniquely trained:** Greg Copeland, "Navy's Most Powerful Weapons Are Submarines Based in Puget Sound," King 5 News, February 27, 2019.

181 **authenticated and decoded:** Reed, *At the Abyss*, 332.

181 **plan of action:** "Nuclear Matters Handbook 2020," 34–35, 41, 99; Dave Merrill, Nafeesa Syeed, and Brittany Harris, "To Launch a Nuclear Strike President Trump Would Take These Steps," Bloomberg, January 20, 2017.

182 **card and a fire-control key:** Bruce Blair, "Strengthening Checks on Presidential Nuclear Launch Authority," *Arms Control Today*, January/February 2018; Jeffrey G. Lewis and Bruno Tertrais, "Finger on the Button: The Authority to Use Nuclear Weapons in Nuclear-Armed States," Middlebury Institute of International Studies at Monterey, 2019; David Martin, "The New Cold War," *60 Minutes*, September 18, 2016.

182 **Each warhead . . . 455-kiloton:** Hans M. Kristensen and Matt Korda, "Nuclear Notebook: United States Nuclear Weapons, 2023," *Bulletin of the Atomic Scientists* 79, no. 1 (January 2023): 29, 38. In an interview to discuss 455 kilotons (often reported as 475), Kristensen clarified: "Our number is based on data, good data, not rumor or earlier reporting." Also: "Each Trident can carry up to eight nuclear warheads, but they normally carry an average of four or five warheads, for an average load-out of approximately 90 warheads per submarine." The DoD does not discuss yield; for more on the Trident see: America's Navy, Resources, Fact Files, Trident II (D5) Missile, updated: September 22, 2021, NAVY.

182 **pressure of the expanding gas:** "Nuclear Matters Handbook 2020," 35.

182 **Fifteen seconds pass:** Interview with Ted Postol. U.S. subs fire Trident missiles every fifteen seconds. The Russian subs fire SLBMs faster, as in roughly every five seconds.

183 **fifteen seconds after that:** Dave Merrill, Nafeesa Syeed, and Brittany Harris, "To Launch a Nuclear Strike President Trump Would Take These Steps," Bloomberg, January 20, 2017.

183 **travel time:** Calculations by Ted Postol.

183 **nuclear support operations:** "Defense Information Systems Agency Operations and Maintenance, Defense-Wide Fiscal Year (FY) 2021 Budge Estimates," DoD, 18, author copy. (comptroller.defense.gov).

183 **FPCON Delta:** Nathan Van Schaik, "A Community Member's Guide to Understanding FPCON," U.S. Army Office of Public Affairs, July 1, 2022.

184 **close all U.S. borders:** Interview with Robert Bonner.

186 **"Ignition is complicated":** Interview with Glen McDuff.

186 **"ignition thresholds":** Harry Alan Scarlett, "Nuclear Weapon Blast Effects," LA-UR-20-25058, LANL, July 9, 2020, 14.

186 **"jets of flame":** Glasstone and Dolan, *The Effects of Nuclear Weapons*, 285.

186 **"The energy released":** Lynn Eden, *Whole World on Fire*, 25–30; interview with Lynn Eden.

186 **physicist's point of view:** Interview with Ted Postol.

186 **"fireball will rise buoyantly":** Theodore Postol, "Striving for Armageddon: The U.S. Nuclear Forces Modernization Program, Rising Tensions with Russia, and the Increasing Danger of a World Nuclear Catastrophe Symposium: The Dynamics of Possible Nuclear Extinction," New York Academy of Medicine, February 28–March 1, 2015, slide10–14, with diagrams, author copy.

186 **burns out of control:** Office of Technology Assessment, *The Effects of Nuclear War*, 27–28.

187 **in excess of 1,220 degrees Fahrenheit:** Interview with Glen McDuff.

189 **265,000 square feet:** "'Underground Pentagon' Near Gettysburg Keeps Town Buzzing," *Pittsburgh Press*, November 18, 1991.

191 **UK prime minister:** "NATO's Nuclear Sharing Arrangements," North Atlantic Treaty Organization, Public Diplomacy Division (PDD), Press & Media Section, February 2022.

193 **claiming today not to:** Interview with Pavel Podvig; "Soviets Planned Nuclear First Strike to Preempt West, Documents Show," Electronic Briefing Book No. 154, NSA-GWU, May 13, 2005.

193 **"undermining global stability":** Jaroslaw Adamowski, "Russia Overhauls Military Doctrine," *Defense News*, January 10, 2015.

193 **"preliminary command":** Interview with Pavel Podvig. For Kazbek communications system, see Podvig, *Russian Strategic Nuclear Forces*, 61–62.

194 **2020 computer simulation:** "Plan A: How a Nuclear War Could Progress," Arms Control Association, July/August 2020. To demonstrate how this could happen, Alex Wellerstein, Tamara Patton, Moritz Kütt, and Alex Glaser (with assistance from Bruce Blair, Sharon Weiner, and Zia Mian), of Princeton University's Program on Science & Global Security, developed a video simulation, based on real force postures, targets, and estimates of fatalities. It can be viewed on YouTube, see Alex Glaser, "Plan A," 4:18 minutes.

194 **with the goal of decapitating:** "The North Korean Nuclear Challenge: Military Options and Issues for Congress," CRS Report 7-5700, CRS, November 6, 2017, 31. Noting the degree of risk: "If [a decapitation] attack is suspected . . . the DPRK could begin to disperse and hide units, making them more difficult to attack. Such a large-scale attack . . . could result in an escalation to a full-scale war if North Korea believes the operation is intended to decapitate the regime."

194 **"decision calculus":** "Report on the Nuclear Employment Strategy of the United States—2020," Executive Services Directorate, OSD, 8. The full quote: "One of the means of achieving this is to respond in a manner intended to restore deterrence. To this end, elements of U.S. nuclear forces are intended to provide limited, flexible, and graduated response options. Such options demonstrate the

resolve, and the restraint, necessary for changing an adversary's decision cal-culus regarding further escalation."

194 **"Deterrence day-to-day":** "Speech, Adm. Charles Richard, Commander of U.S. Strategic Command," 2022 Space and Missile Defense Symposium, August 11, 2022.

195 **"for suspicious purposes":** Kim Gamel, "Training Tunnel Will Keep US Soldiers Returning to Front Lines in S. Korea," *Stars and Stripes,* June 21, 2017.

195 **"It is one of the hardest":** Testimony of the Honorable Daniel Coats, Hearing before the Committee on Armed Services, U.S. Senate, May 23, 2017. See also Ken Dilanian and Courtney Kube, "Why It's So Hard for U.S. Spies to Figure Out North Korea," NBC News, August 29, 2017. They write: "North Korea is a nightmare of an intelligence target: A brutal police state with limited internet usage in mountainous terrain laced with secret tunnels."

195 **"The possibility of intelligence gaps":** Bruce G. Blair with Jessica Sleight and Emma Claire Foley, "The End of Nuclear Warfighting: Moving to a Deterrence-Only Posture. An Alternative U.S. Nuclear Posture Review," Program on Science and Global Security, Princeton University Global Zero, Washington, D.C., September 2018, 38.

196 **"Personal Secretariat manages everything":** Interview with Michael Madden.

196 **"counterforce targets":** "Counterforce Targeting," in "Nuclear Matters Handbook 2020," OSD, 21. "Counterforce targeting plans to destroy the mili-tary capabilities of an enemy force. Typical counterforce targets include bomber bases, ballistic missile submarine bases, intercontinental ballistic missiles (ICBM) silos, air-defense installations, command and control centers, and weapons of mass destruction storage facilities. Because these types of targets may be hardened, buried, masked, mobile, and defended, the forces required to implement this strategy need to be diverse, numerous, and accurate."

196 **nuclear weapons production:** "A Satellite View of North Korea's Nuclear Sites," *Nikkei Asia,* n.d.; "North Korea's Space Launch Program and Long-Range Missile Projects," Reuters, August 21, 2023; David Brunnstrom and Hyonhee Shin, "Movement at North Korea ICBM Plant Viewed as Missile-Related, South Says," Reuters, March 6, 2020.

196 **"humanity and military necessity,":** Mary B. DeRosa and Ashley Nicolas, "The President and Nuclear Weapons: Authority, Limits, and Process," Nuclear Threat Initiative, 2019, 12.

197 **lawn for a parade:** Interview with Joseph Bermudez. See also Joseph S. Bermudez Jr., Victor Cha, and Jennifer Jun, "Undeclared North Korea: Hoejung-ni Missile Operating Base," CSIS, February 7, 2022.

197 **"The mountaintop":** Interview with Joseph Bermudez.

197 **almost nothing is known:** David E. Sanger and William J. Broad, "In North Korea, Missile Bases Suggest a Great Deception," *New York Times,* November 12, 2018.

200 *"Be Prepared for a Nuclear Explosion":* "Be Prepared for a Nuclear Explosion," pictogram, FEMA.

200 **image screen-grabbed:** "Be Informed, Nuclear Blast," California Department of Public Health, n.d.

201 **looks sinister and malevolent:** Interview with Jim Freedman, who photographed many of these thermonuclear explosions for EG&G.

201 *"Get Inside, Stay Inside, and Stay Tuned":* "Be Prepared for a Nuclear Explosion," pictogram, FEMA. Variations include: "Get In. Stay In. Tune In.," Shelter-in-Place, pictogram, FEMA.

201 **135-page guidebook:** "Planning Guidance for Response to a Nuclear Detonation, Second Edition," Federal Interagency Committee, Executive Office of the President, Washington, D.C. Interagency Policy Coordinating Subcommittee for Preparedness & Response to Radiological and Nuclear Threats, June 2010, 14–96. Lines that follow here are from this planning guidance (with firestorm consequences expanded in the third edition).

201 *FEMA and the Office of the President:* Ibid., 11–13.

202 **"priorities are likely to change":** Ibid., 87.

202 **"AVOID FIRE RISKS":** "Planning Guidance for Response to a Nuclear Detonation, Third Edition," Federal Emergency Management Agency (FEMA), Office of Emerging Threats (OET), with the U.S. Department of Homeland Security (DHS), Science and Technology Directorate (S&T), the Department of Energy (DOE), the Department of Health and Human Services (HHS), the Department of Defense (DoD), and the Environmental Protection Agency (EPA), May 2022, 16.

203 **Pocket dosimeters:** "Nuclear Power Preparedness Program," California Office of Emergency Services, 2022.

204 **"unknown warning":** NOAA Weather Radio and DHS together broadcast all-hazards messages to include warnings of terrorist strikes, nuclear accidents, toxic chemical spills, and more. The system is old, with some copper wire technology dating to the mid-nineteenth century. See Max Fenton, "The Radio System That Keeps Us Safe from Extreme Weather Is Under Threat: NOAA Weather Radio Needs Some Serious Upgrades," *Slate*, August 4, 2022.

204 **$13.5 billion settlement:** Richard Gonsalez, "PG&E Announces $13.5 Billion Settlement of Claims Linked to California Wildfires," NPR, December 6, 2019.

204 **microprocessors destroyed:** Interview with Jeffrey Yago.

206 **range angle of 38.26 degrees:** Interview with Ted Postol.

206 **"has no ability":** "Q&A with Steven J. DiTullio, VP, Strategic Systems," *Seapower*, October 2020.

207 **combined explosive power:** Sebastien Roblin, "Ohio-Class: How the U.S. Navy Could Start a Nuclear War," *19FortyFive*, December 3, 2021. Kristensen and Korda believe the average load out of around ninety warheads per sub.

207 **DUGA-2:** Jesse Beckett, "The Russian Woodpecker: The Story of the Mysterious Duga Radar," War History Online, August 12, 2021.

208 **notorious counterpart:** Dave Finley, "Radio Hams Do Battle with 'Russian Woodpecker,'" *Miami Herald,* July 7, 1982. For a modern summary, see Alexander Nazaryan, "The Massive Russian Radar Site in the Chernobyl Exclusion Zone," *Newsweek*, April 18, 2014. For an excellent documentary, watch Chad Gracia, dir., *The Russian Woodpecker*, Roast Beef Productions, 2015.

208 **"missile salvos":** Interview with Thomas Withington.

209 **"pieces of crossed wire":** Interview with Ted Postol; George N. Lewis and Theodore A. Postol, "The European Missile Defense Folly," *Bulletin of the Atomic Scientists* 64, no. 2 (May/June 2008): 39.

210 **"mass decapitation":** "Presidential Succession: Perspectives and Contemporary Issues for Congress," R46450, CRS, July 14, 2020.

210 **Title 3, Section 19:** Ibid.

212 **quick reaction force:** Interview with Craig Fugate; interview with William Perry.

212 **"Thousands of bodies":** Haruka Sakaguchi and Lily Rothman, "After the Bomb," *Time*, n.d.

214 **radiation sickness:** L. H. Hempelmann and Hermann Lisco, "The Acute Radiation Syndrome: A Study of Ten Cases and a Review of the Problem," vol. 2, Los Alamos Scientific Laboratory, March 17, 1950; Slotin is Case 3. Prior to August 1945, effects of radiation poisoning were not known because no data existed. Doctors in Hiroshima and Nagasaki called this mysterious new disease "Disease X."

214 **"blue glow":** "Official Letter Reporting on the Louis Slotin Accident," from Phil Morrison to Bernie Feld, June 4, 1946, Los Alamos Historical Society Photo Archives, author copy.

216 **Cyanosis:** "Second and the Last of the Bulletins," from Phil Morrison to Bernie Feld, June 3, 1946, Los Alamos Historical Society Photo Archives, author copy.

217 **slicing him open:** Ibid. For further reading, see Alex Wellerstein, "The Demon Core and the Strange Death of Louis Slotin," *New Yorker*, May 21, 2016. Wellerstein located documents at the New York Public Library. "The photographs were, well, terrible," he writes. "Some showed Slotin naked, posing with his injuries. The look on his face was tolerant. There were a few more of his hand injuries, and then the time skips: internal organs, removed for autopsy. Heart, lungs, intestines, each arranged cleanly and clinically. But it's jarring to see photographs of him on the bed, unwell but alive, and then in the next frame, his heart, neatly prepared."

217 **"pleasant way to die":** William Burr, ed., "77th Anniversary of Hiroshima and Nagasaki Bombings: Revisiting the Record," Electronic Briefing Book No. 800, NSA-GWU, August 8, 2022.

218 **location could be:** For more about Russia's nuclear bunkers: Jess Thomson, "Would Putin's Nuclear Bunker in Ural Mountains Save Him from Armageddon?" *Newsweek*, November 10, 2022; Michael R. Gordon, "Despite Cold War's End, Russia Keeps Building a Secret Complex, *New York Times*, April 16, 1996.

218 **three nuclear briefcases:** "General Gerasimov, Russia's Top Soldier, Appears for First Time Since Wagner Mutiny," Reuters, July 12, 2023.

218 **"We are aware":** "Meeting with Heads of Defence Ministry, Federal Agencies and Defence Companies," President of Russia/Events, November 11, 2020, author copy. For summation and further context: Joseph Trevithick, "Putin Reveals Existence of New Nuclear Command Bunker," Drive, January 26, 2021.

218 **off and on:** "Revealed: Putin's Luxury Anti-Nuclear Bunker for His Family's Refuge," *Marca*, March 3, 2022.

220 **"lightning fast":** Amanda Macias et al., "Biden Requests $33 Billion for Ukraine War; Putin Threatens 'Lightning Fast' Retaliation to Nations That Intervene," CNBC, April 28, 2022.

220 **"Not . . . Formula 1 fast,":** Hans M. Kristensen, Matt Korda, and Eliana Reynolds, "Nuclear Notebook: Russian Nuclear Weapons, 2023," *Bulletin of the Atomic Scientists* 79, no. 3 (May 8, 2023): 174.

221 *siloviki* **(the enforcers)**: Paul Kirby, "Ukraine Conflict: Who's in Putin's Inner Circle and Running the War?" BBC News, June 24, 2023.

221 **running out of time:** Bruce G. Blair, Harold A. Feiveson, and Frank N. von Hippel, "Taking Nuclear Weapons off Hair-Trigger Alert," *Scientific American*, November 1997. "It is obvious that the rushed nature of this process, from warning to decision to action, risks causing a catastrophic mistake. The danger is compounded by the erosion of Russia's ability to distinguish reliably between natural phenomena or peaceful ventures into space and a true missile attack. Only one third of its modern early-warning radars are working at all, and at least two of the nine slots in its constellation of missile-warning satellites are empty."

221 **Podvig tells us:** Interview with Pavel Podvig. See also Pavel Podvig, "Does Russia Have a Launch-on-Warning Posture? The Soviet Union Didn't," *Russian Strategic Nuclear Forces* (blog), April 29, 2019. Podvig's copy of *Russian Strategic Nuclear Forces*, given to him by Gennady Khromov of the Soviet Military Industrial Commission, includes Khromov's handwritten notes stating as much.

222 **Putin said:** Vladimir Solovyov, dir., *The World Order 2018*, Masterskaya, 2018, 1:19:00; translation from the Russian by Julia Grinberg. Solovyov's film about Putin is available on YouTube. See also Bill Bostock, "In 2018, Putin Said He Would Unleash Nuclear Weapons on the World If Russia Was Attacked," *Business Insider*, April 26, 2022.

225 **chilling example:** Hoffman, *The Dead Hand*, 23–24, 421–23.

225 **Hoffmann says:** Terry Gross and David Hoffman, "'Dead Hand' Re-Examines the Cold War Arms Race," *Fresh Air*, NPR, October 12, 2009.

226 **opens the Cheget:** "Factbox: The Chain of Command for Potential Russian Nuclear Strikes," Reuters, March 2, 2022.

227 **Son of Satan:** Lateshia Beachum, Mary Ilyushina, and Karoun Demirjian, "Russia's 'Satan 2' Missile Changes Little for U.S., Scholars Say," *Washington Post*, April 20, 2022.

227 **Russia's ICBMs:** Hans M. Kristensen, Matt Korda, and Eliana Reynolds, "Nuclear Notebook: Russian Nuclear Weapons, 2023," *Bulletin of the Atomic Scientists* 79, no. 3 (May 2023): 174–99, table 1.

228 **ICBM divisions:** Ibid., 180.

228 **70,000:** Robert S. Norris and Hans M. Kristensen, "Nuclear Weapon States, 1945–2006," *Bulletin of the Atomic Scientists* 62, no. 4 (July/August 2006): 66.

228 **Russia's 312 nuclear-armed ICBMs:** Hans M. Kristensen, Matt Korda, and Eliana Reynolds, "Nuclear Notebook: Russian Nuclear Weapons, 2023," *Bulletin of the Atomic Scientists* 79, no. 3 (May 2023): 179.

228 **"about 640":** Ibid., 174.

229 **"two scorpions in a bottle":** J. Robert Oppenheimer, "Atomic Weapons and American Policy," *Foreign Affairs*, July 1, 1953.

229 **All but a few headed for targets:** In addition to its long-range, so-called "strategic nuclear weapons," Russia keeps roughly seventy "nonstrategic" nuclear warheads (aka "tactical nukes") loaded onto short-range missiles, like the Iskander-M. They carry 10- to 100-kiloton warheads, and have a range of ~300 miles (500 km).

231 **"anything fixed is destroyable":** Interview with Michael J. Connor.

PART IV: THE NEXT (AND FINAL) 24 MINUTES

235 **Hayden says:** "Defense Primer: Command and Control of Nuclear Forces," CRS, November 19, 2021, 1.

236 **same as three Russian subs did:** "Three Russian Submarines Surface and Break Arctic Ice during Drills," Reuters, March 26, 2021. Later, one of the three subs was revealed to be a special mission spy submarine. See H. I. Sutton, "Spy Sub among Russian Navy Submarines Which Surfaced in Artic," Covert Shores, March 27, 2021.

236 **Soviet-era predecessors:** "Russia Submarine Capabilities," Fact Sheet, Nuclear Threat Initiative, March 6, 2023.

236 **five-second intervals:** Interview with Ted Postol. Trident subs launch at fifteen-second intervals.

237 **unnervingly close:** "Defense Budget Overview," Fiscal Year 2021 Budget Request, DoD, May 13, 2020, 9–12; map, fig. 9.1.

238 **how it ends:** William Burr, ed., "Long-Classified U.S. Estimates of Nuclear War Casualties during the Cold War Regularly Underestimated Deaths and Destruction," Electronic Briefing Book No. 798, NSA-GWU, July 14, 2022. "Key internal analyses over the years concluded nuclear weapons would not compel the USSR to surrender and that a nuclear war could never produce a 'winner.'"

239 **"Not a place you want":** Interview with Leon Panetta.

240 **"combat-ready force":** Statement of Commander Charles A. Richard, U.S. Strategic Command, before the Senate Committee on Armed Services, February 13, 2020, 21.

240 **NATO jet fighters:** Interview with Hans Kristensen. NATO nuclear-bomb sharing protocols are difficult to report on. Kristensen tells us the loading process alone could take hours.

241 **"rationality of irrationality":** Schelling, *Arms and Influence*, 219–33; Hans J Morgenthau, "The Four Paradoxes of Nuclear Strategy," *American Political Science Review* 58, no. 1 (1964): 23–35.

242 **"Everything unravels":** Rachel S. Cohen, "Strategic Command's No. 2 Picked to Run Air Force Nuclear Enterprise," *Air Force Times*, October 12, 2022.

242 **"Until his untimely death":** Frank N. von Hippel, "Biden Should End the Launch-on-Warning Option," Bulletin of the Atomic Scientists, June 22, 2021.

242 **This allowed Blair:** Interview with Frank von Hippel.

242 **"There are 975 [targets] in Russia":** Bruce G. Blair with Jessica Sleight and Emma Claire Foley, "The End of Nuclear Warfighting: Moving to a Deterrence-Only Posture. An Alternative U.S. Nuclear Posture Review," Program on Science and Global Security, Princeton University Global Zero,

Washington, D.C., September 2018, 35. Blair notes: "All estimates are the author's."

243 **975 targets:** This follows the one-to-one (at minimum calculus) General Hyten shared with CNN. General Hyten with Barbara Starr, "Exclusive: Inside the Base That Would Oversee a US Nuclear Strike," CNN, March 27, 2018, 3:30.

243 **"Maximum warfighting":** Bruce G. Blair with Jessica Sleight and Emma Claire Foley, "The End of Nuclear Warfighting: Moving to a Deterrence-Only Posture. An Alternative U.S. Nuclear Posture Review," Program on Science and Global Security, Princeton University Global Zero, Washington, D.C., September 2018, 35.

243 **ICBM missile fields:** "LGM-30G Minuteman III Fact Sheet," U.S. Air Force, February 2019.

244 **"alert status":** Hans M. Kristensen and Matt Korda, "Nuclear Notebook: Russian Nuclear Weapons, 2022," *Bulletin of the Atomic Scientists* 78, no. 2 (February 2022): 171.

245 **"The special alarm sounds":** Interview with Julian Chesnutt.

245 **come out of the WS3 vaults:** It's plausible this action could take hours, even days, as per my interview with Hans Kristensen.

245 **"NATO pilots know":** Interview with David Cenciotti.

245 **nuclear gravity bomb:** NATO pilots carry the B61 gravity bomb, outfitted with a nuclear warhead that adjusts to different yields. "B61-12: New U.S. Nuclear Warheads Coming to Europe in December," ICAN, December 22, 2022. "These bombs can detonate beneath the Earth's surface, increasing their destructiveness against underground targets to the equivalent of . . . 83 Hiroshima bombs."

246 **boasted publicly:** "W88 Warhead Program Performs Successful Tests," Phys.org, October 28, 2014.

247 **"brains of the warhead":** Michael Baker, "With Redesigned 'Brains,' W88 Nuclear Warhead Reaches Milestone," *Lab News*, SNL, August 13, 2021.

247 **destroyed Hiroshima:** John Malik, "The Yields of the Hiroshima and Nagasaki Nuclear Explosions," LA-8819, LANL, September 1985, 1.

247 **"And we call ourselves":** William Burr, ed., "Studies by Once Top Secret Government Entity Portrayed Terrible Costs of Nuclear War," Electronic Briefing Book No. 480, NSA-GWU, July 22, 2014.

248 **"This step":** Carla Pampe, "Malmstrom Air Force Base Completes Final MMIII Reconfiguration," Air Force Global Strike Command Public Affairs, June 18, 2014. See also Adam J. Hebert, "The Rise and Semi-Fall of MIRV," *Air & Space Forces*, June 1, 2010.

248 **palaces and villas:** "Kim Jong Il, Where He Sleeps and Where He Works," *Daily NK*, March 15, 2005; interview with Michael Madden.

249 **mass of particulates:** Steven Starr, Lynn Eden, Theodore A. Postol, "What Would Happen If an 800-Kiloton Nuclear Warhead Detonated above Midtown Manhattan?" Bulletin of the Atomic Scientists, February 25, 2015.

250 **impaled by flying shards:** Glasstone and Dolan, *The Effects of Nuclear Weapons*, 549.

250 **nuclear facilities:** Olli Heinonen, Peter Makowsky, and Jack Liu, "North Korea's Yongbyon Nuclear Center: In Full Swing," 38 North, March 3, 2022.

252 **UGFs:** "North Korea Military Power: A Growing Regional and Global Threat," Defense Intelligence Agency, 2021, 30, DIA.

253 **"made into a fortress":** Ibid.

253 **tunnel-boring machine:** Interview with Michael Madden.

253 **"in wet soil":** Blair, *The Logic of Accidental Nuclear War*, 138.

253 **no early-warning system:** Interview with William Perry.

254 **"embedded telephonic system":** Interview with Michael Madden.

254 **favorite nightmare scenario:** Elizabeth Jensen, "LOL at EMPs? Science Report Tackles Likelihood of a North Korea Nuclear Capability," NPR, May 30, 2017.

255 **doubled down on its warning:** Testimony of Dr. Graham and Dr. Peter Pry, "Empty Threat or Serious Danger? Assessing North Korea's Risk to the Homeland," U.S. House of Representatives, Committee on Homeland Security, October 12, 2017.

255 **"Electric Armageddon":** Interview with Peter Pry. A common phrase in Pry's writing.

255 **NORAD ID: 41332:** Anton Sokolin, "North Korean Satellite to Fall toward Earth after 7 Years in Space, Experts Say," *NK News*, June 30, 2023. Popular satellite apps include Heavens-Above, N2YO, and Pass Predictions API by Re CAE.

256 **"fears expressed":** Jim Oberg, "It's Vital to Verify the Harmlessness of North Korea's Next Satellite," *The Space Review*, February 6, 2017. "What might be inside that half-ton package is literally anybody's guess. That it might be a functioning applications satellite for the betterment of the population is harder and harder to believe. That it might be something harmful—and no heat shield would be needed if it were supposed to be triggered in space—is getting terrifyingly easier to consider."

257 **unusual south-to-north orbit:** David Brunnstrom, "North Korea Satellite Not Transmitting, but Rocket Payload a Concern: U.S.," Reuters, February 10, 2016. Space-Track.org website shows the satellite's orbit.

257 **EMP Might:** Kim Song-won, "The EMP Might of Nuclear Weapons," *Rodong Sinmun* (Pyongyang), September 4, 2017. North Korea's official public statement: "The H-Bomb, the explosive power of which is adjustable from tens of kilotons to hundreds of kilotons, is a multi-functional thermonuclear weapon with great destructive power which can be detonated even at high altitudes for super-powerful EMP attack according to strategic goals."

257 **Oberg's Doomsday Scenario:** In *The Space Review*, Oberg wrote: "These certainly don't convey the appearance of the features of a peaceful, harmless space program, and could possibly indicate something far more ominous. . . . There's another feature of the orbit, possibly accidental, possibly not. It's determined by the immutable laws of orbital motion, my specialty in Mission Control for more than 20 years. On the very first pass around Earth, after crossing near Antarctica, the satellite tracks northwards off the west coast of South America, over the Caribbean, and right up the U.S. East Coast. Sixty-five minutes after launch, it's passing a few hundred miles west of Washington, D.C. And with a minor steering adjustment during launch it could pass right overhead."

257 **"Russia, China, and North Korea now have":** "Assessing the Threat from Electromagnetic Pulse (EMP), Volume I: Executive Report," Report of the

Commission to Assess the Threat to the United States from Electromagnetic
Pulse (EMP) Attack, July 2017, 5.

257 **"'Super' EMP weapons":** Testimony of Ambassador Henry F. Cooper,
"The Threat Posed by Electromagnetic Pulse and Policy Options to Protect
Energy Infrastructure and to Improve Capabilities for Adequate System
Restoration," May 4, 2017, 23.

258 **"Russian secret weapon":** Dr. Peter Pry, "North Korea EMP Attack: An
Existential Threat Today," Cipher Brief, August 22, 2019. See also Dr. Peter Pry,
"Russia: EMP Threat: The Russian Federation's Military Doctrine, Plans, and
Capabilities for Electromagnetic Pulse Attack," EMP Task Force on National
and Homeland Security, January 2021.

258 **Pry was privy to . . . Russian generals:** Interview with Peter Pry. The
information about the Russian generals can be found in "Threat Posed by
Electromagnetic Pulse (EMP) Attack," Committee on Armed Services, House
of Representatives, July 10, 2008. Q: "It is my understanding that, in interview-
ing some Russian generals, that they told you that the Soviets had developed
a 'Super-EMP' enhanced weapon that could produce 200 kilovolts per meter
at the center? . . . This is about, what, four times higher than anything we ever
built or tested to, in terms of EMP hardening?" Dr. William Graham, chairman of the EMP Commission: "Yes."

258 **"The result could be":** "Empty Threat or Serious Danger? Assessing
North Korea's Risk to the Homeland," Statement for the Record, Dr. William
R. Graham, Chairman, Commission to Assess the Threat to the United States
from Electromagnetic (EMP) Attack, to U.S. House of Representatives,
Committee of Homeland Security, October 12, 2017, 5. Graham read Cooper's
testimony from the year before.

258 **360 nuclear . . . war games:** Statement of Charles A. Richard,
Commander, United States Strategic Command, before the House
Appropriations Subcommittee on Defense, April 5, 2022.

258 **Intelligence Community reports:** One example of a still classified report
is: "Volume III: Assessment of the 2014 JAEIC Report on High-altitude
Electromagnetic Pulse (HEMP) Threats, SECRET//RD-CNWDI//
NOFORN, 2017."

258 **that mad king logic:** Interview with Richard Garwin.

258 **pre-electric times:** In discussing this part of the scenario with Gregory
Touhill, he commented on how bad this would be: "Nobody wants to party like
it's 1799."

259 **Osan's tarmac:** Interview with Julian Chesnutt.

259 **ground forces:** "North Korea Military Power: A Growing Regional and
Global Threat," Defense Intelligence Agency, 2021, 28–29, DIA.

260 **launch vehicles:** Ibid., 29.

260 **railcars stop:** Vann H. Van Diepen, "It's the Launcher, Not the Missile:
Initial Evaluation of North Korea's Rail-Mobile Missile Launches," 38 North,
September 17, 2021.

260 **"several thousand metric tons":** "North Korea Military Power: A Growing
Regional and Global Threat," Defense Intelligence Agency, 2021, 28, DIA. See

also U.S. Central Intelligence Agency, "Unclassified Report to Congress on the Acquisition of Technology Relating to Weapons of Mass Destruction and Advanced Conventional Munitions, 1 July through to 31 December 2006," n.d.

260–61 **240-millimeter launchers:** Interview with Reid Kirby.

261 **"THAAD can handle":** Interview with Reid Kirby.

261 **Kirby did the math:** Reid Kirby, "Sea of Sarin: North Korea's Chemical Deterrent," Bulletin of the Atomic Scientists, June 21, 2017. Kirby's calculations, which we discussed, are presented in graph form and take into account the assumed higher lethal dosage versus lower lethal dosage of Sarin nerve agent.

262 **helicopter pilots and crews:** Interview with Richard "Rip" Jacobs, who was rescued in Vietnam. For more on this amazing and improbable rescue see: Jacobsen, *The Pentagon's Brain*, 197–202.

263 **sword of Damocles:** JFK used the phrase in a speech before the UN about the threat of nuclear war. "Every man, woman and child lives under a nuclear sword of Damocles hanging by the slenderest of threads."

263 **"A nuclear detonation":** "Burst Height Impacts EMP Coverage," *Dispatch* 5, no. 3, June 2016. Wax currently serves as assistant secretary of defense for science and technology at the Pentagon.

264 **"An air-burst EMP . . . still classified":** Interview with Gregory Touhill. For more on Touhill, see Robert Hackett, "Meet the U.S.'s First Ever Cyber Chief," *Fortune*, September 8, 2016.

264 **begins to fail:** "Electromagnetic Pulse: Effects on the U.S. Power Grid," U.S. Federal Energy Regulatory Commission, Interagency Report, 2010, ii–iii.

264 **EMP collateral effects:** To note: while real-world effects of a Super-EMP get debated among analysts, the most significant truth is often ignored: the government keeps classified its data on how networked infrastructure systems will actually be impacted. For example, in its report, "High-Altitude Electromagnetic Pulse Waveform Application Guide," in March 2023, the DOE wrote: "HEMP [high-altitude EMP] is considered a credible threat to the electric power grid and other critical infrastructure sectors," followed by, "The DOE recommends that asset owners, operators, and stakeholders focus on simulating, testing, assessing, and protecting the assets and systems in their care, and not on becoming experts in nuclear weapons effects, which requires years to master and data that are not publicly available"—meaning they're not going to share classified data with asset owners, so good luck.

264 **11,000 utility-scale:** "Electric Power Sector Basics," U.S. Environmental Protection Agency (epa.gov), author copy.

264 **22,000 generators . . . 6.3 million miles:** "TRAC Program Brings the Next Generation of Grid Hardware," U.S. Department of Energy (energy.gov), author copy.

264 **"10 percent of the vehicles":** Testimony of Dr. William Graham, "Threat Posed by Electromagnetic Pulse (EMP) Attack," Committee on Armed Services, July 10, 2008, 22.

265 **"SCADA systems going down":** Interview with Richard Garwin. Garwin wrote the first paper on EMP, in 1954, and has studied EMP effects for decades. He was an author on the Jason Report of 2001, "Impacts of Severe Space

Weather on the Electrical Grid." In our interviews, he insisted there are ways to counter catastrophic effects of high-altitude EMP, but that as of 2023, no countering has been done. See also Richard L. Garwin, "Prepared Testimony for the Hearing, 'Protecting the Electric Grid from the Potential Threats of Solar Storms and Electromagnetic Pulse,'" July 17, 2015.

266 **all hell breaks loose . . . Earth:** Interview with Yago; interview with Pry. See also: Yago, *ABCs of EMP*, 118.

266 **subway trains:** Yago, *ABCs of EMP*, 118; interview with Peter Pry.

266 **fifty-three remaining nuclear power plants:** "U.S. nuclear industry explained" (eia.gov), author copy. "As of August 1, 2023, the United States had 93 operating commercial nuclear reactors at 54 nuclear power plants in 28 states."

266 **fly-by-wire technology:** Interview with Jeffrey Yago; Yago, *ABCs of EMP*, 116.

266 **Yago tells us:** Interview with Yago. "Many people refuse to believe this," he says, with magazines reporting that commercially available products like trash cans and paint cans can protect against EMP. "Pretty much the only electronics that will work after a Super-EMP pulse are items stored inside a metal box that's been sealed shut." See: James Conca, "How to Defend against the Electromagnetic Pulse Threat by Literally Painting over It," *Forbes*, September 27, 2021.

269 **"Apes on a Treadmill":** Paul C. Warnke, "Apes on a Treadmill," *Foreign Policy* 18 (Spring 1975): 12–29.

269 **fascinating new twist:** Michael D. Sockol, David A. Raichlen, and Herman Pontzer, "Chimpanzee Locomotor Energetics and the Origin of Human Bipedalism," *Proceedings of the National Academies of Science* 104, no. 30 (July 24, 2007).

270 **"smart enough":** Will Dunham, "Chimps on Treadmill Offer Human Evolution Insight," Reuters, July 16, 2007.

272 **Site R was designed:** "Site R Civil Defense Site," FOIA documents, Ref 00-F-0019, February 18, 2000.

273 **"beloved one spared":** Clark, *Beaches of O'ahu*, 148.

275 **Flying in circles:** Tyler Rogoway, "Here's Why an E-6B Doomsday Plane Was Flying Tight Circles off the Jersey Shore Today," The War Zone, December 13, 2019.

275 **one digit at a time:** Interview with Craig Fugate.

277 **"envy the dead":** Ed Zuckerman, "Hiding from the Bomb—Again," *Harper's*, August 1979. In Russia it's said to be taken from Nikolay Chukovsky's *Treasure Island*. "Those of you who will be still alive will envy the dead."

PART V: THE NEXT 24 MONTHS AND BEYOND

281 **very cold and it is very dark:** This is a variation on the title of a book by Paul Ehrlich, Carl Sagan, Donald Kennedy, and Walter Orr Robert called *The Cold and the Dark: The World after Nuclear War*. The book was written after a gathering in Washington, D.C., of 200 scientists in the fall of 1983, for "The Conference of the World after Nuclear War."

281 **smog of pyrotoxins:** Ehrlich et al., *The Cold and the Dark*, 25.

282 **lethal smoke and gases:** Interview with Brian Toon.

282 **Coniferous trees:** "Sources and Effects of Ionizing Radiation," United Nations Scientific Committee on the Effects of Atomic Radiation, UNSCEAR 1996 Report to the General Assembly with Scientific Annex, United Nations, New York, 1996, 21. Chernobyl demonstrated that some trees are remarkably resilient, others, like pine trees, turn rust-orange red and die. See also Jane Braxton Little, "Forest Fires are Setting Chernobyl's Radiation Free," *Atlantic*, August 10, 2020.

282 **peat bogs:** Henry Fountain, "As Peat Bogs Burn, a Climate Threat Rises," *New York Times*, August 8, 2016.

282 **150Tg (about 330.6 billion pounds):** Li Cohen, "Nuclear War between the U.S. and Russia Would Kill More Than 5 Billion People—Just from Starvation, Study Finds," CBS News, August 16, 2022.

282 **black, powdery soot:** Owen B. Toon, Alan Robock, and Richard P. Turco, "Environmental Consequences of Nuclear War," *Physics Today* 61, no. 12 (December 2008): 37–40.

282 **"27 degrees Fahrenheit,":** Interview with Alan Robock. To note: Robock and colleagues, in modeling nuclear winter effects, almost always use degrees Celsius in their papers; some news outlets convert these numbers in error, and report them incorrectly.

282 **called nuclear winter:** R. P. Turco et al., "Nuclear Winter: Global Consequences of Multiple Nuclear Explosions," *Science* 222, no. 4630 (1983): 1283–92.

282 *Parade* **magazine:** For a summation of the drama that unfolded around the initial reporting on nuclear winter, see Matthew R. Francis, "When Carl Sagan Warned the World about Nuclear Winter," *Smithsonian*, November 15, 2017.

283 **Consequences that:** R. P. Turco et al., "Nuclear Winter: Global Consequences of Multiple Nuclear Explosions," *Science* 222, no. 4630 (1983): 1283–92.

283 **attacked by other scientists:** Stephen H. Schneider and Starley L. Thompson, "Nuclear Winter Reappraised," *Foreign Affairs*, 981–1005.

283 **"Soviet disinformation,":** Interview with Brian Toon.

283 **recently seen the light of day:** William Burr, ed., "Nuclear Winter: U.S. Government Thinking during the 1980s," Electronic Briefing Book No. 795, NSA-GWU, June 2, 2022.

283 **"atmospheric trauma":** Peter Lunn, "Global Effects of Nuclear War," Defense Nuclear Agency, February 1984, 13–14.

283 **"Of course there are uncertainties":** Interview with Frank von Hippel.

283 **more severe:** Owen B. Toon, Alan Robock, and Richard P. Turco, "Environmental Consequences of Nuclear War," *Physics Today* 61, no. 12 (December 2008): 37–40.

283 **"more like ten years":** Interview with Brian Toon.

283 **70 percent:** L. Xia et al., "Global Food Insecurity and Famine from Reduced Crop, Marine Fishery and Livestock Production Due to Climate Disruption from Nuclear War Soot Injection," *Nature Food* 3 (2022): 586–96. For a summation: "Rutgers Scientist Helps Produce World's First Large-Scale Study on How Nuclear War Would Affect Marine Ecosystems," *Rutgers Today*, July 7, 2022.

284 **troposphere changes:** Paul Jozef Crutzen and John W. Birks, "The Atmosphere after a Nuclear War: Twilight at Noon," *Ambio,* June 1982; Ehrlich et al., *The Cold and the Dark*, 134.

284 **troposphere is:** "Earth's Atmosphere: A Multi-layered Cake," NASA, October 2, 2019.

284 **Temperatures plunge:** C. V. Chester, A. M. Perry, B. F. Hobbs, "Nuclear Winter, Implications for Civil Defense," Oak Ridge National Laboratory, U.S. Department of Energy, May 1988, ix. In a treatise on "Nuclear Winter, Implications for Civil Defense," even the Defense Department conceded a "temperature depression of the order of 15 degrees Celsius averaged over the temperate regions of the Northern Hemisphere . . . [and] as large as 25 degrees Celsius are predicted in the interiors of the continents."

285 **"like Iowa and Ukraine":** Interview with Brian Toon.

285 **thick sheets of ice:** Alan Robock, Luke Oman, and Georgiy L. Stenchikov, "Nuclear Winter Revisited with a Modern Climate Model and Current Nuclear Arsenals: Still Catastrophic Consequences," *Journal of Geophysical Research Atmospheres* 112, no. D13 (July 2007), fig. 4 (pages 6–7 of 14, author copy of Robock's pdf).

285 **"Nuclear Little Ice Age":** Harrison et al., "A New Ocean State After Nuclear War," AGU Advancing Earth and Space Sciences, July 7, 2022.

285 **grueling maladies:** Glasstone and Dolan, *The Effects of Nuclear Weapons*, ch. 7 and 9; Paul Craig and John Jungerman, "The Nuclear Arms Race: Technology and Society," glossary, "Effects of Levels of Radiation on the Human Body."

285 **chromosomal damage and blindness:** Per Oftedal, Ph.D., "Genetic Consequences of Nuclear War," in *The Medical Implications of Nuclear War*, eds. F. Solomon and R. Q. Marston (Washington, D.C.: National Academies Press, 1986), 343-45.

285 **sterile:** "Sources and Effects of Ionizing Radiation," United Nations Scientific Committee on the Effects of Atomic Radiation, UNSCEAR 1996 Report to the General Assembly with Scientific Annex, United Nations, New York, 1996, 35.

286 **reduced by 50 percent:** C. V. Chester, A. M. Perry, B. F. Hobbs, "Nuclear Winter, Implications for Civil Defense," Oak Ridge National Laboratory, U.S. Department of Energy, May 1988, x–xi.

286 **starving to death:** Matt Bivens, MD. "Nuclear Famine," International Physicians for the Prevention of Nuclear War, August 2022.

286 **temperatures destroy crops:** Ehrlich et al., *The Cold and the Dark*, 53, 63; L. Xia et al., "Global Food Insecurity and Famine from Reduced Crop, Marine Fishery and Livestock Production Due to Climate Disruption from Nuclear War Soot Injection," *Nature Food* 3 (2022): 586–96.

286 **damaged or dead:** Alexander Leaf, "Food and Nutrition in the Aftermath of Nuclear War," in *The Medical Implications of Nuclear War*, eds. F. Solomon and R. Q. Marston (Washington, D.C.: National Academies Press, 1986), 286–87.

287 **under a foot of ice:** Interview with Brian Toon.

287 **surface water:** L. Xia et al., "Global Food Insecurity and Famine from Reduced Crop, Marine Fishery and Livestock Production Due to Climate Disruption from Nuclear War Soot Injection," *Nature Food* 3 (2022): 586–96; interview with Brian Toon; interview with Alan Robock.

287 **thawing corpses:** Alexander Leaf, "Food and Nutrition in the Aftermath of Nuclear War," in *The Medical Implications of Nuclear War*, eds. F. Solomon and R. Q. Marston (Washington, D.C.: National Academies Press, 1986), 287; Ehrlich et al., *The Cold and the Dark*, 113.

287 **killing aquatic life:** Ehrlich et al., *The Cold and the Dark*, caption to fig. 3, center insert, n.p.

287 **mussels:** "Sources and Effects of Ionizing Radiation," United Nations Scientific Committee on the Effects of Atomic Radiation, UNSCEAR 1996 Report to the General Assembly with Scientific Annex, United Nations, New York, 1996, 16.

287 **microscopic aquatic plant life:** Ehrlich et al., *The Cold and the Dark*, 112. "Food chains composed of phytoplankton, zooplankton, and fish are likely to suffer greatly from light extinction. Within roughly two months in the temperate zone in late spring or summer, and within three to six months in that zone in winter, aquatic animals would show dramatic population declines that for many species could be irreversible."

287 **marine food chain disrupts:** Interview with Walter Munk.

287 **"starved or froze to death":** "I've studied nuclear war for 35 years—you should be worried," transcript of Brian Toon, TEDxMileHigh, November 2017.

288 **Southern Hemisphere:** Interview with Brian Toon; discussion on the *Nature Food* paper, Toon's slide presentation, author copy.

288 **"more than 5 billion":** L. Xia et al., "Global Food Insecurity and Famine from Reduced Crop, Marine Fishery and Livestock Production Due to Climate Disruption from Nuclear War Soot Injection," *Nature Food* 3 (2022): 586–96.

288 **lethal consequences:** Interview with Brian Toon; interview with Alan Robock.

288 **ultraviolet rays:** Ehrlich et al., *The Cold and the Dark*, 24.

288 **shielding power worldwide:** Charles G. Bardeen et al., "Extreme Ozone Loss Following Nuclear War Results in Enhanced Surface Ultraviolet Radiation," *JGR Atmospheres* 126, no. 18 (September 27, 2021), pages 10–18 of 22. See also Ehrlich et al., *The Cold and the Dark*, 50.

289 **A study by:** "Sources and Effects of Ionizing Radiation," United Nations Scientific Committee on the Effects of Atomic Radiation, UNSCEAR 1996 Report to the General Assembly with Scientific Annex, United Nations, New York, 1996, 38.

289 **insect-borne diseases:** Ehrlich et al., *The Cold and the Dark*, 24–25, 123–24.

289 **question remains:** Ibid., 35. "Prophecy is a lost art," Carl Sagan wrote.

290 **Temperatures return:** Alan Robock, Luke Oman, and Georgiy L. Stenchikov, "Nuclear Winter Revisited with a Modern Climate Model and Current Nuclear Arsenals: Still Catastrophic Consequences," *Journal of Geophysical Research Atmospheres* 112, no. D13 (July 2007), fig. 10., page 11 of 14; Ehrlich et al., *The Cold and the Dark*, 113.

290 **societies that we once built, advanced:** Interview with Charles H. Townes (on dual-use technologies).

292 **told Schmidt, yes:** Schmidt, *Göbekli Tepe*, 12.

292 **the wishing tree:** Morsch notes, "The tree is dedicated to the graves of three innocent people regarded as saints. Therefore the place became a pilgrimage for the locals. Pieces of fabric are tied to the tree and a wish or vow is made. This is a custom that dates back to pre-Islamic times and is widespread in Turkey."

292 **"Hundreds of square miles":** Interview with Michael Morsch.

292 **"bizarre landscape":** Schmidt, *Göbekli Tepe*, 15. Interview with Michael Morsch.

294 **Schmidt had found something:** Schmidt, *Göbekli Tepe*, 89–92.

295 **"We can tell you what they ate":** Interview with Michael Morsch.

296 **"The population size":** Ehrlich et al., *The Cold and the Dark*, 160. To note: no governmental agency currently has an unclassified program to evaluate the impact of nuclear winter.

297 **"The enemy of us all":** Ehrlich et al., 129. This idea, that "nuclear weapons themselves" are the real enemy, was made forty years ago. And still, here we are.

BIBLIOGRAPHY

BOOKS

Blair, Bruce. *The Logic of Accidental Nuclear War*. Washington, DC: Brookings Institution Press, 1993.

Bracken, Paul. *The Second Nuclear Age: Strategy, Danger, and the New Power Politics*. New York: Macmillan, 2012.

Clark, John R. K. *Beaches of O'ahu*. Honolulu: University of Hawaii Press, 2004.

Clarke, Richard. *Against All Enemies: Inside America's War on Terror*. New York: Free Press, 2004.

Eden, Lynn. *Whole World on Fire: Organizations, Knowledge, and Nuclear Weapons Devastation*. Ithaca, NY: Cornell University Press, 2004.

Ehrlich, Paul R., et al. *The Cold and the Dark: The World after Nuclear War*. London: Sidgwick & Jackson, 1985.

Ellsberg, Daniel. *The Doomsday Machine: Confessions of a Nuclear War Planner*. New York: Bloomsbury, 2017.

Glasstone, Samuel, and Philip J. Dolan, eds. *The Effects of Nuclear Weapons*, 3rd ed. Washington, DC: Department of Defense and Department of Energy [formerly the Atomic Energy Commission]), 1977.

Graff, Garrett M. *Raven Rock: The Story of the U.S. Government's Secret Plan to Save Itself— While the Rest of Us Die*. New York: Simon & Schuster, 2017.

Hachiya, Michihiko. *Hiroshima Diary: The Journal of a Japanese Physician, August 6–September 30, 1945*. Chapel Hill: University of North Carolina Press, 1995.

Harwell, Mark A. *Nuclear Winter: The Human and Environmental Consequences of Nuclear War*. New York: Springer-Verlag, 1984.

Hershey, John. *Hiroshima*. New York: Alfred A. Knopf, 1946.

Hoffman, David E. *The Dead Hand: The Untold Story of the Cold War Arms Race and Its Dangerous Legacy*. New York: Doubleday, 2009.

Jacobsen, Annie. *Operation Paperclip: The Secret Intelligence Program That Brought Nazi Scientists to America*. New York: Little, Brown, 2014.

Jacobsen, Annie. *The Pentagon's Brain: An Uncensored History of DARPA, America's Top Secret Military Research Agency*. New York: Little, Brown, 2015.

Jones, Nate. *Able Archer 83: The Secret History of the NATO Exercise That Almost Triggered Nuclear War*. New York: New Press, 2016.

Kaplan, Fred. *The Wizards of Armageddon*. New York: Simon & Schuster, 1983.

Kearny, Cresson H. *Nuclear War Survival Skills: Lifesaving Nuclear Facts and Self-Help Instructions*. Updated and expanded 1987 edition, with foreword by Dr. Edward

Teller and introduction by Don Mann. Washington, DC: U.S. Department of Energy, 1979.

Otterbein, Keith F. *How War Began*. College Station: Texas A&M University Press, 2004.

Perry, William J., and Tom Z. Collina. *The Button: The New Nuclear Arms Race and Presidential Power from Truman to Trump*. Dallas: BenBella Books, 2020.

Podvig, Pavel, ed. *Russian Strategic Nuclear Forces*. Cambridge, MA: MIT Press, 2001.

Reagan, Ronald. *An American Life: Ronald Reagan*. New York: Simon & Schuster, 1990.

Reed, Thomas. *At the Abyss: An Insider's History of the Cold War*. New York: Presidio Press, 2005.

Rubel, John H. *Doomsday Delayed: USAF Strategic Weapons Doctrine and SIOP-62, 1959–1962: Two Cautionary Tales*. Lanham, MD: Hamilton Books, 2008.

Sagan, Carl, and Richard Turco. *A Path Where No Man Thought: Nuclear Winter and the End of the Arms Race*. New York: Random House, 1990.

Sakharov, Andrei. *Memoirs*. New York: Alfred A. Knopf, 1990.

Schelling, Thomas C. *Arms and Influence*. New Haven, CT: Yale University Press, 1966.

Schlosser, Eric. *Command and Control: Nuclear Weapons, the Damascus Accident, and the Illusion of Safety*. New York: Penguin Press, 2013.

Schmidt, Klaus. *Göbekli Tepe: A Stone Age Sanctuary in South-Eastern Anatolia*. München: C. H. Beck, 2006.

Schwartz, Stephen I., ed. *Atomic Audit: The Costs and Consequences of U.S. Nuclear Weapons Since 1940*. Washington, DC: Brookings Institution Press, 1998.

Sekimori, Gaynor. *Hibakusha: Survivors of Hiroshima and Nagasaki*. Tokyo: Kosei, 1989.

Shurkin, Joel N. *True Genius: The Life and War of Richard Garwin*. New York: Prometheus Books, 2017.

Yago, Jeffrey. *The ABCs of EMP: A Practical Guide to Both Understanding and Surviving an EMP*. Virginia Beach, VA: Dunimis Technology, 2020.

MONOGRAPHS

Agnew, Harold, and Glen McDuff. "How the President Got His 'Football.'" Los Alamos National Laboratory, LAUR-23-29737, n.d.

"Air Force Doctrine Publication 3-72, Nuclear Operations." U.S. Air Force, Department of Defense, December 18, 2020.

Alvarez, Robert, et al. "Reducing the Hazards from Stored Spent Power-Reactor Fuel in the United States." *Science and Global Security* 11 (2003): 1–51.

"Assessing the Threat from Electromagnetic Pulse (EMP), Volume I: Executive Report." Report of the Commission to Assess the Threat to the United States from Electromagnetic Pulse (EMP) Attack, July 2017.

"Atomic Weapons Requirements Study for 1959 (SM 129-56)." Strategic Air Command, June 15, 1956. Top Secret Restricted Data, Declassified August 26, 2014.

Blair, Bruce G., with Jessica Sleight and Emma Claire Foley. "The End of Nuclear Warfighting: Moving to a Deterrence-Only Posture. An Alternative U.S. Nuclear Posture Review." Program on Science and Global Security, Princeton University Global Zero, Washington, D.C., September 2018.

"A Brief History of the Sea-Based X-Band Radar-1 (SBX-1)." Missile Defense Agency History Office, May 1, 2008.

Brode, Harold L. "Fireball Phenomenology." Santa Monica, CA: RAND Corporation, 1964.

Chester, C. V., and R. O. Chester. "Civil Defense Implications of a Pressurized Water Reactor in a Thermonuclear Target Area." *Nuclear Applications and Technology* 9, no. 6 (1970).

Chester, C. V., A. M. Perry, B. F. Hobbs. "Nuclear Winter, Implications for Civil Defense." Oak Ridge National Laboratory, U.S. Department of Energy, May 1988.

Chester, C. V., F. C. Kornegay, and A. M. Perry. "A Preliminary Review of the TTAPS Nuclear Winter Scenario." Emergency Technology Program Division, Federal Emergency Management Agency, July 1984.

"Defense Budget Overview." Fiscal Year 2021 Budget Request, U.S. Department of Defense, May 13, 2020.

"Defense Primer: Command and Control of Nuclear Forces." Congressional Research Service, November 19, 2021.

"Defense Primer: Command and Control of Nuclear Forces." Congressional Research Service, December 15, 2022.

Office of Technology Assessment. *The Effects of Nuclear War.* Senate Committee on Foreign Relations, United States Congress, Washington, D.C., May 1979.

"Enclosure 'A.' The Evaluation of the Atomic Bomb as a Military Weapon: The Final Report of the Joint Chiefs of Staff Evaluation Board for Operation Crossroads." Evaluation Board Part III—Conclusions and Recommendations, Joint Chiefs of Staff, June 30, 1947.

"Ensuring Electricity Infrastructure Resilience against Deliberate Electromagnetic Threats." Congressional Research Service, December 14, 2022.

"The Evolution of U.S. Strategic Command and Control and Warning, 1945–1972: Executive Summary (Report)." Vol. Study S-467. Institute for Defense Analyses, June 1, 1975.

Garwin, Richard L. "Technical Aspects of Ballistic Missile Defense." Presented at Arms Control and National Security Session, APS, Atlanta, March 1999.

Hempelmann, L. W., and Hermann Lisco. "The Acute Radiation Syndrome: A Study of Ten Cases and a Review of the Problem." Los Alamos Scientific Laboratory, March 17, 1950.

"History of the Joint Strategic Target Planning Staff: Background and Preparation of SIOP-62." History & Research Division, Headquarters Strategic Air Command. (Top Secret Restricted Data, Declassified Feb 13, 2007).

"History of the Joint Strategic Target Planning Staff SIOP—4 J/K, July 1971–June 1972." (Top Secret Restricted Data, Declassified 2001)

Leaf, Alexander. "Food and Nutrition in the Aftermath of Nuclear War." Institute of Medicine (U.S.) Steering Committee for the Symposium on the Medical Implications of Nuclear War. In *The Medical Implications of Nuclear War.* Edited by F. Solomon and R. Q. Marston. Washington, D.C.: National Academies Press, 1986.

"Lessons Learned from the Fukushima Nuclear Accident for Improving Safety and Security of U.S. Nuclear Plants." National Research Council, National Academies Press, 2014.

Lunn, Peter. "Global Effects of Nuclear War." Defense Nuclear Agency, February 1984.

Malik, John. "The Yields of the Hiroshima and Nagasaki Explosions." LA-8819, UC-34. Los Alamos National Laboratory, September 1985.

"Mortuary Services in Civil Defense." Technical Manual: TM-11-12, United States Civil Defense, 1956.

"North Korea Military Power: A Growing Regional and Global Threat." Defense Intelligence Agency, U.S. Government Publishing Office, Washington, D.C., 2021.

"The North Korean Nuclear Challenge: Military Options and Issues for Congress." CRS Report 7-5700, Congressional Research Service, November 6, 2017.

"Nuclear Command, Control, and Communications: Update on Air Force Oversight Effort and Selected Acquisition Programs." U.S. Government Accountability Office, August 15, 2017.

"Nuclear Matters Handbook 2020." Deputy Assistant to the Secretary of Defense for Nuclear Matters, Department of Defense, 2020.

"Nuclear Matters Handbook 2020 [Revised]." Deputy Assistant to the Secretary of Defense for Nuclear Matters, Department of Defense, 2020.

ODR&E Report. "Assessment of Ballistic Missile Defense Program." PPD 61–33, 1961. York Papers, Geisel Library.

Oftedal, Per Ph.D., "Genetic Consequences of Nuclear War." Institute of Medicine (U.S.) Steering Committee for the Symposium on the Medical Implications of Nuclear War. In *The Medical Implications of Nuclear War.* Edited by F. Solomon and R. Q. Marston. Washington, D.C.: National Academies Press, 1986.

"Operation Ivy: 1952." United States Atmospheric Nuclear Weapons Tests, Nuclear Test Personnel Review, Defense Nuclear Agency, Department of Defense, December 1, 1982.

Oughterson, W., et al. "Medical Effects of Atomic Bombs: The Report of the Joint Commission for the Investigation of Effects of the Atomic Bomb in Japan," vol. 1. Army Institute of Pathology, April 19, 1951.

"Planning Guidance for Response to a Nuclear Detonation, First Edition." Homeland Security Council Interagency Policy Coordination Subcommittee for Preparedness & Response to Radiological and Nuclear Threats, January 16, 2009.

"Planning Guidance for Response to a Nuclear Detonation, Second Edition." Federal Interagency Committee, Executive Office of the President, Washington, D.C. Interagency Policy Coordinating Subcommittee for Preparedness & Response to Radiological and Nuclear Threats, June 2010.

"Planning Guidance for Response to a Nuclear Detonation, Third Edition." Federal Emergency Management Agency (FEMA), Office of Emerging Threats (OET), with the U.S. Department of Homeland Security (DHS), Science and Technology Directorate (S&T), the Department of Energy (DOE), the Department of Health and Human Services (HHS), the Department of Defense (DoD), and the Environmental Protection Agency (EPA), May 2022.

"Presidential Succession: Perspectives and Contemporary Issues for Congress." Congressional Research Service, July 14, 2020.

"Proud Prophet-83, After Action Report." Joint Exercise Division, J-3 Directorate, Organization of the Joint Chiefs of Staff, Pentagon, Room 2B857, Washington, D.C., January 13, 1984.

Pry, Peter Vincent, Dr. "Russia: EMP Threat: The Russian Federation's Military Doctrine, Plans, and Capabilities for Electromagnetic Pulse (EMP) Attack." EMP Task Force on National and Homeland Security, January 2021.

———. "Surprise Attack: ICBMs and the Real Nuclear Threat." Task Force on National and Homeland Security, October 31, 2020.

"Report of Advisory Task Force on Power Reactor Emergency Cooling." U.S. Atomic Energy Commission, 1968.

"Report on the Nuclear Employment Strategy of the United States—2020." Executive Services Directorate, Office of the Secretary of Defense, n.d.

"Russia's Nuclear Weapons: Doctrine, Forces, and Modernization." Congressional Research Service, April 21, 2022.

"SIOP Briefing for Nixon Administration." XPDRB-4236-69. National Security Council, Joint Chiefs of Staff, January 27, 1969.

"Sources and Effects of Ionizing Radiation." United Nations Scientific Committee on the Effects of Atomic Radiation, UNSCEAR 1996 Report to the General Assembly with Scientific Annex, United Nations, New York, 1996.

"Threat Posed by Electromagnetic Pulse (EMP) Attack." Committee on Armed Services, House of Representatives, 110th Congress, July 10, 2008.

Townsend, Frances. "National Continuity Policy Implementation Plan." Homeland Security Council, August 2007.

U.S. Central Intelligence Agency. "Unclassified Report to Congress on the Acquisition of Technology Relating to Weapons of Mass Destruction and Advanced Conventional Munitions, 1 July through to 31 December 2006." Office of the Director of National Intelligence, n.d.

"Who's in Charge? The 25th Amendment and the Attempted Assassination of President Reagan." National Archives, Ronald Reagan Presidential Library, n.d.

ARTICLES

"$10 Billion Flushed by Pentagon in Missile Defense." *Columbus Dispatch*, April 8, 2015.

Adamowski, Jaroslaw. "Russia Overhauls Military Doctrine." *Defense News*, January 10, 2015.

"A New Supercomputer Has Been Developed in Russia." Fact Sheet, Ministry of Science and Education of the Republic of Azerbaijan, June 14, 2017.

Aggarwal, Deepali. "North Korea Claims Its Leader Kim Jong-Un Does Not Pee, Poop." *Hindustan Times*, September 7, 2017.

"Assessing Threats to U.S. Vital Interests, North Korea." Heritage Foundation, October 18, 2022.

Avey, Julie, Senior Master Sgt. "Long-Range Discrimination Radar Initially Fielded in Alaska." U.S. Space Command, 168th Wing Public Affairs, December 9, 2021.

"B61-12: New US Nuclear Warheads Coming to Europe in December." International Campaign to Abolish Nuclear Weapons, December 22, 2022.

Babb, Carla. "VOA Exclusive: Inside US Military's Missile Defense Base in Alaska." *Voice of America*, June 24, 2022.

Bailey, Ronald. "Quality of Life Key Priority for SMDC's Missile Defenders and MPs in Remote Alaska." U.S. Army Space and Missile Defense Command, February 8, 2023.

Baker, Michael. "With Redesigned 'Brains,' W88 Nuclear Warhead Reaches Milestone." *Lab News*, Sandia National Laboratories, August 13, 2021.

Bardeen, Charles G., et al. "Extreme Ozone Loss Following Nuclear War Results in Enhanced Surface Ultraviolet Radiation." *JGR Atmospheres* 126, no. 18, September 27, 2021.

Barrett, Anthony M. "False Alarms, True Dangers: Current and Future Risks of Inadvertent U.S.-Russian Nuclear War." RAND Corporation, 2016.

Beachum, Lateshia, Mary Ilyushina, and Karoun Demirjian. "Russia's 'Satan 2' Missile Changes Little for U.S., Scholars Say." *Washington Post*, April 20, 2022.

Beckett, Jesse. "The Russian Woodpecker: The Story of the Mysterious Duga Radar." War History Online, August 12, 2021.

Behar, Michael. "The Secret World of NORAD." *Air & Space*, September 2018.

Bermudez, Joseph S., Jr., Victor Cha, and Jennifer Jun. "Undeclared North Korea: Hoejung-ni Missile Operating Base." Center for Strategic and International Studies, February 7, 2022.

Bivens, Matt, MD. "Nuclear Famine." International Physicians for the Prevention of Nuclear War, August 2022.

Blair, Bruce. "Strengthening Checks on Presidential Nuclear Launch Authority." Arms Control Association, January/February 2018.

Blair, Bruce G., Harold A. Feiveson, and Frank N. von Hippel. "Taking Nuclear Weapons off Hair-Trigger Alert." *Scientific American*, November 1997.

Blair, Bruce G., Sebastien Philippe, and Sharon K. Weiner. "Right of Launch: Command and Control Vulnerabilities after a Limited Nuclear Strike." War on the Rocks, November 20, 2020.

Blanc, Alexis A., et al. "The Russian General Staff: Understanding the Military's Decision Making Role in a 'Besieged Fortress.'" RAND Corporation, 2023.

Bostock, Bill. "In 2018, Putin Said He Would Unleash Nuclear Weapons on the World If Russia Was Attacked." *Business Insider*, April 26, 2022.

Bremer, Ifang. "3 Years into Pandemic, Fears Mount That North Korea Is Teetering toward Famine." *NK News*, February 15, 2023.

Brunnstrom, David. "North Korea Satellite Not Transmitting, but Rocket Payload a Concern: U.S." Reuters, February 10, 2016.

Brunnstrom, David, and Hyonhee Shin. "Movement at North Korea ICBM Plant Viewed as Missile-Related, South Says." Reuters, March 6, 2020.

"Cabinet Kept Alarming Nuke Report Secret." *Japan Times*, January 22, 2012.

Carroll, Rory. "Ireland Condemns Russian TV for Nuclear Attack Simulation." *Guardian*, May 3, 2022.

Cheslow, Daniella. "U.S. Has Made 'Dramatic Change' in Technology Used for Nuclear Code System." *Wall Street Journal*, October 14, 2022.

Choi, David. "South Korean Presidential Candidates Spar over Need for More THAAD Missile Defense." *Stars and Stripes*, February 4, 2022.

Church, Aaron M. U. "Nuke Field Vigilance." *Air & Space Forces*, August 1, 2012.

Clark, Carol A. "LANL: Top-Secret Super-Secure Vault Declassified." *Los Alamos Daily Post*, July 23, 2013.

CNN Editorial Research. "North Korea Nuclear Timeline Fast Facts." CNN, March 22, 2023.

Cockburn, Andrew. "How to Start a Nuclear War." *Harper's*, August 2018.

Cohen, Li. "Nuclear War between the U.S. and Russia Would Kill More Than 5 Billion People—Just from Starvation, Study Finds." CBS News, August 16, 2022.

Cohen, Rachel S. "Does America Need Its 'Doomsday Plane'?" *Air Force Times*, May 10, 2022.

———. "Strategic Command's No. 2 Picked to Run Air Force Nuclear Enterprise." *Air Force Times*, October 12, 2022.

Cohen, Zachary, and Barbara Starr. "Air Force 'Doomsday' Planes Damaged in Tornado." CNN, June 23, 2017.

Conca, James. "How to Defend against the Electromagnetic Pulse Threat by Literally Painting Over It." *Forbes*, September 27, 2021.

"Coordinating the Destruction of an Entire People: The Wannsee Conference." National WWII Museum, January 19, 2021.

Copeland, Greg. "Navy's Most Powerful Weapons Are Submarines Based in Puget Sound." KING 5 News, February 27, 2019.

Crawford, Jamie, and Barbara Starr. "Exclusive: Inside the Base That Would Oversee a US Nuclear Strike." CNN, March 27, 2018.

Crutzen, Paul Jozef, and John W. Birks. "The Atmosphere after a Nuclear War: Twilight at Noon." *Ambio*, June 1982.

Dahlgren, Masao. "North Korea Tests Submarine-Launched Ballistic Missile." Missile Threat, Center for Strategic and International Studies, October 22, 2021.

Daugherty, William, Barbara Levi, and Frank von Hippel. "Casualties Due to the Blast, Heat, and Radioactive Fallout from Various Hypothetical Nuclear Attacks on the United States." National Academy of Sciences, 1986.

DeRosa, Mary B., and Ashley Nicolas. "The President and Nuclear Weapons: Authority, Limits, and Process." Nuclear Threat Initiative, 2019.

Dilanian, Ken, and Courtney Kube. "Why It's So Hard for U.S. Spies to Figure Out North Korea." NBC News, August 29, 2017.

"Donald Trump's Flying Beast: 7 Things about the World's Most Powerful Helicopter." *Economic Times*, February 21, 2020.

"DPRK Strategic Capabilities and Security on the Korean Peninsula: Looking Ahead." International Institute for Strategic Studies and Center for Energy and Security Studies, July 1, 2019.

Dunham, Will. "Chimps on Treadmill Offer Human Evolution Insight." Reuters, July 16, 2007.

"Ex-Defense Chief William Perry on False Missile Warnings." NPR, January 16, 2018.

"Factbox: The Chain of Command for Potential Russian Nuclear Strikes." Reuters, March 2, 2022.

Fenton, Max. "The Radio System That Keeps Us Safe from Extreme Weather Is Under Threat: NOAA Weather Radio Needs Some Serious Upgrades." *Slate*, August 4, 2022.

Finley, Dave. "Radio Hams Do Battle with 'Russian Woodpecker.'" *Miami Herald*, July 7, 1982.

Fountain, Henry. "As Peat Bogs Burn, a Climate Threat Rises." *New York Times*, August 8, 2016.

Francis, Matthew R. "When Carl Sagan Warned the World about Nuclear Winter." *Smithsonian*, November 15, 2017.

Gamel, Kim. "Training Tunnel Will Keep US Soldiers Returning to Front Lines in S. Korea." *Stars and Stripes*, June 21, 2017.

"General Gerasimov, Russia's Top Soldier, Appears for First Time Since Wagner Mutiny." Reuters, July 12, 2023.

Gordon, Michael R. "Despite Cold War's End, Russia Keeps Building a Secret Complex." *New York Times*, April 16, 1996.

"Greater Seoul Population Exceeds 50% of S. Korea for First Time." *Hankyoreh*, January 7, 2020.

Gwynne, Peter. "Scientists Warn of 'Trillion-Dollar' Spent-Fuel Risk." *Physics World* 29, no. 7, July 2016.

Harrison, C. S., et al. "A New Ocean State after Nuclear War." AGU: Advancing Earth and Space Sciences, July 7, 2022.

Hendrickx, Bart. "EKS: Russia's Space-Based Missile Early Warning System." *The Space Review*, February 8, 2021.

Hebert, Adam J. "The Rise and Semi-Fall of MIRV." *Air & Space Forces*, June 1, 2010.

Heinonen, Olli, Peter Makowsky, and Jack Liu. "North Korea's Yongbyon Nuclear Center: In Full Swing." 38 North, March 3, 2022.

Hodgman, James. "SLD 45 to Support SBIRS GEO-6 Launch, Last Satellite for Infrared Constellation." Space Force, August 3, 2022.

Hoffman, David E. "Four Minutes to Armageddon: Richard Nixon, Barack Obama, and the Nuclear Alert." *Foreign Policy*, April 2, 2010.

Jeong, Jeff. "North Korea's New Weapons Take Aim at the South's F-35 Stealth Fighters." *Defense News*, August 1, 2019.

Judson, Jen. "Pentagon Terminates Program for Redesigned Kill Vehicle, Preps for New Competition." *Defense News*, August 21, 2019.

Kaplan, Fred. "How Close Did the Capitol Rioters Get to the Nuclear 'Football'?" *Slate*, February 11, 2021.

Kartapolov, Andrei. "The Higher the Combat Capabilities of Russian Troops, the Stronger the CSTO." Parliamentary Assembly of the Collective Security Treaty Organization (RU), December 22, 2022.

Kearns, R. D., et al. "Actionable, Revised (v.3), and Amplified American Burn Association Triage Tables for Mass Casualties: A Civilian Defense Guideline." *Journal of Burn Care & Research* 41, no. 4 (July 3, 2020): 770–79.

"Kim Jong Il, Where He Sleeps and Where He Works." *Daily NK*, March 15, 2005.

Kirby, Paul. "Ukraine Conflict: Who's in Putin's Inner Circle and Running the War?" BBC News, June 24, 2023.

Kirby, Reid. "Sea of Sarin: North Korea's Chemical Deterrent." Bulletin of the Atomic Scientists, June 21, 2017.

Klingner, Bruce. "Analyzing Threats to U.S. Vital Interests, North Korea." Heritage Foundation, October 18, 2022.

Kristensen, Hans M. "Russian ICBM Upgrade at Kozelsk." Federation of American Scientists, September 5, 2018.

Kristensen, Hans M., and Matt Korda. "Nuclear Notebook: Russian Nuclear Weapons, 2022." *Bulletin of the Atomic Scientists* 78, no. 2 (February 2022): 98–121.

———. "Nuclear Notebook: United States Nuclear Weapons, 2022." *Bulletin of the Atomic Scientists* 78, no. 3 (May 2022): 162–84.

———. "Nuclear Notebook: United States Nuclear Weapons, 2023." *Bulletin of the Atomic Scientists* 79, no. 1 (January 2023): 28–52.

Kristensen, Hans M., Matt Korda, and Eliana Reynolds. "Nuclear Notebook: Russian Nuclear Weapons, 2023." *Bulletin of the Atomic Scientists* 79, no. 3 (May 2023): 174–99.

Kwong, Jamie. "How Climate Change Challenges the U.S. Nuclear Deterrent." Carnegie Endowment for International Peace, July 10, 2023.

Lapp, Ralph E. "Thoughts on Nuclear Plumbing." *New York Times*, December 12, 1971.

"Leaders Urge Taking Weapons off Hair-Trigger Alert." Union of Concerned Scientists, January 15, 2015.

LeRoy, George V. "The Medical Sequelae of the Atomic Bomb Explosion." *Journal of the American Medical Association* 134, no. 14 (August 1947): 1143–48.

Lewis, George N., and Theodore A. Postol. "The European Missile Defense Folly." *Bulletin of the Atomic Scientists* 64, no. 2 (May/June 2008): 39.

Lewis, Jeffrey G., and Bruno Tertrais. "Finger on the Button: The Authority to Use Nuclear Weapons in Nuclear-Armed States." Middlebury Institute of International Studies at Monterey, 2019.

Little, Jane Braxton. "Forest Fires Are Setting Chernobyl's Radiation Free." *Atlantic*, August 10, 2020.

Losey, Stephen. "After Massive Flood, Offutt Looks to Build a Better Base." *Air Force Times*, August 7, 2020.

Macias, Amanda, et al. "Biden Requests $33 Billion for Ukraine War; Putin Threatens 'Lightning Fast' Retaliation to Nations That Intervene." CNBC, April 28, 2022.

Mann, James. "The World Dick Cheney Built." *Atlantic*, January 2, 2020.

Martin, David. "The New Cold War." *60 Minutes*, September 18, 2016.

Martin, Glen. "Diablo Canyon Power Plant a Prime Terror Target/Attack on Spent Fuel Rods Could Lead to Huge Radiation Release." *San Francisco Chronicle*, March 17, 2003.

Martinez, Rachel, Senior Airman. "Daedalians Receive First-Hand Account of National Military Command Center on 9/11." Joint Base McGuire-Dix-Lakehurst News, April 9, 2007.

Matos, Amanda. "Thousands of Half-Lives to Go: Weighing the Risks of Spent Nuclear Fuel Storage." *Journal of Law and Policy* 23, no. 1 (2014): 305–49.

McCurdy, Jack. "Diablo Nuclear Plant: Disaster Waiting to Happen?" Cal Coast News, April 7, 2011.

McLaughlin, Tim. "Defense Agency Stopped Delivery on Raytheon Warheads." *Boston Business Journal*, March 25, 2011.

McLoon, Alex. "Inside Look at Offutt Air Force Base's Airborne 'Survivable' Command Center." Transcript. KETV, ABC-7, April 27, 2022.

Mehta, Aaron. "US Successfully Tests New Homeland Missile Defense Capability." Breaking Defense, September 13, 2021.

Merrill, Dave, Nafeesa Syeed, and Brittany Harris. "To Launch a Nuclear Strike, President Trump Would Take These Steps." Bloomberg, January 20, 2017.

Mohr, Charles. "Preserving U.S. Command after a Nuclear Attack." *New York Times*, June 29, 1982.

Moore, George M. "How International Law Applies to Attacks on Nuclear and Associated Facilities in Ukraine." Bulletin of the Atomic Scientists, March 6, 2022.

"Navy Aegis Ballistic Missile Defense (BMD) Program: Background and Issues for Congress." Congressional Research Service, April 20, 2023.

Nazaryan, Alexander. "The Massive Russian Radar Site in the Chernobyl Exclusion Zone." *Newsweek*, April 18, 2014.

Norris, Robert S., and Hans M. Kristensen. "Nuclear Notebook: U.S. Nuclear Warheads, 1945–2009." *Bulletin of the Atomic Scientists* 65, no. 4 (July 2009): 72–81.

"North Korea—Navy." Janes, March 21, 2018.

"North Korea Submarine Capabilities." Fact Sheet, Nuclear Threat Initiative, October 14, 2022.

"Nuclear Briefcases." Nuclear Issues Today, Atomic Heritage Foundation, June 12, 2018.

Oberg, Jim. "It's Vital to Verify the Harmlessness of North Korea's Next Satellite." *The Space Review*, February 6, 2017.

"On the Record; Reagan on Missiles." *New York Times*, October 17, 1984.

Oppenheimer, J. Robert. "Atomic Weapons and American Policy." *Foreign Affairs*, July 1, 1953.

O'Rourke, Ronald. "Sea-Based Ballistic Missile Defense—Background and Issues for Congress." Congressional Research Service for Congress, December 22, 2009.

Osborn, Kris. "The Air Force Has Plans for the B61-12 Nuclear Bomb." *National Interest*, October 7, 2021.

Panda, Ankit. "North Korea's New Silo-Based Missile Raises Risk of Prompt Preemptive Strikes." *NK News*, March 21, 2023.

Park, Rosa, ed. "Kim Family Regime Portraits." HRNK Insider, Committee for Human Rights in North Korea, 2018.

Parsons, Dan. "VH-92 Closer to Being 'Marine One' but Comms System Could Still Cause Delays." The War Zone, May 2, 2022.

Podvig, Pavel. "Does Russia Have a Launch-on-Warning Posture? The Soviet Union Didn't." *Russian Strategic Nuclear Forces* (blog), April 29, 2019.

Postol, Theodore A. "North Korean Ballistic Missiles and US Missile Defense." *Newsletter of the Forum on Physics and Society*, March 3, 2018.

———. "Possible Fatalities from Superfires Following Nuclear Attacks in or Near Urban Areas." Institute of Medicine (U.S.) Steering Committee for the Symposium on the Medical Implications of Nuclear War. In *The Medical Implications of Nuclear War*. Edited by F. Solomon and R. Q. Marston. Washington, D.C.: National Academies Press, 1986.

"President of State Affairs Kim Jong Un Watches Test-Firing of New-Type Tactical Guided Weapon." Voice of Korea, March 17, 2022.

"Q&A with Steven J. DiTullio, VP, Strategic Systems." *Seapower*, October 2020.

"Revealed: Putin's Luxury Anti-Nuclear Bunker for His Family's Refuge." *Marca*, March 3, 2022.

Robles, Pablo, and Choe Sang-Hun. "Why North Korea's Latest Nuclear Claims Are Raising Alarms." *New York Times*, June 2, 2023.

Roblin, Sebastien. "Armed to the Teeth, America's Ohio-Class Submarines Can Kill Anything." *National Interest*, August 31, 2021.

———. "Ohio-Class: How the US Navy Could Start a Nuclear War." *19FortyFive*, December 3, 2021.

Robock, Alan, Luke Oman, and Georgiy L. Stenchikov. "Nuclear Winter Revisited with a Modern Climate Model and Current Nuclear Arsenals: Still Catastrophic Consequences." *Journal of Geophysical Research Atmospheres* 112, no. D13 (July 2007).

Rogers, Katie, and David E. Sanger. "Biden Calls the 'Prospect of Armageddon' the Highest Since the Cuban Missile Crisis." *New York Times*, October 6, 2022.

Rogoway, Tyler. "Here's Why an E-6B Doomsday Plane Was Flying Tight Circles off the Jersey Shore Today." The War Zone, December 13, 2019.

———. "Trump Said He Found the Greatest Room He'd Ever Seen Deep in the Pentagon, Here's What He Meant." The War Zone, December 1, 2019.

Roughton, Randy. "Beyond the Blast Doors." *Airman*, April 22, 2016.

"Rule 42. Work and Installations Containing Dangerous Forces." International Committee of the Red Cross. In *Customary International Humanitarian Law, Volume*

1: Rules. Edited by Jean-Marie Henckaerts and Louise Doswald-Beck. Cambridge, UK: Cambridge University Press, 2005.

"Russia Submarine Capabilities." Fact Sheet, Nuclear Threat Initiative, March 6, 2023.

"Russia to Keep Notifying US of Ballistic Missile Launches." Reuters, March 30, 2023.

Sagan, Carl. "Nuclear War and Climatic Catastrophe: Some Policy Implications." *Foreign Affairs*, Winter 1983/84.

Sanger, David E., and William J. Broad. "In North Korea, Missile Bases Suggest a Great Deception." *New York Times*, November 12, 2018.

Saslow, Eli. "The Nuclear Missile Next Door." *Washington Post*, April 17, 2022.

Schneider, Stephen H., and Starley L. Thompson. "Nuclear Winter Reappraised." *Foreign Affairs*, 981–1005.

Shim, Elizabeth. "CIA Thinks North Korean Missiles Could Reach U.S. Targets, Analyst Says." United Press International, November 18, 2020.

Shin, Hyonhee. "North Korea's Kim Oversees ICBM Test, Vows More Nuclear Weapons." Reuters, November 19, 2022.

Shipper, David K. "Russia's Antiquated Nuclear Warning System Jeopardizes Us All." *Washington Monthly*, April 29, 2022.

Smith, Josh. "Factbox: North Korea's New Hwasong-17 'Monster Missile.'" Reuters, November 19, 2022.

Smith, Josh, and Hyunsu Yi. "North Korea Launches Missiles from Submarine as U.S.–South Korean Drills Begin." Reuters, March 13, 2023.

Sockol, Michael D., David A. Raichlen, and Herman Pontzer. "Chimpanzee Locomotor Energetics and the Origin of Human Bipedalism." *Proceedings of the National Academies of Science* 104, no. 30 (July 24, 2007): 12265–69.

Sokolin, Anton. "North Korean Satellite to Fall toward Earth after 7 Years in Space, Experts Say." *NK News*, June 30, 2023.

Starr, Steven, Lynn Eden, and Theodore A. Postol. "What Would Happen If an 800-Kiloton Nuclear Warhead Detonated above Midtown Manhattan?" Bulletin of the Atomic Scientists, February 25, 2015.

Stewart, Phil, and Idrees Ali. "Exclusive: U.S., Russia Have Used Their Military Hotline Once So Far during Ukraine War." Reuters, November 29, 2020.

Stone, Mike. "Pentagon Evaluating U.S. West Coast Missile Defense Sites: Officials." Reuters, December 2, 2017.

Stone, Richard. "Spent Fuel Fire on U.S. Soil Could Dwarf Impact of Fukushima: New Study Warns of Millions Relocated and Trillion-Dollar Consequences." *Science*, May 24, 2016.

Sutton, H. I. "New North Korean Submarine: ROMEO-Mod." Covert Shores Defense Analysis, July 23, 2019.

———. "New Satellite Images Hint How Russian Navy Could Use Massive Nuclear Torpedoes." United States Naval Institute, August 31, 2021.

———. "Spy Sub among Russian Navy Submarines Which Surfaced in Arctic." Covert Shores, March 27, 2021.

Thomson, Jess. "Would Putin's Nuclear Bunker in Ural Mountains Save Him from Armageddon?" *Newsweek*, November 10, 2022.

"Three Russian Submarines Surface and Break Arctic Ice During Drills." Reuters, March 26, 2021.

Thurlow, Setsuko. "Setsuko Thurlow Remembers the Hiroshima Bombing." Arms Control Association, July/August 2020.

Toon, Owen B., Alan Robock, and Richard P. Turco. "Environmental Consequences of Nuclear War." *Physics Today* 61, no. 12 (December 2008): 37–40.

Trevithick, Joseph. "Putin Reveals Existence of New Nuclear Command Bunker." Drive, January 6, 2021.

Turco, R. P., et al. "Nuclear Winter: Global Consequences of Multiple Nuclear Explosions." *Science* 222, no. 4630 (1983): 1283–92.

"US Strategic Command's New $1.3B Facility Opening Soon at Offutt Air Force Base." Associated Press, January 28, 2019.

Van Diepen, Vann H. "It's the Launcher, Not the Missile: Initial Evaluation of North Korea's Rail-Mobile Missile Launches." 38 North, September 17, 2021.

———. "March 16 HS-17 ICBM Launch Highlights Deployment and Political Messages." 38 North, March 20, 2023.

Van Schaik, Nathan. "A Community Member's Guide to Understanding FPCON." U.S. Army Office of Public Affairs, July 1, 2022.

Von Hippel, Frank N., and Michael Schoeppner. "Reducing the Danger from Fires in Spent Fuel Pools." *Science and Global Security* 24, no. 3 (September 2016): 141–73.

"W88 Warhead Program Performs Successful Tests." Phys.org, October 28, 2014.

Warnke, Paul C. "Apes on a Treadmill." *Foreign Policy* 18 (Spring 1975): 12–29.

Wellerstein, Alex. "The Demon Core and the Strange Death of Louis Slotin." *New Yorker*, May 21, 2016.

Wesolowsky, Tony. "Andrei Sakharov and the Massive 'Tsar Bomba' That Turned Him against Nukes." Radio Free Europe, May 20, 2021.

Willman, David. "The Pentagon's 10-Billion-Dollar Radar Gone Bad." *Los Angeles Times*, April 5, 2015.

Wolfsthal, Jon. "We Never Learned the Key Lesson from the Cuban Missile Crisis." *New Republic*, October 11, 2022.

Xia, L., et al. "Global Food Insecurity and Famine from Reduced Crop, Marine Fishery and Livestock Production Due to Climate Disruption from Nuclear War Soot Injection." *Nature Food* 3 (2022): 586–96.

Yamaguchi, Mari, and Hyung-Jin Kim. "North Korea Notifies Neighboring Japan It Plans to Launch Satellite in Coming Days." Associated Press, May 29, 2023.

Youssef, Nancy A. "U.S., Russia Establish Hotline to Avoid Accidental Conflict." *Wall Street Journal*, March 4, 2022.

Zeller, Tom, Jr. "U.S. Nuclear Plants Have Same Risks, and Backups, as Japan Counterparts." *New York Times*, March 14, 2011.

Zuckerman, Ed. "Hiding from the Bomb—Again." *Harper's*, August 1979.

TESTIMONY & TRANSCRIPTS

"Admiral Charles A. Richard, Commander, U.S. Strategic Command, Holds a Press Briefing." Transcript, Department of Defense, April 22, 2021.

"Authority to Order the Use of Nuclear Weapons." Hearing before the Committee on Foreign Relations, United States Senate, November 14, 2017.

"Meeting with Heads of Defence Ministry, Federal Agencies and Defence Companies." President of Russia/Events, Sochi, November 11, 2020.

"National Reconnaissance Office, Mission Ground Station Declassification, 'Questions and Answers.'" National Reconnaissance Office, October 15, 2008.

"Spent Nuclear Fuel, Options Exist to Further Enhance Security." Report to the Chairman, Subcommittee on Energy and Air Quality, Committee on Energy and Commerce, U.S. House of Representatives, U.S. General Accounting Office, July 2003.

Statement of Charles A. Richard, Commander, United States Strategic Command, before the House Appropriations Subcommittee on Defense, April 5, 2022.

Statement of Charles A. Richard, Commander, United States Strategic Command, before the House Armed Services Committee, March 1, 2022.

Statement of Commander Charles A. Richard, United States Strategic Command, before the Senate Committee on Armed Services, February 13, 2020.

Statement of Dr. Bruce G. Blair, House Armed Services Committee Hearing on Outside Perspectives on Nuclear Deterrence Policy and Posture, March 6, 2019.

Statement of General C. Robert Kehler, U.S. Air Force (Ret.), before the Senate Foreign Relations Committee, November 14, 2017.

Statement of Theodore A. Postol. "Why Advances in Nuclear Weapons Technologies Are Increasing the Danger of an Accidental Nuclear War between Russia and the United States." Hart Senate Office Building, Washington, D.C., March 26, 2015.

"Strategic Warning System False Alerts." Committee on Armed Services Hearing, House of Representatives, U.S. Congress, June 24, 1980.

Testimony of Ambassador Henry F. Cooper. "The Threat Posted by Electromagnetic Pulse and Policy Options to Protect Energy Infrastructure and to Improve Capabilities for Adequate System Restoration." May 4, 2017, 23.

Testimony of Dr. William Graham. "Threat Posed by Electromagnetic Pulse (EMP) Attack." Committee on Armed Services, U.S. House of Representatives, July 10, 2008.

Testimony of Dr. William R. Graham and Dr. Peter Vincent Pry. "Empty Threat or Serious Danger? Assessing North Korea's Risk to the Homeland." U.S. House of Representatives, Committee on Homeland Security, October 12, 2017.

Testimony of Richard L. Garwin. "Prepared Testimony for the Hearing, 'Protecting the Electric Grid from the Potential Threats of Solar Storms and Electromagnetic Pulse.'" July 17, 2015.

Testimony of Setsuko Thurlow. "Disarmament and Non-Proliferation: Historical Perspectives and Future Objectives." Royal Irish Academy, Dublin, March 28, 2014.

———. "Vienna Conference on the Humanitarian Impact of Nuclear Weapons." Federal Ministry, Republic of Austria, December 8, 2014.

Testimony of Vice Admiral Jon A. Hill, USN Director, Missile Defense Agency, before the Senate Armed Services Committee Strategic Forces Subcommittee, May 18, 2022.

Transcript of Vladimir Solovyov and Vladimir Putin. "The World Order 2018," 1:19:00. Translation from the Russian by Julia Grinberg. Russia-1 Network, March 2018.

BRIEFING BOOKS

Burr, William, ed. "77th Anniversary of Hiroshima and Nagasaki Bombings: Revisiting the Record." Electronic Briefing Book No. 800, National Security Archive, George Washington University, August 8, 2022.

———. "The Creation of SIOP-62: More Evidence on the Origins of Overkill." Electronic Briefing Book No. 130, National Security Archive, George Washington University, July 13, 2004.

———. "The 'Launch on Warning' Nuclear Strategy and Its Insider Critics." Electronic Briefing Book(s) No. 43, National Security Archive, George Washington University, April 2001, updated No. 674, June 11, 2019.

———. "Nuclear Winter: U.S. Government Thinking during the 1980s." Electronic Briefing Book No. 795, National Security Archive, George Washington University, June 2, 2022.

———. "Studies by Once Top Secret Government Entity Portrayed Terrible Costs of Nuclear War." Electronic Briefing Book No. 480, National Security Archive, George Washington University, July 22, 2014.

Mastny, Vojtech, and Malcolm Byrne. "Soviets Planned Nuclear First Strike to Preempt West, Documents Show." Electronic Briefing Book No. 154, National Security Archive, George Washington University, May 13, 2005.

"Site R Civil Defense Site." FOIA documents Ref 00-F-0019. Acquired by John Greenwald Jr., Black Vault, February 18, 2000.

SLIDE PRESENTATIONS

"Diablo Canyon Decommissioning Engagement Panel Spent Fuel Workshop." Embassy Suites Hotel, San Luis Obispo, February 23, 2019. 116-page slide presentation.

Garwin, Richard L., and Theodore A. Postol. "Airborne Patrol to Destroy DPRK ICBMs in Powered Flight." Science, Technology, and National Security Working Group, MIT, Washington, D.C., November 27–29, 2017. 26-page slide presentation.

McDuff, Glen. "Ballistic Missile Defense," LAUR-18-27321. Los Alamos National Laboratory, n.d.

———. "Effects of Nuclear Weapons," LAUR-18-26906. Los Alamos National Laboratory, n.d.

———. "Nuclear Weapons Physics Made Very Simple," LAUR-18-27244. Los Alamos National Laboratory, n.d.

———. "Underground Nuclear Testing," LAUR-18-24015. Los Alamos National Laboratory, n.d.

McDuff, Glen, and Alan Carr. "The Cold War, the Daily News, the Nuclear Stockpile and Bert the Turtle," LAUR-15-28771. Los Alamos National Laboratory, n.d.

McDuff, Glen, and Keith Thomas. "A Tale of Three Bombs," LAUR-18-26919. Los Alamos National Laboratory, January 23, 2017.

Moser, D. "Physics/Global Studies 280: Session 14, Module 5: Nuclear Weapons Delivery Systems, Trajectories and Phases of Flight of Missiles with Various Ranges." 110-page slide presentation.

Postol, Theodore A. "CNO Brief Showing Closely Spaced Basing Was Incapable of Launch." U.S. Department of Defense Pentagon Briefing, 1982. 22-page slide presentation.

———."The North Korean Ballistic Missile Program and U.S. Missile Defense." MIT Science, Technology, and Global Security Working Group, Forum on Physics and Society, Annual Meeting of the American Physical Society, April 14, 2018. 100-page slide presentation.

———. "Striving for Armageddon: The US Nuclear Forces Modernization Program, Rising Tensions with Russia, and the Increasing Danger of a World Nuclear Catastrophe Symposium: The Dynamics of Possible Nuclear Extinction." New York Academy of Medicine, March 1, 2015. 13-page slide presentation.

Scarlett, Harry Alan. "Nuclear Weapon Blast Effects," LA-UR-20-25058. Los Alamos National Laboratory, July 9, 2020.

PODCASTS

Carlin, Dan, and Fred Kaplan. "Strangelove Whisperings." *Dan Carlin's Hardcore History: Addendum* podcast, March 1, 2020.

Coyle, Philip. *Nukes of Hazard* podcast, The Center for Arms Control and Non-Proliferation, May 31, 2017.

Gross, Terry, and David Hoffman. "'Dead Hand' Re-Examines the Cold War Arms Race." *Fresh Air* podcast, NPR, October 12, 2009.

Perry, Lisa and Dr. William J. Perry. *At the Brink: A William J. Perry Project* podcast, Season 1, July 2020.

Rogan, Joe, and Yeonmi Park. "The Joe Rogan Experience #1691, Yeonmi Park." *The Joe Rogan Experience* podcast, August 2021.

"Salt Life: Go on Patrol with an Ohio-Class Submarine That's Ready to Launch Nuclear Warheads at a Moment's Notice." *National Security Science* podcast, LA-UR-20-24937, U.S. Department of Defense, August 14, 2020.

INDEX

Note: Page numbers in *italics* refer to drawings and photographs.

ABOUT THE AUTHOR

Annie Jacobsen is a 2016 Pulitzer Prize finalist and *New York Times* bestselling author of *Area 51, Operation Paperclip, Surprise, Kill, Vanish* and others. Her books have been translated into twelve languages. She also writes and produces TV, including Tom Clancy's *Jack Ryan*. A graduate of Princeton University, she lives in Los Angeles with her husband and their two sons.